World Protein Resources

A symposium sponsored by the
Division of Agricultural and
Food Chemistry at the 150th
Meeting of the American
Chemical Society, Atlantic
City, N. J., Sept. 13-15, 1965.

Aaron M. Altschul, *Symposium Chairman*

ADVANCES IN CHEMISTRY SERIES **57**

AMERICAN CHEMICAL SOCIETY

WASHINGTON, D.C. 1966

Advances in Chemistry Series

Robert F. Gould, *Editor*

AMERICAN CHEMICAL SOCIETY | PUBLICATIONS

FOREWORD

ADVANCES IN CHEMISTRY SERIES was founded in 1949 by the American Chemical Society as an outlet for symposia and collections of data in special areas of topical interest that could not be accommodated in the Society's journals. It provides a medium for symposia that would otherwise be fragmented, their papers distributed among several journals or not published at all. Papers are refereed critically according to ACS editorial standards and receive the careful attention and processing characteristic of ACS publications. Papers published in ADVANCES IN CHEMISTRY SERIES are original contributions not published elsewhere in whole or major part and include reports of research as well as reviews since symposia may embrace both types of presentation.

CONTENTS

PREFACE

In the totality of the problem of overcoming the world food shortage, providing sufficient protein occupies a special place, first because it affects primarily children—not only as children in terms of their survival, but also in terms of their growth and development. Evidence is accumulating that protein deficiency during the preschool years could result in retarded mental and physical development. This problem also occupies a special place because it is becoming clear that to produce the amounts of protein concentrate needed, it will not be enough to extend the present "classical" methods of producing animal protein; there will be the need to develop and exploit other sources of protein concentrate ranging from fish and oilseeds to petroleum.

It is not so easy to estimate accurately the extent of the problem. Abbot concludes (p. 13):

The longer term view, taking account of expected population increases to 1975 and beyond, opens up a truly immense demand for protein. To eliminate malnutrition would mean a 45% increase in total protein supplies for the period 1960–1975. Allowing also for a hoped for annual income growth of 5% in the developing countries, the demand in the year 2000 will be 2-1/2 times that of 1960. More than twice as much protein will still be needed, even if there is no improvement in diets.

Some have other ways of presenting the extent o the problem. A considerable literature is building up on this subject (1, 2, 4, 5). All agree that this is a most serious problem.

It is not uniformly recognized that we do not now have all the means of solving this problem. It has been said often that if all the accumulated knowledge of food and agriculture were applied to the present problems of food deficiency, these could be solved (3). All that is needed is to raise the economic level, to modernize farming, to educate the people, and to industrialize. No one can quarrel with this point of view. If all this could be done, the problems would be solved; and it is happening in some selected countries. But it is not happening rapidly enough in the places where the need is the greatest. And there is the question of whether it can be done at all in that way in many places.

There is a certain soporific quality about this idea: the contention that there is no need to think of new approaches to food—particularly protein food. It is suggested that one merely transfers what is already known; the problems of the protein-poor countries are considered to be no different qualitatively from the problems facing the industrialized countries.

However, the question of competency to solve the protein problem is an open one; we can examine with profit our current methodology and thinking and judge whether our attacks on this problem are consistent with the state of our accumulated knowledge and technology. It is appropriate that this be done at a meeting of the American Chemical Society. After all, this is basically a problem in chemistry; can we, through the various aspects of chemical manipulation, provide the world with sufficient protein? Therefore, in the background is the question, "What can chemical science contribute to the enhancement of the present protein forms and to the development of new protein concentrates?"

It is also appropriate that we dedicate this meeting to the memory of Maurice Pate of UNICEF. He and his agency distributed milk protein to women and children all over the world. They established the value of protein concentrates and the validity of the special character of the protein deficiency problem; they pioneered in recognizing the need for protein concentrates from new sources and stimulated research and development on new protein food forms.

If our general analysis is correct, we can expect that the solutions will be manifold, dictated by national and regional capabilities, and local conditions and cultures. There probably will be areas of the world where mere application of the present knowledge will be sufficient, but in many other places radical new approaches will be necessary. We have brought together at this symposium a sampling of the wide range of possibilities. We are evaluating the possibilities of the classical sources of protein concentrates—meat and milk. We are looking at the status and possibilities of seed proteins, fish, and some of the newer ideas.

I detect a sense of urgency about the world protein food problem. It is not improving with time and the chances of its worsening are good. It is the hope of those who organized this symposium that this exchange of information and ideas will improve chances of specific solutions and accelerate development of a general solution to this problem.

Literature Cited

(1) Altschul, A. M., "Proteins, Their Chemistry and Politics," Basic Books, New York, 1965.
(2) Food and Agriculture Organization, United Nations, Rome, "The State of Food and Agriculture 1964," p. 98, 1964.
(3) Russell, E. J., Wright, N. C., eds., "Hunger: Can It Be Averted?," British Association for Advancement of Science, London, 1961.
(4) Sen, B. R., "The Basic Freedom—Freedom from Hunger," Food and Agriculture Organization, United Nations, Rome, 1960.
(5) Sukhatme, P. V., *J. Roy. Stat. Soc.* **124**, part 4, 463 (1961).

New Orleans, La.

AARON M. ALTSCHUL

October 1965

Maurice Pate

Maurice Pate: 1894-1965

M aurice Pate, Executive Director of the United Nations Children's Emergency Fund (UNICEF) since its founding in 1946 until his death on January 19, 1965, was a practical humanitarian and, in his characteristically unassuming way, a stubborn idealist.

Mr. Pate has been called the foster-father to tens of millions of children of every race and nationality. A Phi Beta Kappa graduate of Princeton University (Class of 1915), Mr. Pate was UNICEF's first Executive Director. Under his direction, UNICEF became a world-wide operation assisting 118 nations in more than 540 programs for children. A tireless traveler, he visited almost all of the 118 countries in which UNICEF aids projects affecting the health, nutrition, and education of children. "It's inspiring," he once said, "to see children more alert, with healthier bodies, in part because of our aid."

Born in Pender, Neb., on October 14, 1894, Mr. Pate began his career in a small country bank in Iowa, but World War I awakened his zeal for public service. He soon volunteered for work with the Commission for Relief in Belgium under its chief, Herbert Hoover, who remained a long-time colleague and close friend. Following a year's service in the U.S. Army in France, Mr. Pate directed the Child Feeding Program of the American Relief Administration, which provided a daily meal to 1,300,000 Polish children. His administrative ability led him to work in Poland for the Standard Oil Co. of New Jersey, and to start his own private import and banking business.

Once again world crisis summoned him to public service, and he served as president of the Commission for Polish Relief from 1939 to 1941. A year later he became director of the American Red Cross Relief to Prisoners of War. In his five years in office, he succeeded in moving $170,000,000 in relief supplies to aid American and Allied prisoners of war.

While making a world food survey with Herbert Hoover following World War II, Pate was struck by the terrible conditions affecting children. The report of this survey was a moving factor in the creation of UNICEF by the United Nations General Assembly in 1946. The first private contribution to UNICEF—a check for $2000—was made by Pate himself.

Mr. Pate carried in his wallet a slip of paper with a quotation that summarized his philosophy of life. "A true reformer," it read, "is one who recognizes in human nature a higher quality than its average performance." His extraordinary ability to find a "humanitarian consensus" that cut across national and political lines reflected his faith that people all over the world could best be reached by appealing to the nobler impulses of their common humanity. He would have desired only one tribute to his memory: the rededication of his friends and colleagues to the cause of children and to the cause of international cooperation.

Modesty, dignity, and quiet determination characterized everything Mr. Pate did. He learned the art of being a practical humanitarian under the most difficult conditions. In occupied Belgium, during the First World War, and in Eastern Europe during the chaotic years that immediately followed, profiting by the inspiration and tutelage of Herbert Hoover, he discovered the power of disinterested goodwill, sometimes managing to obtain the cooperation of governments that were actually fighting each other to get shipments of food and medicine through to devastated areas.

Mr. Pate's 18 years with UNICEF were also years of considerable international tension, but he succeeded in gaining the cooperation of governments all over the world by his firm determination that UNICEF should be absolutely above international politics. "My personal position is simple," he stated. "I believe in universality based on the factor of needs. I believe in extending relief to children without distinction, either within countries or between countries." A true international civil servant, he insisted that UNICEF's mandate to deal with the outstanding needs of children, regardless of their own or their parents' race, creed, nationality status, or political belief, be respected to the letter.

Under Mr. Pate's leadership, UNICEF evolved from a relief organization into one of the most effective instruments yet devised for long-term aid through international cooperation. UNICEF supplies and equipment, the training programs it aids, and the over-all advice and stimulus it has given have enabled 133 countries or territories to launch and strengthen vital programs to improve the health, nutrition, and education of the rising generation. Always foremost in Mr. Pate's mind was the question, "What can we do? What action can we take now?" In accordance with his pragmatic approach, UNICEF aid took whatever form was needed to unlock local resources. It might be bicycles to enable midwives to make their rounds more quickly, educational toys for a model kindergarten, a printing press to produce primary textbooks, or the equipment for an entire milk plant.

As a result of his persistent efforts, the number of governments pledging voluntary contributions to UNICEF increased from 35 in 1951 to 121 (including the U.S.A.) in 1964. He spoke extremely slowly and in a quiet voice. Though appealing to the conscience of humanity, he was not a sentimentalist. He would merely ask, "How can we build a peaceful and prosperous world without healthy, well-nourished youngsters who have been trained to contribute to their countries' development?" His argument was that sick children, hungry children, children deprived of schooling were not only a burden on humanity's conscience but a criminal waste of essential human resources.

Although he had no children of his own, Mr. Pate could appreciate the tragedy of families where a bare majority of children survive to reach school age. The eldest of seven children, he saw three of the others die in infancy—one of polio, one of diphtheria, and one of an intestinal infection brought on by drinking unpasteurized milk. He once remarked to a friend, "They all could have been saved if we'd known then what we know today." With what we know today, he always pointed out, countless children in the developing countries, now doomed to hunger, sickness, and ignorance, could be saved to build a better world. Maurice Pate dedicated his life to this task; and the millions of children who have been protected from crippling disease and given a better chance in life through the intervention of UNICEF are the most fitting memorial he could have desired.

His work for UNICEF and the world's children took Pate to the offices of presidents and prime ministers, leaders and kings, as well as to the papal apartments of Popes Pius XII, John XXIII, and Paul VI.

Because of his reputation as an expert on food distribution, the late United Nations Secretary-General Dag Hammarskjold appointed Maurice Pate as his special representative during the Congo crisis in 1960 to open up emergency food distribution.

His work for children was the focus of Maurice Pate's life. For these efforts, he earned a host of decorations, including an honorary doctorate of philanthropy from Princeton University in 1958, the Albert and Mary Lasker Award in 1959 for notable service in improving child and mother welfare, as well as other awards. The governments of Belgium, France, the Netherlands, Poland, and other countries decorated him. In 1960, the Norwegian National Committee for UNICEF suggested Pate be nominated for the Nobel Peace Prize. He said he would not accept such an honor for himself, suggesting that UNICEF itself be nominated.

Five U.S. Presidents—Johnson, Kennedy, Eisenhower, Truman, and Hoover—have hailed UNICEF's work under Maurice Pate's leadership. Lyndon B. Johnson said: "UNICEF's helping hand has been extended to children in the underdeveloped countries of the world . . . . . . Even in this era of highly advanced science and technology three out of four of all the world's children today still live in the shadow of poverty, hunger, and disease." John F. Kennedy said, "Through the years, the efforts of UNICEF . . . . have met with a remarkable measure of success." Said Harry S. Truman: "I have followed with satisfaction the humanitarian services performed by UNICEF in many countries the world over," while Dwight D. Eisenhower commented, "It is heartwarming to follow the work of UNICEF which contributes much to the lives of millions in need."

The late Herbert Hoover made this assessment of the unassuming, tireless, persistent man, who led UNICEF for so long: "He has given his life to restoring life and chatter among the world's children .... the most efficient and dedicated human angel that I have ever known."

United Nations Secretary-General U Thant said, "The credit for UNICEF's unique achievement belongs to Maurice Pate..... He was truly a great humanitarian."

Donald R. Sabin, *Director*
Food Conservation Division
UNICEF
United Nations, New York

August 6, 1965

EDITOR'S NOTE: In October following the symposium it was announced that the Nobel Peace Prize for 1965 would be awarded to UNICEF. I, speaking about Mr. Pate in connection with his announcenment, U Thant Secretary-General of the United Nations, said that "in a sense, this is a posthumous tribute to his selfless work as Executive Director of UNICEF for so many years."

INTRODUCTIONS

This Symposium on Evaluation of World Protein Resources deals with proteins from plants, both the higher green plants and the lower plant forms, bacteria and fungi. Fifteen of the 22 papers are devoted to plant proteins. This emphasis on proteins from plants is proper for plants are the primary and greatest source of amino acids and proteins. Almost all of the essential amino acids which animals, including man, consume are initially produced in plant cells, most frequently in the cells of green leaves and must generally be concentrated into proteins of seed or tubers or converted into animal protein before they can be used by man.

In my estimation we should greatly increase our research on all forms of plant proteins and ways of concentrating and converting them into edible and acceptable forms. In "the horse and buggy days" we used to feed grain and forage to animals to convert the stored energy into animal power useful for work or transportation. However, scientists found other ways to convert and utilize different forms of energy, including that in fossil fuels and the primary ones of fission and fusion.

I wonder if the conversion of plant proteins into animal proteins may not some day be considered a remnant of the horse and buggy days in which animals were used to concentrate the protein from plants. The challenge that faces the protein chemist today is to find ways to use new, untapped sources of protein, which may, in the end, be as important to a protein-hungry humanity as was developing and utilizing new forms of energy.

Plant biochemists and geneticists have cooperated to search for and find mutants in maize that produce protein of a much better quality. This growing corn with a higher lysine content may have an impact upon agriculture and human nutrition in some countries which will be as important as the introduction of hybrid corn.

Methods have been developed for processing lower plant forms such as bacteria to produce protein concentrates. Microorganisms, including bacteria, have been proposed as a potential source of protein, but much remains to be done to develop suitable processing techniques for producing a high quality protein from this little explored source.

Fungi represent another lower plant form which might contribute to the world protein supply. Protein production from mold has potential for a fungal protein process.

MARK H. STAHMANN
Department of Biochemistry
University of Wisconsin
Madison, Wis.

September 1965

The poor peoples of the world do not get enough good protein, and the deficit is especially serious in young children. Rapidly growing children have greater protein requirements than adults and yet are fed even more exclusively than adults on the local starchy food, usually a grain. The grains have enough, or almost enough protein but are deficient in certain amino acids. The main problem, then, is how to add the missing amino acids.

This is precisely the problem faced in formulating feeds for non-ruminant animals. Animal feeds must be based on locally available materials, be nutritionally complete, and be as cheap as possible. The same requirements must be met in foods for poor, underfed children, and in addition these foods must be made safe and acceptable at as little extra cost as possible. Similar requirements lead to similar solutions. Therefore, cheap adequate foods for underfed children are of the same materials and the same general technological character as the proved animal feeds. In all feed and foods, adjustments in composition must be made to meet specific nutritional needs.

In animal feeds, and in the related foods for children, the protein of grain is upgraded by adding fish or oilseed materials which are concentrated in protein and provide the amino acids lacking in the grain.

An alternative approach to fish and oilseed protein concentrates, which will become more and more important in time, is to upgrade the proteins of grains, not with protein concentrates, but, either completely or partially, with industrially produced amino acids.

Present knowledge of protein nutrition, although less complete so far as children are concerned than nutritionists often pretend, is adequate for going ahead in a big way. Technological knowledge about producing suitable protein-adequate foods, although even less complete than nutritional knowledge, is not the main bottleneck. The main bottleneck is in marketing, in solving the social and economic problems involved in getting protein-adequate foods produced, sold, and used, and in getting the foods into the normal internal economy through normal commercial channels.

In the richer countries of the world, more expensive processing of cheap protein materials can be considered, with the object of obtaining more attractive foods similar in general character to the much appreciated animal protein foods. And it is now basically understood how to achieve in a factory the sort of transformation of crude plant materials into attractive protein foods which is achieved by processing in the animal. A technical revolution is one of man's major ancient activities. The main technical problem is how to obtain desirable structure from a mushy precipitate of isolated protein.

Finally, the protein upgrading of foods for underfed children has so far made only a trivial quantitative impression on the satisfaction of the global needs. Structured products are as yet of trivial commercial importance in the markets of the richer countries. We are just at the starting point of great developments.

For a dozen years or so a relatively small group of interested men has understood the protein needs of underfed children and the general technological approach to satisfying these needs. More than a dozen years ago some basic ways of producing structured foods from plant protein materials were worked out, but interest in the field was limited to laboratories, and to very few of these. Recently, and rather suddenly, the picture has changed. A symposium such as this one, which reflects very broad interest in its subject matter, would have been unthinkable not long ago. And who would have predicted not long ago that our foreign food policy would veer from primary concern with the mere disposal of surplus crops to an emphasis on satisfying human nutritional needs, that it would be declared government policy to help with the protein upgrading of grains, especially for foods for children in the undeveloped countries? So far as structured plant protein foods are concerned, work is going on in various large industrial research laboratories and products are at last beginning to appear on the market. Further rapid progress is now assured.

Thus for the problems and products discussed we are proceeding from understanding and preliminary work of all kinds to interest and development and action on a large scale. We are at the exciting take-off point. The timing of our discussion, therefore, is peculiarly well chosen.

M. L. ANSON
September 1965
18 East 81st St.
New York, N. Y.

Protein Supplies and Prospects: The Problem

J. C. ABBOTT

Marketing Branch, Food and Agriculture Organization, Rome, Italy

While animal protein resources are rising in the developed countries, in the developing countries the total per capita protein supply has declined by about 6% since World War II, with increased dependence on protein from grain. On an average, present supplies are generally adequate for nutrition; in practice, variations in individual requirements and economic and social impediments to distribution mean that substantial segments of the population do not receive enough. The prospects of meeting these needs through protein from cereals, oilseeds, pulses and nuts, fruits and vegetables, livestock products, fish, and less conventional sources of protein are appraised, with indications of relative cost. Immediate deficiencies could be met by specific programs to correct distributional discrepancies. To cover future requirements massive increases in protein food production must be envisaged.

This paper introduces an evaluation of protein resources and requirements on a world basis. It attempts first to summarize available data on the supply of food protein, then appraise these supplies in terms of the quantities and per capita distribution necessary for adequate nutrition. Then the prospects of expanding the supply of protein from different sources are reviewed and some of the economic issues identified.

Supplies of Food Protein

Table I sets out the quantities of protein obtained from various groups of foods in the major regions of the world. These figures are recent estimates of production adjusted by net trade and allowances for seed, livestock use, waste, etc., divided by the estimated total population. Some 70% of the world's protein supply comes from vegetable sources and 30%

from animal sources.   The penultimate two lines of Table I are a measure of the contrast between the situation in the well-fed parts of the world and the others.   Protein supplies through grains are strikingly similar on a per capita basis.   In contrast, availabilities of protein from meat and dairy products are of the order of 20 grams daily per capita, respectively, as against 3 to 4 grams in the developing countries, with only a somewhat higher supply from pulses and oilseeds as a partial compensation.

Grains, the staple food in most countries, are also the main source of protein, furnishing almost half the total supply.   This proportion ranges from 72% in Pakistan to 16% in the United States (Table II).   Grains are the main source of protein in all countries except Argentina, Australia, Canada, New Zealand, and the United States (where it is meat) and Ireland and Sweden (where dairy products are more important).

Pulses, oilseeds, and nuts provide almost 13% of the world's protein supplies.   Their contribution is as high as 27% in India and probably of the same order in mainland China.   They provide 23% of the protein in Brazil and 19% in Japan and Mexico, but in most countries much less.

Starchy roots account for about 5% of protein supplies, rising to 12% in Peru, and perhaps even more in those African countries where cassava or yams are the staple food.

Vegetables and fruits provide only about 3% of the world's protein; their contribution rises to 9% in Spain and 8% in Libya, Peru, the Philippines, and Portugal.

Among animal products, meat and dairy products are of almost equal importance in the world's protein supply, the former contributing about 13% and the latter about 11%.   Meat ranges from 44% in Argentina to 2% in Ceylon, India, and Pakistan, and dairy products from 35% in Finland to 1% in Japan.

Although eggs provide only about 2% of the world's protein, they amount to as much as 7% in Israel and the United States.

Fish too accounts for only about 3% on a world basis but is the main source of animal protein in countries such as Ceylon, Japan, the Philippines, Portugal, and China (Taiwan).   In Portugal fish supplies 23% of the total protein and in Japan, 18%.

Supply trends on a world basis become evident only slowly.   In the economically more developed countries protein intake has increased by some 6% since before World War II; in the developing countries where increases are most needed, there has been a decline of about 6%.   The main change in the composition of protein supplies since before the war has been a reduction in the protein derived from grains in the better-off countries and a large increase in that obtained from animal sources.

Table I. Protein Supplies Per Capita by Major Food Groups and Regions (*3*)

	Vegetable Protein				Animal Protein			
	Grains	Starchy Roots	Pulses, Oil-seeds, and Nuts	Vege-tables and Fruit	Meat and Poul-try	Eggs	Fish	Milk and Milk Products
					Grams per Day			*Total*
North America	15.7	2.3	4.7	4.6	31.9	6.0	2.5	25.3	93
Australia and New Zealand	24.3	2.4	2.1	3.1	36.8	3.5	2.2	19.5	94
Western Europe	30.5	4.4	5.0	4.1	16.2	3.1	2.4	17.3	83
Eastern Europe and USSR	48.3	8.2	2.0	2.5	12.9	2.2	1.9	16.1	94
Latin America	26.5	2.7	10.7	2.8	13.8	1.2	1.5	7.4	67
Far East	32.2	1.8	12.0	1.7	3.0	0.4	2.2	2.2	56
Near East	48.5	0.7	9.5	3.6	4.6	0.5	1.1	7.4	76
Africa	32.2	7.1	9.0	1.7	5.8	0.4	1.3	3.5	61
Europe, North America, Australia, New Zealand, Argentina, Paraguay, Uruguay	33.4	5.2	3.8	3.6	19.8	3.3	2.4	18.5	90
Far East, Near East, Africa, Latin America (except Argentina, Paraguay, and Uruguay)	33.2	2.3	11.6	1.8	3.8	0.4	1.9	2.9	58
World	33.4	3.2	9.0	2.4	8.8	1.2	2.3	7.7	68

Adequacy of Present Level of Supplies

The Joint FAO/WHO Expert Group on Protein Requirements, in October 1963, recommended the following broad basis for assessing protein requirements (grams per kilogram of body weight per day according to age group): years 1 to 3, 0.9 gram; 4 to 9, 0.8 gram; 10 to 15, 0.7 gram; 16 upward, 0.6 gram; with due allowance for the value of the type of food protein.

Average protein requirements estimated accordingly vary from 40 grams per capita per day in the United States to 52 grams in Yugoslavia, for example. This reflects in part the age, sex, and body weight of the population, but principally the biological quality of the protein as measured in terms of net protein utilization (NPU) or protein efficiency ratio (PER). Good quality proteins are widely present in animal products such as milk, meat, fish, cheese, and eggs, and in the seeds of many legumes and pulses. Starchy foods such as cassava and plantains, and to a large extent maize and wheat, contain protein of relatively poor quality. Estimates of requirements in a number of countries are contrasted with available supplies in Table III. The low requirement in the United States results mainly from the high quality of the dietary protein, while in the developing countries the requirements are higher because protein quality is lower.

On an average basis available supplies exceed requirements in most of the countries for which there are data. However, national average figures do not reveal the real situation so far as individuals are concerned. For two sets of reasons these averages cannot be accepted as satisfactory. Because of individual variations in requirements 20% more than the average is recommended to cover the needs of most of the population (5). Economic and social factors further impede the allocation of supplies according to physiological needs. Thus, in India lower income groups in the urban areas of Maharashtra, for example, amounting to between a quarter and a third of the households do not receive enough protein (13). The proportion of persons with inadequate protein supplies would be still higher since in households where food supplies are limited the productive members or wage earners may take all the protein they need and more, at the expense of the nutritionally vulnerable groups—children, and expectant and nursing mothers. Surveys of rural households in Uttar Pradesh indicate similar deficiencies (11). Consequently, considerable proportions of the population probably receive inadequate supplies of protein in countries such as Colombia, Peru, Ceylon, India, Pakistan, and the Philippines, and in various parts of Africa, where total average requirements seem to be just covered. Similarly, while it is probable that even on a world basis the total available supplies of protein are enough to satisfy the calculated requirements of the whole population, in actual fact many people consume much more protein than they need; supplies must be sufficient to take account of this as well as to satisfy minimum requirements. Thus, with distribution according to effective demand, supplies considerably in excess of the calculated average requirement will be needed. The amount of the excess needed will differ from country to country, according to the degree of income disparity, family atittudes as to food appropriate for women and children, spoilage during preparation, availability at the proper time and place, etc.

Prospects for Protein Supplies

Grains. Grains provide nearly half of man's total supply of protein directly, plus much of that obtained via livestock products. As staple foods providing the bulk of the calorie supply, grains will continue to be the main sources of protein in the foreseeable future. Since almost half the present supply, including by-products of processing for human consumption, is fed to livestock, and output in some of the most productive areas is restricted administratively, supplies for human consumption could be expanded rapidly.   It is unlikely, however, that the proportional contribution of grains to the world's protein supplies will be increased greatly.   There is a limit to the amount of such relatively bulky foods a person can consume, especially young children who suffer from protein malnutrition in developing countries, while with rising incomes grain consumption tends to decrease.   Grains are likely to have their main importance as a source of additional protein in those tropical areas where the staple foods are now starchy roots, such as cassava, yams, and sweet potatoes, or starchy fruits such as plantains.

Consumers in the developing countries generally show an increasing preference for wheat and rice.   Wheat, however, does not usually thrive in the tropics except at considerable altitude.   Large areas of tropical Africa, where starchy roots are now staple crops, are believed to be suitable for rice production, but development has been slow because of the arduous work involved with traditional rice cultivation methods and the capital investment needed for satisfactory irrigation.

Pulses, Oilseeds, and Nuts.   Pulses, oilseeds, and nuts are the main protein-rich vegetable crops.   They play a vital role in relieving protein malnutrition in many areas where animal products cannot be afforded. Pulses or grain legumes, such as beans, peas, and lentils, contain 20 to 40% protein on a dry basis.

Prospects for expanding production are favorable because of the range and adaptability of species and varieties.   In the Far East soybean products have long been an important source of protein in the daily diet.   Tofu, miso, shoyu, and natto and other soybean products absorb some 500,000 tons of soybeans in Japan and constitute 10% of total individual protein intake (*12*).   Ten per cent of the more than 90 million population of Indonesia eat 100 grams of tempeh (soybeans fermented by mold action) daily (*10*).   However, in many of the countries producing peanuts, soybeans, sesame seed, and coconuts, the bulk of the potential protein supply for human use is exported, used locally as animal feed, fertilizer, or fuel, or even wasted altogether.   Table IV indicates the contribution which available supplies of oilseeds could make to daily human protein intake in some countries where current levels are so low that vulnerable groups do not receive enough.

Vegetables.   Of all cultivated plants leafy vegetables such as spinach and sorrel give the highest protein yield per unit of area and time.   One acre of vegetable land can produce in 3 to 4 months about 8 tons of fresh spinach containing 160 kg. (350 pounds) of protein.   The same land sown to pasture will feed milking cows producing 530 gallons of milk, or only 220 pounds of protein, though of better quality (*8*).

Table II.   Per Capita Protein
(Averages

	Total Protein	Animal Protein	Grain	Starchy Roots
U. S. A.				
Grams per day	92	65	15	2
% of total protein		70	16	2
Canada				
Grams per day	95	63	23	3
% of total protein		66	24	3
Argentina				
Grams per day	98	57	34	3
% of total protein		58	35	3
Brazil				
Grams per day	61	19	24	2
% of total protein		31	39	3
Colombia				
Grams per day	48	23	15	2
% of total protein		48	31	4
Mexico				
Grams per day	68	20	33	—
% of total protein		30	49	—
Peru				
Grams per day	49	12	22	6
% of total protein		24	45	12
Ireland				
Grams per day	96	57	29	7
% of total protein		59	30	7
Finland				
Grams per day	94	53	34	5
% of total protein		56	36	5
Portugal				
Grams per day	72	26	29	6
% of total protein		37	41	8
Sweden				
Grams per day	61	52	22	4
% of total protein		64	27	5
Israel				
Grams per day	84	33	39	2
% of total protein		40	47	2
Libya				
Grams per day	53	10	34	1
% of total protein		20	64	2
Turkey				
Grams per day	91	15	61	2
% of total protein		17	68	2
United Arab Republic				
Grams per day	76	13	51	—
% of total protein		17	67	—

Supplies in Selected Countries
1957–59) (*6*)

Pulses, Oilseeds, and Nuts	Vegetables	Fruit	Meat and Poultry	Eggs	Fish	Milk and Products
5	4	1	32	6	3	24
5	4	1	35	7	3	26
3	2	1	29	5	4	25
3	2	1	31	5	4	26
1	2	1	43	2	1	11
1	2	1	44	2	1	11
14	—	2	11	1	2	5
23	—	3	18	2	3	8
5	1	2	15	1	—	7
10	2	4	31	2	—	15
13	1	1	9	2	1	8
19	1	1	13	3	1	12
5	3	1	6	—	3	3
10	6	2	12	—	6	6
1	2	—	20	5	2	30
1	2	—	21	5	2	31
1	1	—	12	2	6	33
1	1	—	13	2	6	35
4	5	1	6	1	16	3
6	7	1	8	1	23	4
1	1	1	17	4	7	24
1	1	1	21	5	9	30
4	3	2	10	6	3	14
5	4	2	12	7	4	17
4	2	2	4	—	1	5
7	4	4	8	—	2	9
7	3	2	5	—	1	9
8	3	2	6	—	1	10
7	3	2	5	1	3	4
9	4	3	7	1	4	5

Table II.

	Total Protein	Animal Protein	Grain	Starchy Roots
Ceylon				
Grams per day	45	9	27	1
% of total protein		20	60	2
India				
Grams per day	51	6	30	—
% of total protein		12	59	—
China (Taiwan)				
Grams per day	57	14	31	3
% of total protein		25	54	5
Japan				
Grams per day	67	17	31	2
% of total protein		26	46	3
Pakistan				
Grams per day	46	7	33	—
% of total protein		16	72	—
Philippines				
Grams per day	47	13	26	2
% of total protein		28	55	4
Mauritius				
Grams per day	46	11	27	1
% of total protein		23	59	2
Australia				
Grams per day	92	61	23	3
% of total protein		67	25	3
New Zealand				
Grams per day	105	72	25	3
% of total protein		68	24	3

As with grains, the potential contribution of vegetables to human protein intake is limited by their bulk. Specialized production in the vicinity of large towns in developing countries has often been economically successful. However, major improvements in organization and technique production, transport and marketing are needed if the more perishable vegetables are to be available regularly in quantity and at low prices.

Livestock Products. Animal protein foods are preferred by most consumers and contain other constituents important in human nutrition. Milk is produced in surplus in North America and northern Europe at a high level of consumption, which may recede. In the Far East, excluding Japan, and in Africa, however, milk production per inhabitant is very low and the cost high. In India, a pint of milk daily would absorb half of the average consumer's disposable income. There are many technical difficulties in increasing milk production in the developing countries,

Continued

Pulses, Oilseeds, and Nuts	Vegetables	Fruit	Meat and Poultry	Eggs	Fish	Milk and Products
7	2	—	1	—	6	2
16	4	—	2	—	13	4
14	1	—	1	—	—	5
27	2	—	2	—	--	10
7	2	—	6	—	7	1
12	4	—	11	—	12	2
13	4	—	3	1	12	1
19	6	—	5	1	18	1
4	1	—	1	—	1	5
9	2	—	2	—	2	11
2	3	1	4	1	7	1
4	6	2	9	2	15	2
6	1	—	2	1	4	4
13	2	—	4	2	9	9
2	2	1	37	3	3	18
2	2	1	40	3	3	20
2	2	1	36	5	3	28
2	2	1	34	5	3	27

particularly if it is to be at a low cost.   Consequently skim milk powder produced in surplus to the needs of developed countries has been, as a low-priced protein food, an important element in new milk distribution projects for urban centers.   It is reconstituted with water and mixed with locally produced cow or buffalo milk to produce "toned" milk, or vegetable fats may be added to produce "filled" milk.   These surpluses have been reduced in the last year or two, largely as a result of a strong increase in the use of skim milk powder in animal feeds, but it might be possible with appropriate adjustments in government support programs to induce the production of enough to make a significant impact in developing regions.

The most attractive source of protein in many countries is meat, subject to some religious bans.   Consumption rises sharply with income—e.g., 200 pounds per capita or more annually in North America.   Ghana, relatively prosperous because of cocoa export earnings, was able to attract meat imports from her northern neighbors and from overseas to reach a consumption of 20 pounds per person per annum, as against only 2.2 to 4.4 pounds in nearby Liberia and Sierra Leone. With cocoa prices declining and public nonfood expenditure augmented, these imports have been cut back.

While there are parts of Africa, for example, with good potential for increased livestock production, the pest and disease control measures and changes in management practice required are formidable. It is unlikely that meat production in the developing countries can be increased very rapidly in the immediate future. Prospects of expanding the supply and consumption of poultry meat are perhaps rather brighter than for other meats, given the high feed conversion productivity of modern broiler strains and the general acceptability of chicken meat. However, at present there are no signs of production costs falling below the U.S. level, which means that poultry meat will still be an expensive protein to low income populations. This also applies to eggs, though improvements in the type and management of birds kept on a scavenging basis could help at the local level.

Fish. Marketing problems limit the consumption of fish in many parts of the developing world. However, dried fish is a major source of protein in tropical Africa, as are fermented and dried fish in parts of Asia. Fish and new fish protein concentrates can be expected to compete advantageously with other protein foods up to the limit of the supply. Since some 10 of the estimated 45 million tons of fish caught at present are reduced to meal for animal feeding, there seems no immediate likelihood of a shortage. However, to get these fish to potential consumers would involve major investments in marketing equipment, some extra costs, and the important question of foreign exchange availability.

The long-run prospects for fish as a protein source are of particular interest, both because it competes less directly with other food for productive resources, and because the political and social issues involved in expanding supplies may be much less complicated than for livestock, for example. The potential world harvest of fish, using the traditional hunting-type methods of exploitation, and without endangering known stocks, has been estimated conservatively as approximately 115 million tons, or about 2.5 times the present level (*9*).

Processed Plant Protein Concentrates. While protein from soybeans prepared according to traditional methods has maintained dietary standards in the Far East for centuries, the use of new protein-rich foods based on these sources elsewhere is still very limited (Table V).

It is essential that such products appeal to the consumer and be capable of introduction into existing marketing channels in such a way as to reach consumers who are not otherwise getting enough protein. A difficulty is that commercial feed grade oilcake is not usually a suitable raw material for human food. Special processing is often necessary and also careful selection and handling of raw material to avoid developing toxic substances and to remove or minimize indigenous biologically deleterious compounds. Consequently edible protein concentrates from oilseeds packaged for commercial distribution tend to cost several times as much as commercial feed grade oil cake though they remain a relatively cheap source of protein (*1*)

Table III.   Protein Requirements and Supplies Available
(Grams per capita daily) (*3, 6*)

	Requirements	Supplies
U. S. A.	40	92
Canada	42	95
Australia	45	92
New Zealand	44	105
Britain	44	86
France	47	96
Germany, Federal Republic	44	79
Greece	49	95
Ireland	45	96
Italy	46	77
Sweden	48	81
Switzerland	44	90
Yugoslavia	52	96
Argentina	42	98
Brazil	45	61
Chile	46	77
Colombia	48	48
Mexico	44	68
Peru	48	58
Ceylon	47	45
China (Taiwan)	42	57
India	48	51
Japan	43	67
Pakistan	46	46
Philippines	46	47
Israel	44	83
Libya	47	53
Turkey	45	90
U.A.R.	45	76
Mauritius	42	46
South Africa	41	73

**Table IV.   Protein Intake Daily Per Capita and Potential
Oilseed Availability: Illustrative Countries (1960-62) (3, 4)**

Countries	Population (Millions Average) (1960–62)	Animal Proteins, G.	Oilseed Proteins, G.	
			Actual	Potential on Basis of Production
Mexico	36.1	23	1.4	15.8
Brazil	71.8	18	3.3	15.7
Colombia[a]	14.3	20	0.4	7.3
Peru	9.9	14	0.1	11.6
U.A.R.	26.9	12	0.6	15.8
Nigeria	50.0	5	1.8	14.6
Pakistan	95.8	8	—	5.3
India	450.5	6	0.6	8.8
Ceylon	10.2	8	2.5	15.3
Philippines	28.3	14	1.1	8.8
China (Taiwan)	11.7	15	6.2	8.5

[a] 1960–61.

Protein Isolates.   These products tend to be expensive, and there are still insufficient data for predicting large-scale use in the future.   However, their incorporation in ice cream, as in Japan, is seen as providing an initial basis for commercial processing and marketing operations in a country like India.   It might then be easier to develop less remunerative but more nutritionally desirable lines, possibly with government assistance.

Unconventional Sources of Food Protein.   Food yeast can be produced in large quantities at comparatively low cost.   There are large-scale facilities in several countries, but because of difficulties in making it attractive, its use in human nutrition has met little success.

Problems in using green leaves as a protein food include both color and taste as regards consumer acceptability and also variability in nutritive value.   So far no satisfactory and economic source of suitable raw material has been found.

Algae such as *Chlorella*, and proteins synthesized by solar energy or produced from yeast grown on paraffinic hydrocarbon fractions obtained from petroleum, appear to be promising sources.   Here again the problem is one of acceptability.   It may well be that such sources of protein will provide large quantities of animal feed in the future.   This could both reduce the cost of livestock products from human consumption and release for human use protein feed that would otherwise have been consumed by livestock.

of protein material than by converting it to animal protein. However, as Wright (*14*) has pointed out, many animals do not compete with the human for the type of food they eat. The ruminants, particularly, convert grass and grass products and other forages into more readily available and certainly more desirable forms of protein.

The protein from these sources is not only concentrated to provide a higher protein content of animal protein in the carcass of the animal, but much protein is added through the conversion in the rumen. Even where the animal may be competing with the human for certain types of food, as may be the case with the pig and the hen, these animals are producing a product desired by man. The 1965 estimated total production of meats for the 44 major producing countries is estimated to be 50.3 million tons (*12*).

Figure 1. Available total edible protein supplies

Phillips (*9*) has presented data which show the total protein supplies in grams per person per day for 43 countries and also the total animal protein by source available for those same countries. We have rearranged these data for the 10 high and 10 low countries in Figure 1 to show the available protein in grams per person per day supplied by meat, poultry, and eggs, which are the subject of this particular discussion.

The ten countries low in supplies of animal protein available for human consumption provide from 5 to 14 grams per person per day, in contrast to 51 to 74 grams in countries where edible animal protein is more plentiful. The difference between the part of these totals produced from meat, poultry, and eggs is also striking, ranging from 2 to 6 grams in the lower group to 14 to 44 grams in the higher group. The balance of these animal protein supplies, of course, is provided by fish and by milk and milk products.

The total edible protein in grams per person per day for these same selected countries is presented in Figure 2. The ranges in total protein supply for the ten countries low in dietary animal protein are from 45 to 89.5 grams per person per day, whereas in the ten countries high in animal protein, it is from 60 to 105 grams. All of the high ten, except Sweden, have more than sufficient total supplies to meet the amounts recommended

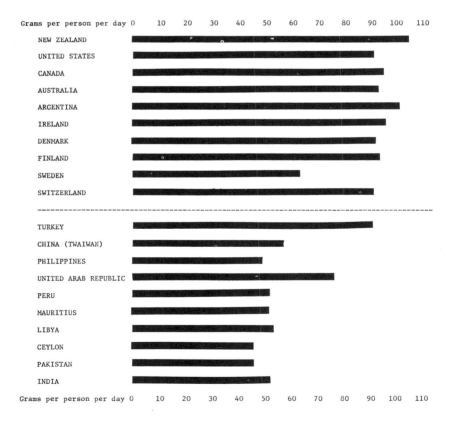

Figure 2. Available edible animal protein supplies

as the daily dietary allowances by the Food and Nutrition Board (*6*), which are 70 grams for men and 58 grams for women, with additional allowances during pregnancy and lactation. In the case of Sweden, the lower total is due to lesser supplies of vegetable protein. At least two (Turkey and the United Arab Republic) have a volume of total protein which will supply sufficient amounts, provided it is nutritionally adequate.

It is evident from these data that there are tremendous differences in the amount of animal protein and of total protein available per person in these selected 20 countries. The question before us is whether these animal protein supplies can be increased in the countries which are now low in their supply of animal protein and whether this is an economically possible or desirable thing to do. Altschul (*2*) has emphasized the inefficient use of great land areas and also the opportunity for improvement in efficiency of animal production.

As has been pointed out by Paddock (*8*), one of the fundamentals in advancement in underdeveloped countries is a determination of natural resources of that country and a concentrated effort to develop those natural resources. We are accepting as fact the thesis that the development of animal populations can be a natural resource in most of the countries that we are considering.

Beef

Beef animals fall within this category most frequently because they can be used as beasts of burden as well as to produce milk and meat. It is not unusual to require from 3 ½ to 6 years to produce a beef animal weighing 300 to 350 kg. and to require from 16 to 20 kg. of feed to produce each kilogram of live-weight animal.

When such is the case, the feed utilized to produce this animal is not material that is suitable for human consumption. It consists primarily of heavy forage grasses and any other forage the animal may be able to find. If we contrast this with the production of beef animals weighing 45 to 500 kg. in one year with the requirement of not more than 8 to 9 kg. of feed to produce each kilogram of live-weight animal, we can see the tremendous opportunity for improvement.

Part of this 8 to 9 kg. of feed is made up of feedstuffs that can be suitable for human consumption. However, much of the difference in time required may be accounted for by the periods of extremely low nutrition of these animals, such as occurs during extreme dry seasons. This may be reduced considerably by supplementing the forage diet of these animals during such periods of poor feed supplies. And this can be done, in part at least, by storing up feeds during the lush seasons and having it available for the animal during the dry seasons in a dry form and also by supplementing the low-protein roughages or grains with either protein supplement or nonprotein nitrogen supplements such as urea, when this commodity is available.

The most important point here, I believe, is that the reduction in time means that the same land area can produce many more animals: at least twice the number being produced today. This, then, means an increased food supply and vastly increases the amount of animal protein per person.

The same principle applies, of course, to the cows used for milk production, whether they be of dairy type, beef type, or a combination of the two. When we think of poultry, meat, and eggs, of course, we are talking about animals that do compete with the human for certain types of foodstuffs. However, the introduction of genetically improved strains has improved the efficiency of conversion very decidedly in our poultry stocks for producing poultry meat and eggs.

Poultry

In this country we have seen the broiler improve in efficiency until we have finally broken the goal of 3-pound broilers, live-weight, in 6 weeks on less than 2 pounds of feed per pound of broiler. This is contrasted with a requirement of approximately 9 weeks and 2.6 pounds of feed per pound of live broiler conversion not more than 10 years ago.

The efficiency of production, of course, varies considerably in different areas of the world, but there are tremendous opportunities for improvement if we accept as typical the production of a 2½ to 3-pound chicken with a feed requirement of at least 3 pounds of feed per pound of live chicken produced in less developed areas.

Eggs, of course, are recognized as one of the most complete and most nutritious sources of protein for the human being. Egg protein is used as a standard in many of the studies conducted today on the adequacy of protein from various sources. Here again there is tremendous room for improvement in both numbers of eggs produced per hen and the amount of feed required to produce those eggs.

When we are thinking of poultry, whether for meat or eggs, we are dealing with a class of animal that lends itself to low investment enterprises which may be started on a rather small scale and developed as the knowledge and economy progress. Man has learned to domesticate the fowl, and poultry production has emerged as a major industry in highly developed countries. The problems usually encountered in starting this type of enterprise in new, undeveloped areas are lack of capital, lack of knowledge of necessary technology, lack of proper feed supplies, and transportation problems. Here is a wonderful opportunity to develop the arts of management and the science of feeding along with the dissemination of highly improved stocks with greatly increased efficiencies and to provide foods that are much desired by the human.

Pigs

Another class of animal which is used to provide tremendous amounts of animal protein is, of course, the pig. Here again there are very decided opportunities to improve efficiencies in meat production from this source. Here also we have an animal that is competing somewhat with the human for the source of food. This animal requires a concentrated rather than a bulky type of feed and as such is competing for grains as a source of energy. The sources of protein are usually obtained primarily from oilseeds utilizing inedible (by humans) as well as edible supplies, but in addition, meat scraps, tankage, and inedible fish meals provide very important sources of protein for this class of animals. This animal also scavenges food waste resulting from the preparation of foods for human use.

It is evident then that there can be great improvements in efficiencies in producing animals as protein sources from the standpoint of both time, which would greatly increase numbers, and also more efficient utilization of the inputs of feed. Additionally, when we consider the fact that ruminants can make efficient use of nonprotein nitrogen in forming proteins

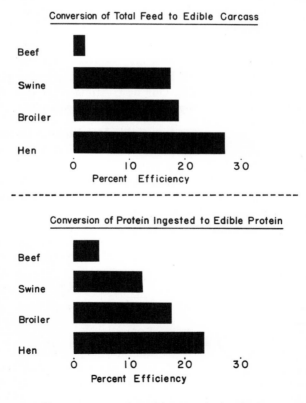

Figure 3. Conversion of ingested feed to food

Table 1.   Amino Acid Composition of

(Amino acids as grams

Amino Acid	Pork (3)	Lamb (3)	Beef (3)	Poultry Meat (4)
Alanine	6.30	6.30	6.40	—
Arginine	6.35	6.86	6.56	6.70
Cystine	1.31	1.34	1.35	1.80
Methionine	2.50	2.32	2.32	1.70
Phenylalanine	4.14	3.94	4.02	3.60
Tyrosine	3.02	3.21	3.24	2.10
Leucine	7.53	7.42	8.40	6.30
Isoleucine	4.89	4.78	5.07	4.20
Lysine	7.77	7.65	8.37	7.40
Threonine	5.12	4.88	4.04	3.90
Valine	4.97	5.00	5.71	6.50
Tryptophan	1.35	1.32	1.10	0.70

suitable for human use, there is an additional economic reason for considering this source of protein in the human dietary.

Efficiency of Conversion

Any discussion of efficiencies of conversion of feeds by animals must consider conversion of total feed to edible carcass and conversion of ingested protein to edible protein. Our best estimates of these conversions are presented in Figure 3. They have been obtained from various sources

Table II.   Vitamin Content of Some

	Thiamine, Mg./100 G.	Riboflavin, Mg./100 G.	Niacin, Mg./100 G.	B₆, Mg./100 G.
Beef (3)				
Chuck	0.08	0.17	4.5	0.38
Round	0.09	0.18	4.8	0.37
Pork (3)				
Ham	0.77	0.19	4.1	0.42
Loin	0.83	0.20	4.4	0.50
Lamb (3)				
Leg	0.16	0.22	5.1	0.26
Loin	0.14	0.20	4.7	0.22
Poultry (11, 13)				
Broiler	0.04	0.26	3.76	2.0(13)
Whole egg (5)	0.10	0.29	0.10	—
Soybean (7)				
(solv. ext.)	0.66	0.33	2.68	—
Cottonseed (7)				
(solv. ext.)	0.81	0.46	4.55	—

Some Selected Food Sources
per 16 G. N)

Whole Egg (1)	Wheat (1)	Corn (1)	Rice (1)	Soybean Meal (1)	Cotton-Seed Flour (1)
—	—	7.50	5.20	—	—
6.49	4.43	4.80	7.20	7.00	11.30
—	—	2.00	1.50	—	—
3.85	0.68	3.10	3.00	1.10	1.61
5.71	3.83	5.00	5.00	4.80	5.20
3.63	3.66	6.00	5.70	3.20	—
8.78	6.30	15.00	8.20	7.60	6.23
5.67	4.68	6.40	5.20	5.80	3.94
7.24	3.06	2.30	3.20	6.60	4.16
5.29	2.81	3.70	3.80	3.90	3.36
8.79	4.00	5.30	6.20	5.20	4.84
1.31	1.36	0.60	1.30	1.20	1.55

but primarily from unpublished data (10). The laying hen, given credit for the carcass as well as the eggs produced, is the most efficient of this group in converting feed to food, from the standpoint of both total feed ingested and conversion of protein to edible protein. The protein in the ration may be partly from inedible sources, such as inedible fish meals and oilseeds, depending upon the area. The broiler, or young meat chicken, ranks second in efficiency while swine, using rations of similar type, rank above beef cattle in converting total feed consumed but approximately the same inconversion of protein (12.5 *vs.* 12.8%). The very poor performance of the

Selected Meat Cuts (Raw)

Pantothenic Acid— Mg./100 G.	Biotin, μ G./100 G.	Choline, Mg./100 G.	B_{12}, μ G./100 G.	Folic Acid, Mg./100 G.
—	—	—	—	0.013
1.0	4.6	68	2.0	0.26
0.72	5.3	120	0.9	0.009
2.0	5.5	77	—	0.007
0.59	5.9	84	2.5	0.009
—	—	—	—	—
6.40(13)	—	—	—	—
2.70	22.5	532.0	28.2	0.009
1.45	—	274.3	—	0.07
1.78	—	286.2	—	0.09

beef animal is mitigated by the fact that the material converted is, in part, very low in nutrient value, and definitely not edible for humans. Conversion of calories in the feed to calories available to the human is likewise of a very low order, but the figures available are much less definitive than those for protein conversion.

However, the beef carcass with 22% fat has an average of 995 calories per pound; the pork carcass with 42% fat has 1827 calories per pound; and chicken fryers with 3.33% fat have only 382 calories per pound. The laying hen carcass with 14.4% fat has 784 calories per pound, and eggs with 10.35% fat have 658 calories per pound (11). These animals do not contribute calories in proportion to their protein efficiencies, but the contribution in this area is significant and must not be ignored.

These figures illustrate dramatically the well-known fact that the production of animals results in much less total food supply where animals are consuming foods that might be used for human consumption. However, lack of precise figures on composition of carcasses, variability in supplementary foods, dietary habits, and other considerations, prevents valid comparisons of the nutritional value to the human of the food eaten by animals and that provided by the animal. This food will vary in different areas and may be principally wheat, corn, or rice, and as available, beans, legumes, or other higher protein sources.

Amino Acids

The amino acid content of selected portions of the carcass of these animals shows marked contrasts as compared with some of the more common vegetable and cereal proteins that are in use (Table I). The lysine content of the meats is noticeably higher and may therefore be used to correct dietary deficiencies. Egg protein is considered one of the most complete proteins for human use, followed very closely by milk.

In general, all of these animal proteins are more nearly complete in their amino acid pattern as required by the human than are the usual vegetable or cereal proteins, particularly those from the cereal grains which provide a very large portion of the protein intake for people in many countries. It is true that the amino acid deficiencies of these cereal proteins can be corrected by adding amino acids. But from a practical standpoint, there are still the problems of, first, the education of the average consumer to know the specific amino acids that are deficient and the means of correcting them; secondly, the quantity of amino acids to be added without creating an imbalance in the resulting product; third, cost of supplementing with synthetic amino acids or with natural food sources which are high in the specific amino acids needed; and, fourth, the availability of the necessary sources of amino acids to correct these deficiencies. In other words, for some time to come, it is going to be necessary to find the most complete diet possible if we are to avoid specific deficiencies. This means that there is a place for meat proteins in the diet.

In Table II we present selected vitamin analysis of some of the more common meats. This is a plus factor, and here again we find instances where meats are the primary sources of certain vitamins. This is particularly true of B-12, and the animal proteins are important sources of many of the others, such as thiamin, niacin, and pantothenic acid.

Conclusions

The controversial subject of animal fats will not be argued here. Suffice it to say that fats are a good source of energy and that inevitably animal proteins are accompanied by a certain quantity of fat, which adds greatly to the energy supply of the world.

Since time immemorial man has looked to animals to supply a very substantial part of his food. He has also learned to make better and more intelligent use of certain vegetable sources of protein, such as soybeans, cottonseed, and peanuts, and we will expect these products to be much more useful as new and more desirable methods of preparation are devised. However, it has been the history of the human race, that as the economic level of the population improves, the quantity of meat, milk, and eggs included in the diet increases.

We are looking forward to an improvement in the economic status of all countries of the world, and as we approach this goal, we expect that the human race will not only continue to use animal proteins as a substantial part of its food but will use increased amounts in proportion to the economic status. Certainly, we are all looking forward to attaining this goal.

Literature Cited

(1) Altschul, A. M., "Processed Plant Protein Foodstuffs," Academic Press, New York, 1958.
(2) Altschul, A. M., "Proteins, Their Chemistry and Politics," Basic Books, New York, 1965.
(3) American Meat Institute Foundation, "Summary of the Nutrient Content of Meat," Bull. **57** (1964).
(4) Block, R. J., Weiss, K. W., "Amino Acid Handbook," Charles C. Thomas, Springfield, Ill., 1956.
(5) Everson, G. J., Souders, H. J., *J. Am. Dietet. Assoc.* **33**, 1244 (1957).
(6) Food and Nutrition Board, Washington, D. C., "Recommended Dietary Allowances," Natl. Acad. Sciences-Natl. Res. Council, Pub. **589** (1958).
(7) Joint United States–Canadian Tables of Food Composition, Natl. Acad. Sci.–Natl. Res. Council, **1232** (1964).
(8) Paddock, W., Paddock, P., "Hungry Nations," Little Brown & Co., Boston, 1964.
(9) Phillips, R. W., "Problems on Increasing Food Production and Their Relation for Future Programs for the Benefit of the Preschool Child," International Conference on Prevention of Malnutrition in the Preschool Child, Washington, D. C., December 1964.

(10) Ralston Purina Co., unpublished data, 1965.
(11) U. S. Dept. Agriculture, "Composition of Foods," Agr. Handbook **8** (1963).
(12) U. S. Dept. Agriculture, Economic Research Service, Foreign Agricultural Economic Report, **22** (1965).
(13) Waisman, H. A., Elvehjem, C. A., "Vitamin Content of Meat," Burgess Publishing Co., Minneapolis, 1941.
(14) Wright, N. C., "Current Food Supply Situation and Present Trends," in "Hunger. Can It be Averted," E. J. Russel and N. C., Wright, eds., British Association for Advancement of Science, London, 1961.

RECEIVED October 12, 1965.

General Outlook For Milk Proteins

D. V. JOSEPHSON

The Pennsylvania State University, University Park, Pa.

Milk protein holds great promise for the future nutrition of man. Unfortunately, three-fourths of today's milk is produced in Europe, North America, and Oceania with only one-fourth of world's population. Milk production is possible in all developing nations, and concerted efforts are being made to establish milk industries throughout the world. Increasing population pressure questions our ability to support animal agriculture which competes for the plant protein supply. Ruminants by their unique microbiological digestive process are capable of utilizing crude forms of protein-free nutrients and synthesizing animal protein; the cow can produce normal milk protein without protein in her diet. Our reservoir of scientific resources should permit milk protein to remain in our scheme of food production for future generations.

As we analyze the present and view the future prospects for milk proteins in the human diet, we must take a very hard look at the problem in all its aspects. From the beginning of recorded history, we find evidence that milk and other animal protein foods have played an important role in man's nutrition and development. The strong and stable nations and cultures have all been developed and maintained with the help of a system of animal agriculture. The ruminant, particularly the dairy cow, has played an important role in this picture through her unique ability to convert crude forms of forage and grains into milk, a high quality protein food for man.

As the human population explodes at an alarming rate, the prospect of man's having to compete with animals for the products of the soil looms larger. We are more frequently being confronted by the question, "How long will we be able to afford the luxury of utilizing our lands for forage and grain production to produce the highly refined animal protein foods?" Domestic animals are admittedly relatively inefficient in their conversion of feed to human foods. The dairy cow converts only 23% of the protein she consumes into milk and meat, the beef animal only 10%, and the pig 12%.

These facts viewed in the light of current food production trends throughout the world add up to a rather dismal picture. One billion of the 3 billion humans on the earth are already underfed or malnourished, and prospects for rapid improvement are not very bright. A recent report by the USDA Economic Research Service (4) suggests that the less-developed countries of the world are clearly losing the capacity to feed themselves and that a growing share of the increase in population is being sustained by food shipments from the developed countries. The report attributes this situation to the fact that the densely populated, less-developed countries have nearly exhausted the supply of new land that can be brought under cultivation. Since nearly half of the world's population lives in these less-developed countries, the problem cannot be passed over lightly.

Irrespective of what has been or will be said about the merits or potential of the protein products of the sea, the plant proteins, the seed proteins, or the synthetic protein foods of the future, the vast majority of humans are not yet prepared to give up the foods that come from an animal agriculture. There are many hopeful signs on the horizon, and I feel confident that with the scientific ingenuity at our disposal and with the many national and international agencies now actively attacking these problems, solutions will be found.

Present Status of Milk Production

Many of the less-developed and emerging nations of the world are in dire need of animal proteins. At the present time the populations of the Far East obtain only 6% of their caloric intake from animal products. Those living in Africa average 7%, while those inhabiting the Near East get 8% of their calories from this source (5). When these are compared with the diet of the North American, who derives 35% of his calories from animal products, the problem begins to come into focus. This disparity exists in spite of the fact that most of the countries in the low animal-calorie regions are basically agricultural and frequently possess large livestock holdings. In Kenya, East Africa, for example, a country of 8,600,000 inhabitants, there are a cattle population of nearly 7 million, about a quarter of a million camels, and 13 million sheep and goats. Most of the cattle are kept for reasons of prestige in the community and with complete disregard for quality and economic considerations. As veterinary services have improved and disease control practices have been adopted, the number of these unproductive cattle has increased, bringing further deterioration of pastures and soil. It has been reported that at least 20 milking cows are required to supply the milk needed by one nomadic farm family (*12*). The calf takes precedence over the needs of man, so a yield of 200 ml. to 2 liters of milk per day is about all that can be expected from these native cattle during their short lactation periods.

India, a predominantly agricultural country with a population of 440 million people, has a cattle population of 220 million. Admittedly a substantial number of these cattle used for draft purposes, and other non-milk producers are kept because of religious beliefs and customs which prohibit their slaughter. Approximately 48.5 billion pounds of milk are produced in India per year, about 5 ounces per person per day. However, 60% of this milk is converted into milk by-products, particularly ghee, the manufacture of which results in an almost total loss of the milk protein (*9*).

Conversely, in the developed nations of Europe, North America, and Oceania, milk production and the milk-processing industries have developed dramatically over the past 25 years. On these three continents where only one fourth of the world population lives, three fourths of the world's milk is produced (*14*). From USDA reports we find that in 1945 the United States had 27.7 million dairy cows that produced slightly less than 120 billion pounds of milk. Today we have 10 million fewer cows (17.6 million) producing nearly 127 billion pounds of milk. The average production per cow per year has risen 2000 pounds in the past 10 years to a present level of 7880 pounds. The cows in herds under the Dairy Herd Improvement programs (1.7 million cows) averaged 11,685 pounds last year and are still increasing at a uniform rate of about 2% per year. This has been possible through genetic improvement, greatly improved methods of feeding and management, and the development of markets and economically sound marketing methods. In North America we consume about 1 quart of milk (in all its forms) per capita per day, while the **average** Asian is limited to about 1 quart equivalent every 14 days (*3*).

The milk production potential of the United States has never been tested. We are producing adequate amounts to meet the needs of our people with a 5 to 7 billion pound surplus annually. Our efficiency of production improves each year and more milk is being produced per acre than ever before. This trend promises to continue for some time to come. The current annual production per cow of 7880 pounds in the United States is far below the potential. Many well managed herds now average 15,000 to 16,000 pounds per cow per year and it is predicted that the national average could reach that level in the foreseeable future. Many other developed countries have the land, climate, cattle, and technical capability to attain much higher levels of milk production if the demand arises. I feel confident that the developed nations of the world will be able to afford the luxury of milk and its products in the foreseeable future and still supply a limited amount of milk protein foods to their less fortunate brothers in the less-developed and emerging nations.

The Problem

Possibly no group now working in the international field is better informed on this problem and its many ramifications than the Animal Production and Health Division of the United Nations Food and Agricultural Organization. The chief of the Dairy Branch of the FAO, Hans Pedersen and his associates have analyzed this problem in the light of the predicted doubling of the world's population by the year 2000 (*14, 15*). They contend, through experience in many countries, that milk production is possible in any country of the world but that production alone without a system of processing and distribution is futile. Native farmers who respond to programs of genetic improvement and forage production are frequently discouraged by the fact that they have no nearby market for their surplus milk over family needs. When they do find a market it is often one for cream, in which case they must feed the skim milk to their cattle or discard it. FAO contends that the need in the world is not for butterfat but for the milk protein in the skim milk. Some very substantial progress has been made on this particular problem. Through FAO and UNICEF cooperation and help several rural cooperative milk processing centers have been developed in Kenya. These diesel-powered plants, which were built in very remote areas of this agricultural country, started by receiving as little as 12 gallons of milk per day (2 gallons per farmer), but now they process over 1000 gallons a day each (*12, 13*). These plants have provided a market for the milk produced and thereby stimulated further production by the native farmers. Contrary to common belief, it has been demonstrated that the climates of the tropics and subtropics are not serious obstacles to milk production by highly productive dairy cattle. Israel and other hot countries have introduced environmental modifications which make it possible for European and American breeds to produce milk at levels comparable to that in their countries of origin (*10*).

Processing Facilities

Assuming that efficient milk production could be established in all of the less-developed countries of the world, a very substantial problem of plant processing facilities would exist. A very recent analysis by the FAO Dairy Branch (*14, 15*) is based on the fact that one billion people in the world are underfed or malnourished. With this existing base and with the assumption that the world population is increasing at a rate of 50 millions per year, they have made some projections as to the need for new dairy processing plants over the next 10 years. Assuming that the present 1 billion underfed were to receive only 0.25 liter (0.26 U.S. quart) of milk equivalent per day, there would be an immediate need for 2500 new processing plants each with a capacity of 100,000 liters per day. In addition, to provide milk at the same rate for the anticipated increase in population over the next ten years would require 125 more new plants of the same size each year.   Put together this means that by 1976, 3650 new plants of 100,000-liter capacity would have to be built.   In other words, one new plant would have to be built, equipped, and opened each day of the year for the next ten years even to catch up.   Then, at the end of 1975, we would have processing capacity to provide milk and milk products for the underfed and the increased population at a consumption rate only one fourth that of the current per capita utilization on the North American continent.

Outlook

The outlook for increasing milk protein resources is not a simple matter.   Were it merely a clear-cut problem of production, processing, and distribution, the future might lend itself to some sort of concrete prediction. Unfortunately, when one considers the problem with its many complicated sociological, political, economic, geographic, climatic, religious, and bio-logical variables intertwined it becomes a far greater problem than a mere dairy and food scientist can cope with.   Of one thing we can be sure, progress will be slow and difficult.   A specific example should demonstrate this point.   One essential step in promoting dairy industry development throughout the world was the establishment of a world-wide code of principles covering standards of identity and analytical methods for milk and milk products.   Such a code, now adopted by 58 countries, required nearly 10 years of intensive work by the International Dairy Federation, the World Health Organization, and FAO (7).

There are, however, a few obvious conclusions that one can draw from history and the experience of those who have been struggling with this problem for a number of years.   There are also some untested possibilities that can and should be considered for the future.

At the outset it is obvious that charity, the shipment of nonfat dry milk or milk in other forms to needy nations, is not the permanent solution to the problem.   Charity temporarily alleviates starvation in periods of famine and will cure infants and children of the protein-deficiency disease kwashiorkor, but it does not begin to provide the basic and continuing needs of the population as a whole.

Likewise, the problem cannot be solved by much talking and quoting of statistics.   Up to a point this defines the problem and helps develop methods for solution, but sooner or later action programs must be initiated.

An oft-quoted ancient Chinese proverb may well be the key to the problem of providing a more adequate supply of milk protein around the world: "Give a man a fish and he will eat for a day.   Teach him to fish and he will eat for the rest of his life."   Education is one of the essential ingredients needed to solve the food problems of the world. Not education as we view it in the United States, where the bachelor's, master's, or doctor's degrees are the goal of millions, but education in the broadest sense, which starts with enlightening the masses at the most elementary level. The heart of the problem starts with the fact that illiteracy and hunger are usually found together. A hungry man cannot work efficiently and thereby develop purchasing power to acquire the food he needs. The internal social and economic status of a country must be conducive to developing the market for milk and other quality foods before production of these foods within that country can be undertaken successfully.

At the level of milk production, education again must play an important role. It is generally recognized that the dairy industry in the less-developed nations must literally emerge from the grass roots and that the mere acquisition of a knowledge of the technology of cattle management, feed, and pasture production is not enough. This knowledge must be conveyed to the peasant. In most of these countries, where the majority of cattle owners are illiterate and the more enlightened have little more than 4 to 5 years of schooling, the problem becomes a real challenge (2). Programs are now emerging in which formal and informal training is being accomplished through such elementary techniques as word of mouth, reading, memorizing, watching, and doing under supervision. It is a monumental task but a necessary one.

Once the markets, the initiative to produce, and the system of distribution are developed, the plane of nutrition should rise and give further impetus to social and economic progress.

No one is so idealistic as to believe that the deficiency of milk protein in the world can be corrected overnight. The best laid plans and goals must be keyed to other related economic, social, and political factors which must evolve through an evolutionary rather than a revolutionary process. The philosophy of FAO on this point is well expressed by the following quotation (14).

Don't try to solve all problems at one go! If you cannot get a pint of milk a day, then get a pint every other day or at least every week. Do whatever you can with the available resources—but do it now!

For the present, therefore, we should be reconciled to the fact that those nations that "have" will need to continue to help provide the milk protein for those that "have not."

This help, both by donation and through normal trade channels, will of necessity be confined largely to nonfat dry milk, which normally contains about 36% milk protein. This product is considered the most valuable source of complementary protein for the malnourished and lends itself to distribution and storage conditions prevalent throughout the world (11, 20). A program has recently been adopted wherein all nonfat dry milk moving overseas under the U.S. Public Law 480 program will be fortified with vitamins A and D (*20*). This product, properly reconstituted in potable water, will at least meet the minimum needs for infants, children, and mothers who might otherwise get little or no animal protein in their diets. For countries with limited milk supplies and for those which will develop modest milk supplies in the future, dry milk can be used for "toning," a practice of blending local high-fat milk supplies with reconstituted nonfat dry milk (*6, 14*). This method of dry milk utilization appears to hold much promise for augmenting the milk protein supplies of countries struggling to develop and expand their own systems of milk production. At about 23 cents per pound of milk protein, nonfat dry milk is one of the cheapest forms of animal protein available on the world market (*6*). For this reason it is particularly well suited to the developing countries which are seeking practical solutions to their animal protein problems. In 1964 the United States produced 2.2 billion pounds of food grade nonfat dry milk, and we have the capability to produce much more.

The ultimate goal, however, should be to develop dairy industries in all countries of the world and, wherever possible, they should be founded predominantly on local milk production. Then, and only then, can a population be assured of a continuous and adequate supply of milk protein

A Bold Look Ahead

We have seen that by expanding the use of our existing scientific knowledge, disseminating the technology of the more developed countries, and sharing our own resources we can help meet the growing need for milk protein for many years in the future. However, we have still not answered the question, "Will the day come when we must begin to think of abandoning our animal agriculture so that released land can be used for more direct and intensive production of human food?" The passing of feed materials through animals is not the most efficient means of human food production, although the quality and palatability of the ultimate product are greatly enhanced. It may not be too early to consider some bold and radical alternatives to our conventional method of producing milk protein. Let's examine one possibility.

Ruminant animals—cattle, sheep, and goats—may offer us a unique opportunity to maintain an animal agriculture almost indefinitely. These animals are all characterized by having a four-part stomach, the first of which is the rumen. This organ does not possess animal enzymes but, rather, contains billions and billions of bacteria and protozoa. These microorganisms actually bring about the digestion of the feed materials which the animals eat. The cow or sheep thereby derives its nutrients by absorbing the soluble products of the microbial fermentations or by actually digesting the microorganisms in the lower digestive tract.

We already know that the rumen microorganisms synthesize the B vitamins and the essential amino acids which are secreted in milk. The question we wish to raise is, "Can we extend the usefulness of the rumen microorganisms beyond what we now require of them?" By this we mean, "Is it possible to have these organisms synthesize more and more of the essential nutrients a cow requires so that they need not be provided in the animal's diet?"

The pioneering studies of A. I. Virtanen, Nobel Laureate from Finland, indicate that this may indeed be feasible (17, 18, 19). Virtanen has been working with highly purified diets for milk production by the bovine species. These diets are composed of purified starch, sucrose, α-cellulose, urea, a mere trace of corn oil, ammonium sulfate, ammonium phosphate, 16 other minerals, and vitamins A and D.

The dairy cows fed this ration over extended periods of time have maintained normal body functions, body weight, and reproduction. Milk production has been maintained at about half the level of normal high producers, or about 4500 pounds per year. The major point of interest here is that this milk is completely normal in every respect—its content of proteins, vitamins, and the other normal chemical constituents is the same as that of milk from animals fed normal, complete diets. This observation has far-reaching implications, because it demonstrates that the ruminant is potentially capable of producing milk protein without competing for the available plant protein supply. In this study, high quality animal protein food was produced without feeding the animal any protein whatsoever. Virtanen states: "If a cheap, sufficiently digestible carbohydrate feed can be prepared from straw, wood, sugar cane waste, or other fast-growing plants of the same kind, or even synthetically, it may be possible to remove, by milk production, protein and vitamin deficiency in vast areas inhabited by undernourished peoples" (18).

An example of a useful raw material of this nature is the 15 billion pounds of whey that is available each year as a by-product of the cheese industry in the United States. At present whey poses a serious disposal problem. A process has been developed in our laboratories at The Pennsylvania State University for the production of a high-nitrogen cattle feed from this whey by fermentation with Lactobacillus bulgaricus, followed by treatment with anhydrous ammonia to neutralize the lactic acid formed (1). Animals performed satisfactorily when this material was included in their ration as a source of nitrogen, although problems of palatability were encountered and are yet to be solved (8).

Research should begin really to test the potential of rumen microorganisms to support animals when they are receiving an odd variety of materials which have little or no food value to man or do not compete with land used for human food production. This work should also extend into studying what chemical or microbiological processes might transform substances, which we do not now consider feed materials, into highly desirable ingredients for the ration of the ruminant. Likewise, extensive studies on ways of improving the palatability of rations are needed. The classic and continuing studies of Virtanen have already shown that one amino acid, histidine, is apparently the most limiting factor in purified diets. This suggests that supplementation with this one amino acid might greatly increase the production of milk protein in animals receiving the purified or exotic diet. Now is the time for this type of information to be obtained so that when and if conditions require a modified animal agriculture, man will be prepared to maintain his plane of nutrition without drastic changes in his diet.

Summary

This discussion on the outlook for milk proteins has dealt primarily with the problems of the less-developed countries of the world because it is in these countries where the problems exist. The developed nations have adequate supplies and even surpluses now and will develop the capabilities needed to continue animal agriculture in their schemes of food production for the generations ahead. We should, nevertheless, be prepared to apply alternative methods of animal protein production which will not compete with supplies of plant protein needed for direct human consumption.

The immediate goal should be that of helping the milk-deficient nations develop independent milk production, processing, and distribution systems which, with some augmentation through imports of nonfat dry milk, will help elevate their plane of nutrition. This promises to be a long, tedious and monumental task which will be compounded by the pressures of population growth. The problem is not one that will be solved with our scientific and technological tools alone but will require an integrated effort in education and social change. With many organizations within the United Nations and other international, national, educational, and private agencies already actively working on these problems, and with the reservoir of scientific and technological resources at our disposal, there is certainly room for optimism.

Literature Cited

(1) Arnott, D. R., Patton, Stuart, Kesler, E. M., *J. Dairy Sci.* **41,** 931 (1958).
(2) Barrett, M. A., Working Paper 6, Agenda V, FAO International Meeting on Dairy Education, Paris, 1964.
(3) Brown, L. R., Proceedings of 60th Annual Meeting, ADSA, Lexington, Ky., 1965.
(4) Brown, L. R., U. S. Dept. Agriculture, Foreign Agr. Econ. Rept. **25** (1965).
(5) Food and Agriculture Organization, United Nations, UN, World Food Problems, No. **4** (1962).
(6) *Ibid.*, No. **5,** 38 (1964).

(7) Food and Agriculture Organization and WHO, "Code of Principles Concerning Milk and Milk Products," 4th ed., 1963.

(8) Hazzard, D. G., Kesler, E. M., Arnott, D. R., Patton, Stuart, *J. Dairy Sci.* **41,** 1439 (1958).

(9) Iya, K. K., Working Paper 7, Agenda V, FAO International Meeting on Dairy Education, Paris, 1964.

(10) Johnson, J. E., Proceedings of 60th Annual Meeting, ADSA, Lexington, Ky., 1965.

(11) Kon, S. K., FAO Nutritional Studies, No. **17** (1959).

(12) Mann, I., communication, Agenda Item 5, FAO International Meeting on Dairy Education, Paris, 1964.

(13) Mann, I., *Milk Hygiene (Geneva)* **647** (1962).

(14) Oberg, S., Alfa-Laval International (Special Issue), Tumba, Sweden, 1965.

(15) Pedersen, H., FAO, Rome, personal communications, 1965.

(16) Phillips, R. W., Publ. *Am. Assoc. Advance Sci.* **76,** 15 (1964).

(17) Virtanen, A. I., *Biochem. Z.* **338,** 443 (1963).

(18) Virtanen, A. I., *Suomen Kemistilehti B.* **36,** 83 (1963).

(19) Virtanen, A. I., Lampila, M., *Ibid.,* **35,** 244 (1962).

20) U.S. Dept. Agriculture, *Foreign Agr.* **3** (23), 8 (1965).

RECEIVED October 12, 1965.

4

General Outlook for Edible Fish Protein Concentrates

JOHN A. LOVERN

Torry Research Station, Ministry of Technology, Aberdeen, Scotland.

Oily species are probably the most abundant potential raw material for fish protein concentrates (FPC). Without solvent extraction FPC will contain up to 10% oil, usually highly rancid. Some people like rancid flavors, but there are nutritional objections. The oil can be stabilized by antioxidants or by partial replacement with vegetable oil, but there are technological problems. Partial removal of oil—e.g., with hexane— gives FPC with some remaining flavor and negligible nutritional hazard. Extraction with ethanol or 2-propanol removes all lipid but also all taste, and the FPC must be added to a staple food. Flavor "reversion" can be troublesome. Technological, economic, and sociological problems must still be overcome before FPC becomes an important commodity, but the outlook is promising.

In many quarters it is being said that man must turn increasingly to the oceans for the extra food needed by the world's growing population. Certainly the biggest part of the world food problem is the over-all deficit of high quality protein, and food from the ocean consists in the main of such protein. It is debatable, however, how far present fish and other seafood supplies can be increased, using the traditional approach in which the fish stocks are exploited by hunting but are not husbanded like farm animals. It may be that fish farming on a major scale will one day be accepted practice, but for the present purposes only the existing fisheries pattern is considered.

The world catch of fish in 1963 was 46.4 million metric tons (*12*). About one quarter of this was not caught for the human food market but for conversion into animal feedstuffs. This is a measure of the extent to which current supplies could yield additional food for direct human consumption. It is worthwhile to consider briefly the pattern of the world fish meal production. In 1963 meal made from oily-fleshed species amounted to 2,450,000 tons, whereas meal made from nonoily species, the so-called "white" fish meal, amounted to only 518,000 tons. By far the greater part of the oily meal was made from fish caught primarily for this purpose, whereas the white fish meal was mainly a by-product of the filleting of fish caught for the human market. On the whole, it is the oily pelagic species of fish that can be caught most cheaply and in the greatest quantities, so favoring their direct use for fish meal manufacture. Indeed, landings are often so heavy that only the fish meal industry could absorb them with present processing and distribution facilities.

It is ironic that some of the world's most protein-deficient populations are engaged in large scale exportation of protein in the form of fish meal. Outstanding is Peru, which in 1963 produced well over a million metric tons of meal from one species of oily fish (anchovy) and exported practically all of it. Other examples are Chile, South Africa, and Morocco. In all these countries schemes have been initiated to divert part of this fish supply for direct local human use, in the form of a fish protein concentrate (FPC), but to date none have gone beyond the pilot plant level of production. The present paper is largely concerned with some of the problems, many of them chemical, encountered in FPC production. The expanding world pattern of animal husbandry has created difficulties in meeting the demand for high quality protein in animal feedstuffs, and the present world demand for fish meal exceeds the supply. If FPC production becomes a ma or industry in such countries as Peru, there will be repercussions in the animal feedstuffs industry mainly affecting the affluent and well-fed countrieś most of which are big importers of fish meal.

It is possible that in some areas large stocks of fish occur which are not at present exploited. Thus the current U.S. Bureau of Commercial Fisheries FPC research project is based on the existence of largely untouched reserves of fish off the coasts of the United States, in particular red hake (24). But in the main any large scale production of FPC would be in direct competition with the fishmeal industry for supplies of raw material. In this respect it would resemble the development of fish-based pet foods and mink foods, and the answer would probably be the same; fishmeal manufacturers would participate in FPC production. There is much to be said for this on technical grounds.

Types of Product

The term "fish protein concentrate" is generally accepted as including any stable preparation from fish, intended for human consumption, in which the protein is more concentrated than in the original fish. The word "stable" is imprecise but in respect of most types of FPC has been tentatively defined as implying no significant deterioration in 6 months at

80°F. (27°C.) when packed in a hermetically sealed container (*11*). Fish meal is undoubtedly the cheapest potential fish protein concentrate, but is not intended for human consumption. Just how much cheaper it is than the more sophisticated products is illustrated by some data cited by Abbott (*1*). Anchovy meal f.o.b. Lima cost 10.5 U.S. cents per kg., with a protein content of 65%, compared with a deodorized, defatted Moroccan FPC, with 80% protein at 40 cents per kg. It is essential that FPC should be as cheap as possible, because of the poverty of its potential consumers. Is there any reason why ordinary fish meal should not be fed to protein deficient populations, even to babies and young children?

First fish meal is not normally made under sufficiently hygienic conditions to rule out the risk of occasional contamination by pathogenic bacteria. No conventional fish meal plant is so designed that all pockets of bacterial reinfection can be eliminated. In any case, it is not acceptable practice to produce human food and animal feed in the same plant. Completely separate premises, plant, and personnel would be needed, which could put up the price a little.

Second, although fish meal has given satisfactory results in animal rations, the animals in question are living on very carefully balanced diets, with adequate amounts of such things as fat-soluble vitamins. Malnourished humans generally suffer from multiple deficiencies. Fish meal typically contains rancid fat, which could conceivably precipitate a deficiency of fat-soluble vitamins. There are, however, a very few and quantitatively unimportant fish meals that do not become rancid.

Third, there is always a slight risk of cumulative toxic effects when a product that is not proved to be wholesome is fed over a very long period. Farm animals do not live out their full lifespan; often their life is extremely brief. Under a thoroughgoing scheme, humans would probably eat FPC every day from weaning to old age. Apart from its destructive effect on fat soluble vitamins, many nutritionists look askance at highly rancid fat, such as occurs in fish meal, as a possible toxic agent.

On the favorable side, many protein-deficient populations actually like the flavor of really rancid fish products. This does not, however, mean that the products are good for them. Some time ago an experiment was made in Peru with dried, whole anchovies. The Indian population in the Sierra country ate these with relish, despite their rancidity, or perhaps because of it! But illness followed, and the experiment had to be abandoned. Dried oily fish have a far higher oil content than fish meal made from the same raw material, so that this experience does not mean that anchovy meal would have produced the same troubles. But it does suggest the desirability of keeping the level of rancid fat in FPC as low as possible. White fish meal, with a crude fat content generally less than 6%, might be satisfactory, but some nutritionists would prefer to see it considerably lower and to think in terms of total fat, rather than crude fat, which means what can be extracted with ethyl ether or light petroleum. Badly oxidized and polymerized fat is not extracted by these solvents.

The amount of FPC suggested for inclusion in human diets should supply about 15 grams of protein; at about 70% protein content this means about 20 grams of FPC which, if it consisted of normal oily fish meal with about 10% residual oil, would contribute some 2 grams of rancid fat. It seems most unlikely that this quantity involves any significant risk and present thinking in the international agencies is that unsophisticated fish meal, if made under satisfactory processing conditions, might well be the best product for a large proportion of the world's potential FPC consumers.

Some workers advocate the use of commercial fish meal as raw material for further processing into FPC, typically by solvent extraction. The extensive South African research and pilot scale developments have been based on fish meal. Such use of fish meal ensures continuity and even rate of supply of raw material and permits maximal recovery of the best type of oil, since oil recovered by cooking and pressing as in fish meal manufacture is in general superior to that extracted by solvent for use in hydrogenated oil and margarine, although careful operation and use of suitable solvents can give oil of high quality. Solvent-extracted fish oil is more uniform and more stable than pressed oil, but where color is a factor, refining losses will be greater.

There is considerable experience showing that fish meal made from very fresh raw material—e.g., made at sea on factory ships—is easier to deodorize and deflavor by subsequent solvent extraction than meal made from staler raw material. A Polish project now in the development stages will be based on fish meal made at sea as raw material for solvent treatment ashore (22). Delay between manufacture of fish meal and subsequent solvent extraction also increases the difficulty of complete removal of odor and taste, because of oxidation and polymerization of the residual oil in the meal. There is much to be said for the use of freshly made press cake as raw material for subsequent solvent treatment, but continuity of supply could not be guaranteed, and no current project appears to be based on it.

Two types of FPC that are really sophisticated fishmeal are envisaged by the Protein Advisory Group of the United Nations Agencies most closely involved (FAO, UNICEF, and WHO). One (type A) is virtually odorless and tasteless and has a maximum total lipid content of 0.75%; the other (type B) has a maximum total lipid content of 3%, with no specified odor and flavor limits. Total lipid means material extracted in 6 hours by boiling ethanol. Much of it may, in fact, be nonlipid material. It is accepted that, even if rancid, the fat level in type B offers no significant nutritional hazard. Inevitably, however, solvent extraction is involved in the manufacture of such products, and the tentative specifications include zero levels of "harmful" solvent residues. As always, zero level specifications give trouble as analytical methods become more sensitive, but for these sophisticated products the tentative specifications also require safety tests with animals. Apart from solvent residues, there is always the possibility of toxic reaction products of solvent and fish.

There are types of FPC that are totally unlike fish meal. These are typically extensively hydrolyzed fish protein that resembles meat extract rather than fish. Hydrolysis may be either chemical or enzymatic, and the final products may be concentrated to a pasty consistency or incorporated into bouillon cubes. An example of the enzymatic approach is that of Bertullo (*3*), employing a proteolytic yeast, while HCl hydrolysis of white fish meal pre-extracted with water was used by Stachowski (*22*). So far the hydrolyzed products are a long way behind the variants of fish meal, in both development and potential demand.

Table I.   Analysis of Some Types of FPC

(G./100 G. dry matter)

Sample[a]	Protein	Fat	Ash
	(N × 6.25)		
Menhaden meal (*15*)	65	11	22
Herring meal (*15*)	76	11	11
Pilchard meal (*14*)	71	7	—
Ethanol-extracted (*8*) pilchard meal	79	0.6	19
2-Propanol extracted (*21*) cod flesh	96	0.03	5

[a] The first three samples are normal commercial fish meals (FPC type C), the fourth is FPC type A made from whole fish, the fifth FPC type A made from fillets only. These products are typical of many others. Type B is intermediate in fat content; it has received far less attention. Fat in the first four samples is crude (hexane) fat; in the last sample it is total ($CHCl_3$/MeOH) lipid.

Production Processes and Problems

It is not intended to discuss in detail all the methods that have been proposed or developed for producing the sophisticated fish meals known as FPC types A and B. A good summary of many of them has been given (*24*). Nor will any attempt be made to describe the manufacture of conventional fish meals. Rather will attention be concentrated on certain general processing features with particular reference to the chemical and physical problems that are associated with them. Any sophistication of conventional fish meal, whether the raw material is fresh fish, commercial fish press cake, or commercial fish meal, is essentially designed to remove undesired odors and flavors, or prevent undesired changes between manufacture and consumption.

The odorous and flavorous components of fish fall broadly into two groups, the water-soluble "extractives" which are largely responsible for the fishy taste and odor, and the water-insoluble lipids, which in their unaltered state have very little odor or taste but soon develop both as a result of atmospheric oxidation. When fish is cooked and pressed in the first stage of fish meal manufacture, no serious oxidation of the lipids occurs and the fresh press cake tastes and smells liked cooked fresh fish. When the press cake is dried into meal, oxidation sets in rapidly, in the dryer if this is of the flame type, or soon after if the dryer is of the steam or vacuum type. If this oxidation could be prevented, or even if its extent could be greatly reduced, the nutritionists' objections to hygienically prepared conventional fish meal would be met. This would seem a suitable item on which to commence more detailed consideration.

Since by the use of a suitable dryer fish meal can be made in which oxidation is scarcely significant, suggestions have been made that it should be gas-packed for storage and distribution. My own feeling is that, apart from expense, this method might well fail in the final stages of distribution and use after the large bulk containers had been opened. It is unrealistic to think in terms of small consumer-size gas-packed containers, remembering that the daily requirement per head is about 20 grams. In many areas where a strongly flavored FPC would be acceptable, it would be added at the domestic level to stews, etc., rather than incorporated into some centrally prepared cereal product such as bread. For a non-extracted oily fish meal we have to contemplate storage in the home, unprotected from atmospheric oxidation, for periods of weeks. It would also cheapen and simplify distribution if the bulk supplies were stable to atmospheric oxygen.

In the fish meal industry it is common practice, at least in the United States, to add about 0.1% of a permitted commercial antioxidant to the product as it leaves the dryer. The primary purpose of this addition is to reduce the subsequent rate of oxidation to the level at which spontaneous heating will not pose a fire hazard, or lead to nutritional damage. There is no intention or hope of preventing all oxidation, which has generally begun in the dryer anyway, and the treated meal has the typical flavor of fish meal, of which oxidized fish oil is a characteristic component. However, the drastic reduction in the extent of oxidation, as compared with fish meal that has had to undergo the alternative treatment known as "curing," should remove some of the nutritionists' doubts about rancid fat and make such fish meal comparable in this respect to FPC type B. The use of antioxidants, even if permitted in fish meal for animal feed in one particular country, is no guarantee that they will be accepted for human use by the authorities in another country, and the tentative specifications already mentioned (11) exclude the addition of antioxidants to oily fish meal (FPC type C) "unless permitted by the consuming country."

It would be a big technological advance if an antioxidant could be efficiently incorporated into press cake and could stabilize the fat right through the dryer. There are two practical difficulties associated, respectively, with addition and with retention of antioxidant. There are obvious difficulties in uniform incorporation of a very small percentage of a typical oil-soluble, water-insoluble antioxidant into a wet press cake, in which the oil droplets are dispersed at various levels. Even if this obstacle could be overcome, the commercial antioxidants normally used have vapor pressures high enough to result in their being largely lost in the dryer effluent gases. At least one manufacturer of solvent-extracted fish meal adds an antioxidant to the solvent. This will result in uniform distribution of antioxidant in any remaining lipid in the meal, as well as stabilizing the recovered oil.

Tocopherols are antioxidants that are both well distributed in fish tissues and have low vapor pressures. The amount of α-tocopherol in the flesh of many species of fish ranges from about 2 to 20 μg. per gram *(4, 19)*, and this amount does not prevent oxidation of meals made from these species. Early reports from FAO that fish meal made in Ghana from a local sardine did not develop rancidity even after a year's exposure to air were received with some scepticism but have been repeatedly confirmed and explained by the high tocopherol content of the species in question, which resulted in the final meal's having a total tocopherol content of 18 μg. per gram *(2)*. Naturally, much of the tocopherol will be lost in the expressed oil, and no value is given for the tocopherol content of the original fish. But 18μg. per gram is far less than 1 mg. per gram of antioxidant usually added to commercial fish meals, and its increased effectiveness can probably be attributed to two factors: better distribution in the product, and absence of oil oxidation before incorporation of antioxidant.

For a long time it seemed that the Ghana sardine was unique, but recently a UNICEF research worker at Torry Research Station found that the sprat *(Clupea sprattus)* caught in British waters gave a meal that was likewise completely stable to atmospheric oxygen. This meal proved to contain 30μg. per gram of total tocopherols *(17)*. We are now going to study seasonal variations in the content of α- and total tocopherols in the sprat. The sprat is closely related to the herring *(Clupea harengus)*, and the oils are virtually indistinguishable chemically, yet herring meal oxidizes readily. That the sprat meal really contains an antioxidant was checked by adding it to a system in which methyl linoleate was undergoing rapid oxidation. Oxygen uptake stopped at once.

Even a relatively poor antioxidant, if efficiently distributed before oil oxidation has commenced, can stabilize a fish meal for many months. This has been shown in the same UNICEF research studies *(17)* by drying commercial herring press cake in a stream of air at 75°C., either with or without introducing some wood smoke. Meal made without smoke readily absorbed oxygen, with rapid fall in iodine value of the fat, and became rancid ; in meal made in the presence of smoke the only absorption of oxygen could be attributed to certain smoke constituents, the iodine value of the fat remained constant, and the meal did not become rancid on exposure to the air. It tasted like a freshly smoked herring product, such as a kipper. As a matter of fact, it was known from wartime dehydration studies that whereas dehydrated herring rapidly became rancid, dehydrated smoked herring did not (7). Wood smoke is also known to prevent oxidation of fish oils as such (20). It is not suggested that simple smoked fish meal would be a suitable type of FPC, in view of the small but definite carcinogen content of wood smoke, but it might prove feasible to incorporate a suitable antioxidant by fine dispersion or vaporization into the dryer gases. Alternatively a carcinogen-free wood smoke might be used, since the smoked FPC flavor should be acceptable to many people.

A different line of approach towards prevention of rancidity in oily fish meal is partial replacement of the residual fish oil by a more stable type of oil, such as a vegetable oil, which furthermore contains natural antioxidants. This has been shown to be technically feasible (9) and should be effected with a freshly made fish meal. Using peanut oil for replacement, the fish meal, while still containing the typical 10% of fat, remained completely free from rancidity during at least 4 months' exposure to the atmosphere. The problem is what to do with the expressed mixture of vegetable and fish oil, which is dark in color and rancid in odor. The amount of it is approximately equal to the amount of vegetable oil originally added to the fish meal, which is then warmed and pressed—in the preliminary South African experiments about 15% by weight of the fish meal. The economics of oil replacement will depend largely on the monetary value of this recovered oil, which has not yet been determined.

Little need be said about production problems for FPC type B. Relatively cheap solvents, such as feed-grade hexane, can be employed either to extract most of the fat from a dry raw material such as fish meal or to remove both water and fat from a wet raw material by a process of combined azeotropic drying and solvent extraction. The solvent with which most experience has been gained in the latter type of operation is 1,2-dichloroethane (5, 16). Manufacture of FPC type B is facilitated and cheapened by the fact that the solvent extraction need not be exhaustive. The problem of residual solvent traces is dealt with under FPC type A, but it is potentially worse for type B because the solvents in question are probably more toxic, or at least suspect.

The cheapest and safest solvent for extraction of a food product is obviously water. Starting with a low-fat fish meal such as cod meal, water extraction will remove not only the water-soluble extractives but at least part of the phospholipids which in such meals form a considerable proportion of the total lipids. The final product could in many cases be regarded as FPC type B, but its flavor is entirely different from that of fish meal extracted with such a solvent as hexane. For certain purposes it is superior —e.g., as raw material for further processing into a bouillon-like seasoning

(6) Connell, J. J., unpublished results.
(7) D.S.I.R. Food Investigation Special Rept. 62, "Dehydration of Fish," H. M. Stationery Office, London, 1956.
(8) Dreosti, G. M., "Fish in Nutrition," E. Heen and R. Kreuzer, eds., p. 425, Fishing News (Books), London, 1962.
(9) Dreosti, G. M, Wieschers, S. G., Fishing Industry Research Institute, Cape Town, Ann. Rept. **15**, 48 (1961).
(10) *Ibid.*, Progr. Rept. **65** (1962).
(11) Food and Agriculture Organization, United Nations, "Draft Specifications for Fish Protein Concentrate," FAO Documents **IFIME (B) R/2, ICFN/WP/1** (March 23 and Sept. 27, 1961).
(12) Food and Agriculture Organization, United Nations, 'Yearbook of Fishery Statistics," Fishery Commodities, **17** (1963).
(13) FAO/UNICEF Report on Processing of Fish Flour from Sardines at Azote Union Plant in Safi, Morocco (September 1960).
(14) Fishing Industry Research Institute, Cape Town, Ann. Rept. **17,** 78 (1963).
(15) Karrick, N. L., "Industrial Fishery Technology," M. E. Stansby, ed., p. 253, Reinhold, New York, 1963.
(16) Levin, E., Finn, R. K., *Chem. Eng. Progr.* **51,** No. 5, 223 (1955).
(17) Loayza Salazar, E., unpublished results.
(18) Loetscher, K. M., Fishing Industry Research Institute, Cape Town, Ann. Rept. **16,** 70 (1962).
(19) Nazir, O. J., Magar, N. G., *Biochem. J.* **90,** 268 (1964).
(20) Nikkilä, O. E., Linko, R. R., *Acta Chem. Fennica,* **B24,** 74 (1951).
(21) Power, H. E., *J. Fisheries Res. Board Can.* **19,** 1039 (1962).
(22) Stachowski, J. K. S., personal communication.
(23) Stachowski, J. K. S., *Przemyst. Spozywczy* **19,** 220 (1965).
(24) Subcommittee on Merchant Marine and Fisheries, Committee on Commerce, United States Senate, hearing Aug. 14, 1964, Serial No. 60, U. S. Government Printing Office, Washington, D. C., 1964.
(25) Thomson, F. A., Merry, E., *Brit. J. Nutr.* **16,** 175 (1962).

RECEIVED October 12, 1965. Prepared as part of the program of the Ministry of Technology. Crown copyright reserved.

Discussion

D. G. Snyder. I should like to present information on two items concerning FPC that Dr. Lovern did not cover in his excellent paper—yet these items I feel are critical to matters being discussed at this symposium. We should first of all have some idea about how much fish is potentially available for FPC manufacture from our world's oceans on an annual sustained basis.

The next obvious point is to indicate how much this high quality 80 to 85% animal protein product prepared from whole fish is going to cost.

There are almost as many estimates of potential fish harvests as there are biologists making these estimates. Let us consider a high, medium, and low estimate.

Wilbert Chapman of the Van Camp Foundation estimates, and provides the calculations to go with his estimate, that the total annual production by the ocean of fish and shellfish of practical usable size is 2 billion tons. This tonnage would supply, in turn, 400 million tons per year of animal protein. This tonnage of protein would, of course, be adequate to meet the annual requirements of a world population ten times the size of the present one.

Bureau biologists estimate that about 500 billion pounds of fish could be harvested annually from our world oceans. Let's assume (and these are my calculations) that from 500 billion pounds of fish we can get roughly 100 billion pounds of FPC. If we consider that 10 grams comprise one supplemental dose of animal protein and 400 days comprise one year (the former value may be just as wrong as the latter one), we could provide 10 billion people with an animal protein supplement each year from now on, assuming all fish harvest would go into FPC production—which it would not. Today about 100 billion pounds of fish are taken and used for purposes other than FPC. Therefore, only four fifths of the potential would be available for FPC production. Instead of 10 billion people, we supply FPC supplements to only 8 billion people.

Herbert W. Graham and Robert L. Edwards, Biological Laboratory, Bureau of Commercial Fisheries, Woods Hole, Mass., have provided one of the most conservative estimates of the annual harvest potential of our oceans. They conclude that under present conditions and with present fishing techniques, the annual harvest of marine fish can be at the very most tripled. At the time of their estimate approximately 80 billion pounds of fish were being taken. Thus they estimate 240 billion pounds could be harvested. This value is roughly half that of the preceding one. Therefore, the conservative estimate provides FPC supplements for 4 billion people.

It is important to recognize that the estimate of Graham and Edwards relates only to present conditions and present harvesting devices. Aquaculture techniques, new gear, and the like would provide many times the fish harvest they say is now possible.

No matter what production figures we use, there appears to be a significant volume of animal protein available from our world's oceans.

The Bureau of Commercial Fisheries, Technological Laboratory, College Park, Md., has recently completed engineering studies on a solvent-extraction method of FPC production including real cost estimates. Based on a minimum-sized small commercial plant with a capacity of 50 tons of raw material per day, the cost of FPC figures out to be about $0.18 to 0.20 per pound. This estimate considers fish to cost about $0.01

a pound and includes a consideration of profit, labor costs, amortization of equipment, etc.   The only item not considered is by-product oil recovery, which may be a plus factor lowering the final cost of the product. The cost of a 10-gram portion of FPC, therefore, would be about one half of a cent.   The price per kilogram on the basis of 100% protein would be $0.50.   Nonfat dry milk on this same basis costs $1.00.

If the price quoted is off by a few pennies (and we cannot be expected to tell industry what to charge), the fact is that FPC is the least expensive source of potentially available animal protein.   We must not forget, too, that the quality of the protein is outstanding—or at least can be, as we have shown from our work at College Park.   And even though we have difficulty in getting biologists to agree on an estimate of the fishery resource, there is a goodly quantity of fish available for the production of this inexpensive marine protein concentrate.

5

General Outlook for Seed Protein Concentrates

MAX MILNER[1]

UNICEF, United Nations, New York, N. Y.

Seed proteins, particularly those of the cereals and legumes, are mainstays of human protein nutrition, providing several times more of this nutrient than animal proteins. The rapidly growing world protein requirement has directed major attention to the food use of oilseed proteins since these are available in roughly equal quantity to animal proteins. Although oilseed proteins are now used mostly for animal feeding or fertilizer, refinements in oil recovery processes as well as new technologies have overcome several problems in the food use of oilseeds, including removal of antibiological factors, toxic plant pigments, and mold metabolites. The increasing variety of protein foods of good nutritive quality and appealing gastronomic character from oilseeds suggests that oilseeds will soon contribute significantly to world protein requirements.

The serious problem of lagging world food production, and particularly the protein supply, is now widely recognized. Altschul (5) has recently written a penetrating analysis of world protein resources, particularly with reference to the possible role which protein materials traditionally unused as human food may play if they can be made available in acceptable edible forms. He is one of the first to make the very important point that limitation in traditional thought and attitude seems to have consigned major resources such as the residues of oilseed processing to fertilizer use or at best to animal feeding as optimum means for their utilization. The implications of this point provide an excellent approach to a discussion of seed protein concentrates, which is that their use as food and their future impact on the world protein scarcity will be related increasingly to the extent of scientific and technological study devoted to their processing

[1] Present address: Office of Technical Cooperation and Research, Agency for International Development, Washington, D. C.

and to improved methods of utilization. It is only in this light that the potential of seed protein, particularly for direct use as human food, can be properly assessed.

The proteins of seeds, particularly those of cereals and legumes, have, since the neolithic agricultural revolution, been the major sources of human protein nutrition. Science and technology notwithstanding, the prottein from these sources will continue for a long time to come to be our dietary mainstays. It is constructive to examine in greater detail the contribuions which various traditional resources are making to the world protein balance sheet.

World Protein Resources

The cereals contribute in round numbers 75 million metric tons of protein, of which wheat provides 25 million, rice 12 million and corn 20 million tons. The legumes, consisting of various beans, peas and lentils, in aggregate, provide, surprisingly, only about 8 million tons. Additional but minor plant sources of protein are tubers, including potatoes, and nuts. The world animal protein supply, including principally meat, milk, eggs, and fish, has been estimated to be about 20 million metric tons. And finally, the potential contribution of the oilseeds, which include principally soybeans, cottonseed, and peanuts, can be considered to be about equal to that of all the animal protein now available, 20 million tons per annum. Abbott (1) has tabulated the contribution to human diets of various protein resources.

No single traditional or novel resource, whether increased through agricultural productivity or by new technology, will itself solve the protein problem. It is the purpose of this symposium to analyze as carefully as we can the role which each and every resource might play and how this contribution may logically develop.

The oilseeds have specific relevance to my topic since at least one of them, the soybean, contains, even prior to processing, as much as 40% protein and thus is one of the few plant materials which approach animal products in protein concentration. By definition, oilseeds are processed primarily for their edible oil constituent, and this traditional treatment alone, whether by pressing, by solvent extraction, or by combination of these techniques, results in a residue with relatively large quantities of protein—i.e., from 30 to 60% (4). These, then, are the major types of seed protein concentrates which I will deal with.

The quantitative contribution which oilseed protein concentrates could make to the human dietary is about equal to that of all the protein of animal origin being produced in the world today. It is pertinent to ask: where are these materials being produced in the world and in what quantities? How are these proteins being disposed of now (I would have preferred to have used the term "utilized")? Why have they not been widely used for human food, and what are some of the reasons for hoping that they will be?

Dealing with the first question, one can point to the fact that soybeans are the world's largest oilseed crop, totaling as much as 35 million metric tons annually, a quantity which is only slightly less than the total production of the next two major oilseeds taken together—peanuts (15 million metric tons) and cottonseed (21 million metric tons). If one includes in the total other significant oil-bearing seeds, such as sesame, sunflower, rape, flaxseed, copra, and palm kernel, the world's production of oilseeds approximates 80 million metric tons (Table I).

Table I. Major Oilseeds Used as Food

Species	Botanical Name	Protein Content (Av.), %	Oil Content (Av.), %	World Production, 1000 Metric Tons	Major Producing Countries	Problems in Processing as Food
Soybean	Glycine max.	42	20	35,000[a]	U. S., China	Antitrypsin factors Hemagglutinin factor
Peanut	Arachis hypogea	27	48	14,800[b]	India, Senegal, Nigeria	Aflatoxin [*]
Cottonseed	Gossypium	30	30	20,600[b]	U. S., India, USSR, Mexico, UAR, Brazil, Pakistan	Gossypol, malvalic acid, aflatoxin
Sesame	Sesamum indicum	25	50	1,500[b]	China, India, Sudan, Mexico	Fiber, oxalate
Sunflower	Helianthus annus	30	40	6,840[b]	USSR, Argentina, Uruguay, S. Africa, Turkey	Fiber
Coconut	Cocus nucifera	8[c]	65[c]	3,200[b,c]	Philippines, Indonesia, Ceylon, India, Malaysia	Fiber

[*] Estimated for 1965.
[b] (6).
[*] Dried meats (copra).

Soybeans alone account for about 40% of the world's total oilseed crop. In 1965, 65% of the world's soybean crop was produced in a single country—the United States. The doubling in the world's soybean resources between the immediate post-World War II period and recently is due primarily to the U.S. crop, which has risen from 300 million to 860 million bushels (23 million metric tons). China is the second major producer (about 8 million tons) and thus the United States and China together produce 90% of the world's crop. Other countries producing soybeans in amounts worth mentioning are Japan, Brazil, and Indonesia. Unfortunately, this valuable protein resource is virtually unknown in many countries where the need for protein is the greatest.

Cottonseed, the next in prevalence, is much more widely distributed than soybeans. Most tropical and subtropical areas of the world, which include many of the developing countries, produce cotton, and the production of this seed has shown a moderate increase in recent years. Major non-U.S. producers are India, the USSR, Mexico, UAR, Brazil, and Pakistan.

Peanut production, like that of cottonseed, is also more spread about than soybeans, India and several countries of West Africa being the major producers. India alone grows about one third of the world's total crop. Sesame, one of the few seed sources rich in the sulfur-containing amino acid methionine, is the only oilseed which has decreased in production since the postwar period.

As for the current channels of utilization of oilseed protein, precise breakdowns in ratios of use for animal feeding and fertilizer are somewhat difficult to come by, but one general rule exists—very little is either processed or used at present for human food. For all practical purposes, about 95% of the U.S. soybean crop not exported is crushed for oil and the meal is fed to livestock, principally poultry. Possibly as much as 2% of the crop is processed for food. The percentage of soybean meal produced in the United States which has been exported has risen in ten years from about 2% of the crop to about 12% at the present time. Export of unprocessed soybeans has grown by a similar amount. Soybeans and their products, including oil, constitute the largest single U.S. agricultural export today. Most of these materials go to Western Europe and Japan, where a rising standard of living is calling for increased amounts of animal protein in the diet. One of the primary reasons for the decrease in availability of skim milk powder for relief feeding from U.S. donations during the past few years, as well as for concessional sale to individual countries, has been the increased demand in Europe for milk products generally and particularly for producing milk-fed veal. The high standard of living in the United States and that developing in other industrialized countries (including Japan) is reflected in an almost insatiable demand for animal protein, whose production is based to a considerable extent on feeding rations supplemented with oilseed protein concentrates. For this reason, incidentally, soybean oil has been a surplus commodity under the U.S. Food for Peace operations, whereas soybeans and soybean meal for which a strong and increasing dollar demand exists, are as yet unavailable in this program.

On the U.S. scene soybean alone accounts for over 55% of the protein concentrates fed to livestock. Cottonseed accounts for about 15%, meat by-products 11%, corn gluten about 7%, and fish meal about 4%.

We may take India as a typical developing country in terms of the pattern of utilization of oilseed protein by-products. There is virtually no soybean production in India. Peanut, the largest oilseed crop, about 5 million tons annually, is the mainstay of the country's edible oil supply. Peanuts are crushed for oil by obsolescent and inefficient technological means. About 10% of the defatted cake may be exported. Only insignificant quantities are used as food and little more for animal feeding. Informed estimates suggest that 80% of the Indian peanut press cake, containing up to about 40% protein (not to mention residual oil of 10% or more), is used primarily as manure. There are obviously both tragedy and challenge here when one considers that this largely vegetarian society, many segments of which suffer from serious protein malnutrition, has developed no effective or rational use for this protein resource.

The utilization of cottonseed, the second oilseed crop of India, is also pertinent. Because of several factors, including the generally obsolescent oilseed processing technology, a ban on the use of petroleum solvents for food processing, and a conviction among farmers that whole seeds are superior to press cake for cattle feeding, only about 20% of this vegetable oil resource is recovered for human food use.

The question becomes urgent: Why do these patterns of utilization exist? Why, except for soybeans to a limited extent, have oilseed proteins been used hardly at all as human food? Why indeed, in its painfully pragmatic approach to food selection, even in times of scarcity and starvation, has the human race rejected these traditional protein concentrates as food?

Much of the answer is obvious from a casual visit even to a modern oilseed plant which is processing peanut or cottonseed for oil. The procedures employed emphasize the recovery of oil as the primary product while the meal or press cake generally receives scant consideration in terms of safeguarding nutritive and sanitary quality. Generally these by-products are fibrous in nature, contain large quantities of hulls and other debris, and in most cases have been overheated to the extent that the protein nutritive quality is severely impaired. The point I am trying to make is simple—that every advantage and economy which have been applied to oil recovery have tended to downgrade those qualities of the protein necessary to provide a palatable, nutritious, and sanitary food.

Some recent scientific discoveries have suggested additional reasons why these materials have not been used traditionally as food. I refer to the problems of fungal toxicity and intrinsic antibiological factors. In retrospect we must acknowledge and indeed endorse the pragmatic wisdom of our ancestors in rejecting materials of this kind as food. By the same token, as scientists and technologists we have taken on a rather major challenge in attempting to reverse these age-old traditions and practices.

Soybeans

The soybean, containing up to 40% of protein, can be considered as a protein concentrate even without defatting. The traditional oriental processing, which involves aqueous extraction of ground beans, tends to retain most of the fat in the final protein curd product. The protein nutritive value of the soybean is among the highest of all proteins of vegetable origin (*3*). In comparison with other plant proteins it is unusually high in lysine and is therefore useful as a supplement to the cereals. Its limitation in terms of protein nutritive quality may be primarily a moderate deficiency in methionine. Breakfast bacon and eggs attest strongly to the nutritive virtue in animal rations of a mixture of corn and soybean meals.

The pragmatic methods developed centuries ago by the people of Southeast Asia to process soybeans into a great variety of foods are widely known. The major problem, and one which must not be minimized, is the bitter flavor principle of mature beans, which is not easy to remove, particularly by home-processing methods. More recently, there has occurred scientific clarification of the variety of deleterious antibiological factors in soybeans, apparently primarily protein in nature, most of which are fortunately destroyed by carefully controlled heat processing.

Among the major oriental foods of value, whose processing represents a uniquely pragmatic answer to these problems, one can list the tofu (soybean curd) of China and Japan and the variety of fermented products derived from it, particularly in mixtures with cereals, including miso and natto. The Indonesian tempeh made by fungal fermentation of soaked soybeans with the mold *Rhizopus*, followed by deep fat frying, has received considerable study in the United States recently. All these products are interesting and nutritious foods, and in a few instances such as tempeh, are actually appealing to the western palate. Their processing and use as protein foods in a number of countries outside of the Orient merit thorough investigation.

Soybean milk, produced by aqueous extraction as the first stage of traditional tofu production, can be a product of considerable merit in its own right. It has never achieved the popularity it deserves even in those cultures where other soybean foods are traditionally accepted, and this I would attribute primarily to the fact that home and village processing are unable to control the critical heat-processing step adequately, and also to the absence of refrigeration which is required to maintain this product safe, as is necessary for fresh dairy products. The greatest promise for its expanded use must be predicated on processing it by sterilization on an industrial scale. Some urban enterprises of this type are already in operation, notably a flourishing one in Hong Kong. In Indonesia a spray-dried soybean extract of this type has been on the market for several years. Additional research and development in these processes are necessary in order to improve the economic aspects, the flavor, and the nutritive quality of the product. Nevertheless it appears certain that soybean milk in liquid or in powdered forms suitable for reconstitution has a bright future, particularly in the rapidly expanding urbanized areas of Southeast Asia.

That the controlled application of steam and heat following solvent defatting of soybean products effects marked improvement in the flavor and feeding value of soybean oil meal, as well as virtual elimination of the deleterious factors, came to be recognized only after the introduction of solvent processing in the United States some 25 years ago. Taking into account minimum sanitary standards and food-grade processing requirements, defatted edible soybean meal containing 50% or more of protein has been shown to be an excellent source of economical protein in a form suitable as human food. The pre-eminent virtue of these nutritious soybean grits and flours is their low cost, representing probably the greatest value in protein available on today's market. If the present U.S. soybean crop were to be processed entirely into such toasted soybean protein products, instead of being used for animal feeding, where 80 to 90% of protein and calorie substance is lost, it could provide 750 million children with a 40-gram ration of high quality protein per day. This calculation may be more than an idle speculation in terms of proposals being discussed in Washington these days to expand U.S. production of soybean protein and other protective foods to meet the most critical aspects of the world's food shortage.

As useful and cheap as defatted, heat-processed soybean meals and flours are as protein supplements, they suffer certain limitations which additional research and process development must seek to remedy. In the first place their appearance and flavor remain a compromise among various processing factors related to the solvent-defatting step. The subsequent desolventizing of the meal with moist heat causes color development (Maillard reaction), yet heat processing is necessary to inactivate the deleterious antibiological factors. Since the protein becomes largely heat-denatured and therefore insoluble, it has serious technological limitations in terms of control or modification of physical properties desirable for a variety of foods. Possibilities for combinations with other foods are also restricted. Much challenge to research exists in finding more effective and economical ways to process soybeans as food and particularly to improve their palatability and flavor. A negative economic factor in a developing country is that efficient production of a solvent-processed product requires considerable capital investment and the installation of expensive ancillary facilities such as grain storage and drying. If the United States should decide to make this protein concentrate available in quantity in an expanded Food for Peace program, the problem of a market outlet for oil might again become a serious factor.

It is for such reasons that much favorable notice has been given to producing edible full-fat soybean flour by a rather straightforward cooking-extrusion technology. This approach to edible soybean processing, particularly in terms of providing low-cost foods in developing countries, seems to represent a major technological advance.

The efforts of the U.S. soybean processing industry to expand its markets have led to a number of interesting modern products and processes which may in the future achieve considerable economic significance. Soybean flour doughs can be extruded and fixed into meatlike forms. Soybean protein concentrates containing 70% protein are prepared by leaching of soluble carbohydrate and mineral components of soybean meals by water, dilute acids, or alcohol. These products because of their blandness and light color are finding their way into many new processed cereal and meat products. A considerable demand has been built up over a number of years in the paper industry for industrial-grade soybean protein isolates prepared by alkali dispersion of defatted raw soybean flakes. Soybean glues are increasingly important. Edible forms of the soluble isolates (spray-dried alkali dispersions) are used in a number of sophisticated food applications such as for foaming and gelling agents, and also as the protein component of coffee whiteners, frozen desserts, and soybean beverages. The increasing demand in the food industry for modified whey, casein, and other high grade dairy by-products has stimulated increased interest in these soybean protein products. All are of a specialized nature and relatively costly, possessing valuable specific properties tailored to a variety of technological needs in U.S. food processing. Their sophistication may appear at this moment to have little relevance to the needs for protein in developing countries, particularly in terms of the economics involved. On the other hand this basic technology may well find early application in some of these countries—for example, to augment the cow's milk supply. Furthermore, protein isolates are pointing the way to entirely new and highly sophisticated foods which may open mass markets for this product. I refer particularly to the production of highly textured meat-like materials, prepared by filament-spinning techniques.

Cottonseed

Cottonseed suffers from several drawbacks in spite of the fact that its protein biological quality, limited to some extent by methionine and lysine deficiency, is not markedly inferior to that of soybean. The most serious problem is the ubiquitous and toxic natural polyphenolic pigment of this species—gossypol—whose presence has until recently restricted even the animal feeding use of cottonseed meals almost entirely to ruminants. The other drawback to wider edible use of cottonseed protein concentrates is that it has been a prisoner of traditional processes, which have been concerned only with oil recovery. Studies during the past 15 years have greatly clarified the effects of heat processing in terms of the basic mechanism of binding the gossypol to proteins, particularly to the detriment of the lysine content, which is already limited. Wider understanding of this problem and adjustment of the traditional operations accordingly can result in marked improvement of cottonseed protein concentrates, many of which are now acceptable for swine and poultry feeding (2). As a matter of fact, some of these heat-processed gossypol-bound materials are already in use in Guatemala, Colombia, and Peru for the production of protein-rich cereal food mixtures highly useful as infant weaning products. A food-grade product of this type has been marketed in the United States for a number of years. Guidelines for producing such edible products by modification of standard oil meal processing have been made available by the United Nations agencies.

Fortunately, biochemical and processing studies on cottonseed are continuing at an accelerated pace, aimed at greatly improved methods for producing low-gossypol cottonseed protein concentrates, of considerably higher nutritive quality and palatability than the traditional meals (2). A commercial firm in Sicily is simultaneously defatting and degossypolizing cottonseed with acetone. Apparently the problem of oil recovery from the acetone miscella has been adequately solved in this process.

The Southern Regional Laboratory has developed a mixed solvent technique, based on acetone, hexane, and water, for simultaneously defatting and degossypolizing, which permits removal of the pigment without prior heating of the raw cottonseed flakes. The protein quality of this product is essentially unharmed, the lysine being virtually fully available. The nutritive quality of the protein remains very close to that of a properly processed soybean flour. This product has already been tested by feeding to young infants as a sole source of dietary protein, with excellent results. In further exploration of this technology, the USDA group has shown that aqueous acetone by itself can selectively remove gossypol, and the way now seems open to low-gossypol meals in which much of the nutritious cottonseed oil is retained. Engineering processes of this type are also under study in Hyderabad, India.

There seems little doubt that techniques of this kind have been perfected to the point where they can be applied quickly on a commercial scale if and when the demand for such products appears. Cottonseed production is widely distributed in a number of developing countries which suffer from protein scarcity. It is my prediction that these new processes will provide the protein feeding component necessary for expanded production of swine and poultry—i.e., an animal protein economy, in these regions. Incidentally, the solvent degossypolizing techniques can provide essentially raw protein and thus this method opens the way for producing protein isolates as a logical development, following the soybean protein model.

Another remarkable advance in cottonseed protein quality has resulted from a recent breakthrough on the genetic front. Gossypol-free varieties of cottonseed have been developed, from which the characteristic pigment glands are virtually absent (*2*). This breeding factor can apparently be introduced into virtually any strain of seed without impairing the fiber quality or desirable agronomic characteristics. The cottonseed meals and flours are considerably lighter in color and of excellent nutritive value. The National Cottonseed Processors Association has developed an active program of seed production and distribution, which should make these new varieties widely available to growers by 1970.

Peanut

The third major oilseed resource, peanut, which suffers least from indigenous or naturally occurring deleterious components, has nevertheless recently weathered a rather difficult and unsettling experience in terms of the problem of aflatoxin (*8*). The recent identification of this fungal-induced toxicity, which can occur on this and other crops including cottonseed when improperly harvested and stored, may indicate another major reason why as a vegetable oil industry by-product, peanut meal, has achieved little traditional food use.

In any event, with means to control the aflatoxin problem at hand, this major protein resource will doubtless achieve wider use for feeding as well as for industrial purposes (*7*). [Careful selection of peanuts can provide flours of good nutritious quality, highly valuable in a variety of diets, and acceptable as components of low-cost protein-rich foods suitable in a number of developing countries.]

I have tried to indicate the impact which seed protein concentrates could make on the world protein needs if they were processed and used more extensively in human foods. As a result of several new technologies, more valuable and sophisticated ways to use them are now available. Nevertheless the art, and to a far greater extent the technology, of their processing and use as food still lag very far behind our knowledge and art in the use of traditional foodstuffs such as cereal grains, dairy foods, and the animal proteins. On the basis of the considerable expansion of the study of nutritional and food technology now under way, it seems certain that these products will soon take their place as major resources in the world's food protein balance sheet.

Literature Cited

(1) Abbott, J. C., ADVAN. CHEM. SER., **57**, 1 (1966).
(2) Agricultural Research Service, U. S. Dept. Agriculture, Proceedings of Conference on Cottonseed Protein Concentrates, New Orleans, La., January 1964.
(3) Agricultural Research Service, U. S. Dept. Agriculture, Proceedings of Conference on Soybean Proteins in Human Foods, Peoria, Ill., September 1961.
(4) Altschul, A. M., "Processed Plant Protein Foodstuffs," Academic Press, New York, 1958.
(5) Altschul, A. M., "Proteins, Their Chemistry and Politics," Basic Books, New York, 1965.
(6) Food and Agricultural Organization, United Nations, "Production Yearbook," Vol. 17, 1963.
(7) Milner, M., *Food Technol.* **16**, 46–53 (1962).
(8) Wogan, G. N., "Mycotoxins in Foodstuffs," Proceedings of Symposium at Massachusetts Institute of Technology, March 1964, MIT Press, Cambridge, Mass., 1965.

RECEIVED October 12, 1965.

Discussion

B. F. Buchanan: It is an interesting and significant observation that there is potentially as much protein available from today's oilseed production as from all edible animal products.

Equally significant is the observation that no single traditional or new protein resource will itself solve the problem of the world dietary protein insufficiency. It is perhaps fortunate that the latter is, indeed, true in view of the fact that no single vegetable protein has the proper amino acid composition for optimum nutrition. Since carbohydrates and fats provide a much more economical source of calories than does protein, it is highly important that insofar as possible, proteins should be utilized for their contribution to the diet as *proteins* and not squandered as calories. Therefore, to get the most mileage from those vegetable proteins available, consideration should be given to combinations from those various sources which yield optimum amino acid balance, thus avoiding the risk of expending valuable amino acids for calories alone in the protein marginal diets.

Now let us consider some of the data presented by Dr. Milner. Current annual production of oilseed of 80 metric tons represents a potential of about 45 billion pounds of protein. At the conservative estimate of feeding only 55 grams of protein per person per day, this 45 billion pounds of protein would feed only about one billion persons for one year. With two-thirds of the world's population suffering from protein-poor diets, this quantity of protein from today's oilseed crop would satisfy only about one-half of that protein deficient population. Although this is a tremendous raw material resource and should not be minimized, the fact that there is not enough to satisfy today's demands is again perhaps fortunate since it virtually forces one to mix protein sources to achieve adequate supplies, thus resulting in finished food products of better nutritional quality.

If one could satisfy the requirements of an adequate supply of nutritionally balanced proteins to feed the world, two important problems would still have to be overcome. First is the matter of developing acceptable food products familiar to the tastes of the population in the country under consideration. Dr. Milner mentioned the great waste in many areas of currently produced oilseed proteins as fertilizers and as animal feeds. This waste is attributable primarily to emphasis on oil recovery at the expense of retaining quality in the protein fraction. But let us assume edible-quality production. Before man will eat these proteins they must be fabricated into acceptable and palatable food products. A hungry person suffering from a protein-deficient diet most frequently lacks the tools to prepare a meal from soy flour, cottonseed flour, peanut flour. Those tools are not necessarily just the hardware for preparation and fuel for heating, but more often the knowledge to help him build attractive, finished foods, ready to be eaten with a minimum of preparation.

Scientifically advanced nations today possess the technologies to produce and to convert protein resources into nutritious, palatable, and acceptable food products. Ample evidence is exhibited, for example, in the fact that the United States uses upwards of 50 million pounds of soy protein per year as ingredients in such items as bakery products, meat products, breakfast cereals, baby foods, milk-like products, and a host of special dietary foods.

Second, even the most nutritious, acceptable food product has to be sold to the consumer. Marketing is a highly developed skill, successfully used in this and many other countries to create awareness in the mind of the consumer.

Therefore, to relieve the problem of world protein malnutrition it is necessary (a) to develop food products indigenous to the population—products that are nutritious, stable, easily prepared for eating, and highly acceptable; (b) to utilize to the fullest our marketing talents, even intrigue if necessary, to bring these products to the attention of those most in need; (c) finally, to use every skill and incentive at our command to encourage these peoples to work and pay for what they get.

Production of Lysine and Methionine

ARCHIBALD T. McPHERSON

4005 Cleveland St., Kensington, Md.

Lysine and methionine are manufactured for use as food supplements in human nutrition and animal feeding. The larger part of present production is feed grade methionine. L-Lysine is made by fermentation, employing selected strains or mutants of microorganisms growing in a solution of glucose or molasses, ammonium compounds, inorganic salts, and other substances. DL-Methionine is synthesized from acrolein, methyl mercaptan, and any readily available sources of cyanide and ammonium ions. Unlike lysine, both the D- and the L-forms of methionine can be utilized by the body; hence resolution is not necessary. A very large demand for lysine, methionine, and other amino acids may be created by the proposed supplementation of the diet in protein-deficient regions. The necessary production is within the capability of the chemical industry.

Each of the major industrial countries of the world engages to some extent in the production of essential amino acids. At present only lysine and methionine are manufactured in commercial quantities and, of the two, methionine is produced in the larger amount. The production of lysine in large volume has lagged for the lack of a sufficiently large market, and the demand, in turn, has been slow in developing because of the relatively high price. The widespread world food shortage, and the protein deficit in particular, may create an urgent demand for lysine, methionine, and certain other essential amino acids to supplement and upgrade the incomplete proteins of the cereals, pulses, and oilseeds that constitute a large part of the diet in the developing countries of Tropical America, Africa, and Asia. Anticipating this demand, Japan has been particularly active in research on the production of amino acids by fermentation.

Lysine and methionine, as well as most of the other amino acids can be made either by chemical synthesis or by the culture of microorganisms on suitable substrates. Methionine is currently produced by synthesis while the fermentation method for lysine has supplanted the chemical syntheses formerly used. Production by microorganisms is the more economical method for lysine because it yields only the levo enantiomorph, the form in which lysine occurs in nature and is required for nutritional purposes. With methionine, however, both the dextro- and the levo- forms can be utilized by the body; hence resolution of the racemate obtained by chemical synthesis is not necessary.

Methods of Synthesis

Various synthetic routes are available for producing amino acids, but he route most commonly followed in manufacturing lysine and methionine by chemical synthesis involves the Bucherer modification of the Strecker synthesis. In this route an aldehyde, on reaction with $(NH_4)^+$ and $(CN)^-$, yields a hydantoin which, on hydrolysis, yields the amino acid. The ultimate raw materials required are petroleum and/or coal, inorganic salts, sulfur, and atmospheric nitrogen. All of the raw materials and most of the intermediates, as well, are in abundant supply. The quantities of raw materials that would be required for the largest production that can be foreseen would amount to only a small fraction of the quantities now ut lized for other purposes.

Methionine. The present commercial synthesis of methionine starts with acrolein (25). Successive steps are: reaction of acrolein with methyl mercaptan to yield 3-(methylthio)-propionaldehyde; reaction of this aldehyde with sodium cyanide and ammonium carbonate, or other sources of cyanide and ammonium ions, to yield 5-[(2-methylthio(ethyl)] hydantoin; and hydrolysis of this hydantoin to yield methionine. Alternatively, the 3-(methylthio)-propionaldehyde may be made to react with hydrogen cyanide to yield the corresponding 2-hydroxynitrile; the hydroxyl is then rep aced by an amino group by reaction with ammonia under pressure; hydrolysis of the nitrile then yields methionine. The reactions by the two routes are shown diagrammatically as follows:

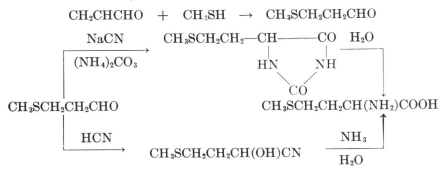

The acrolein required in this synthesis can be made by oxidizing propylene obtained in petroleum refining. Methyl mercaptan may be obtained by reaction of methanol and hydrogen sulfide; and hydrogen cyanide, by reaction of ammonia and methane.

If the hydroxyl of the 2-hydroxy-4-(methylthio) butylnitrile is not replaced by an amino group, the nitrile yields, on hydrolysis, the hydroxy analog of methionine. This product, in the form of its calcium salt, is manufactured in quantity for use in animal feeding where it serves the same nutritional functions as methionine.

Lysine. Lysine can be made synthetically from a variety of intermediates, including dihydropyran (*18, 20*), caprolactam (*2, 21*), piperidine (*22*), and cyclohexanone (*4*). In the synthesis of lysine from dihydropyran the first step is opening of the ring by hydration to yield 5-hydroxyvaleraldehyde. This aldehyde, on reaction with sodium cyanide and ammonium carbonate or other sources of cyanide and ammonium ions, yields 5-(4-hydroxybutyl) hydantoin. The hydroxyl group of this hydantoin is replaced by a halogen on reaction with hydrogen chloride or hydrogen bromide. The halogen, in turn, is replaced by an amino group on treatment with ammonia, and the hydantoin on hydrolysis yields lysine. Following is a sketch of the reactions.

Resolution of the DL-lysine obtained by chemical synthesis may be effected by reaction with an optically active acid selected so as to form two diastereoisomers that differ sufficiently in solubility to permit separation by fractional crystallization. Among the acids which have been proposed for this purpose are L-glutamic (*3, 17*), D-camphoric (*26*) and, D-homocysteinic acid (*7*). With the first of these, the L-lysine-L-glutamate separates out from a water-alcohol mixture, and, on treatment with hydrochloric acid the lysine is obtained as the monohydrochloride and the glutamic acid is recovered. The unwanted D-lysine is recovered as the monohydrochloride from the filtrate from the L-lysine-L-glutamate, and is converted by heating with alkali to the racemate, which is then recycled in the process.

Biochemical Production

The chemical synthesis of lysine has been supplanted by fermentation processes in which selected microorganisms are grown in a broth containing a nutrient such as glucose or molasses, together with an ammonium compound, small amounts of inorganic salts, and other materials necessary for the growth of the microorganisms, notably biotin and small amounts of certain amino acids. Lysine accumulates in the broth, together with other amino acids in smaller amounts, vitamins, and other substances. The lysine may be recovered conveniently by passing the filtrate from the broth through a column of an acidic ion-exchange resin which takes up the lysine. The lysine is eluted from the resin by a solution of ammonium hydroxide. On evaporation of this solution to dryness the ammonia volatilizes, leaving a residue of lysine which is converted to the mono-hydrochloride, and this, in turn, is purified by recrystallization.

The efficiency of the fermentation process depends on selecting a strain of microorganisms capable of producing a relatively high concentration of lysine in the broth. Not only have thousands of naturally occurring organisms been investigated, but in addition mutant strains of various organisms have been produced by irradiation with cobalt-60 and with x-rays.

The economic advantage of the fermentation process lies not only in the direct production of the desired L-isomer of lysine, but also in the use of cheap by-products such as molasses and corn-steep liquor as the nutrient.

A typical lysine fermentation is described by Kinoshita in a review on the production of amino acids (12). The organism employed was a special strain of *Micrococcus glutamicus*.

A graph relating the production of lysine to the disappearance of glucose showed the maximum accumulation to be about 2.5% of lysine, expressed as the monohydrochloride.

The industrial production of L-lysine in Japan, the United States, and France, according to Kinoshita (12), employs special strains of *M. glutamicus* growing on a culture medium containing molasses as the principal nutrient. Molasses is preferable to pure glucose because it contains biotin, other vitamins, and small amounts of certain amino acids, all of which are necessary or desirable for the growth of the microorganisms. While Kinoshita states that it is not unusual to obtain a broth containing 2% of lysine, lower percentages are more commonly reported in experiments described in the literature. The yields in commercial production apparently have not been disclosed.

The development of fermentation processes has been greatly aided by research on the ways in which amino acids are formed in nature. Present knowledge of the biosynthesis of lysine is summarized as follows in a recent book by Meister (15).

Two distinct pathways are known that lead to the synthesis of lysine. In certain fungi and algae the carbon skeleton of lysine arises from acetate and alpha-ketoglutarate by a biosynthetic sequence that includes alpha-aminoadipic acid. The other pathway has been found in bacteria, higher plants, blue-green and green algae, and certain fungi; in these organisms, the lysine carbon chain is synthesized from pyruvate and aspartate, and alpha, epsilon-diaminopimelic acid is the key intermediate. At the ime of this writing more is known about the diaminopimelic acid pathway. . . .

Some fermentation processes are conducted in two stages, the first leading to the production of aminoadipic acid or diaminopimelic acid, and the second being the enzymatic conversion of these acids to lysine. In one such process (*14*) a mutant of *Escherichia coli* was used which, itself, required a low concentration of lysine for its growth. When an inoculum of this organism was added to a culture medium containing 4% of sugar beet molasses and 3% of glycerol as nutrients, diaminopimelic acid accumulated to the extent of 0.7%. Some back-mutation of the organism evidently occurred since, on addition of toluene to rupture cell walls, sufficient diaminopimelic acid carboxylase was released to convert the diaminopimelic acid completely to lysine on standing.

World Production of Amino Acids

Statistics regarding the production of amino acids seem to be limited to those collected and reported by the U. S. Tariff Commission in connection with the production and sale of synthetic organic chemicals in the United States. Lysine, methionine, and other amino acids except glutamic are classified as medicinal chemicals, while glutamic acid, as monosodium glutamate, is shown as a flavor and perfume material because of its use as a condiment.

Data on the production, sales, and value of amino acids since 1945 are summarized in Table I. The maximum annual production shown is 5,946,000 pounds, or a little under 3000 tons, for 1961. In 1961 the detailed statistics show the sales of lysine as 296,000 pounds, or slightly less than 150 tons. Since 1961 too few firms have been making lysine to admit the separate reporting of production or sales figures, inasmuch as so doing might disclose the output of individual firms. For the same reason the hydroxy analog of methionine, prior to 1964, was not shown as a separate item but was blanketed in a general "all other" item. In a preliminary report for 1964, however, methionine and the hydroxy analog are grouped together with a total production of 6,049,000 pounds. When this figure is compared with the total production of amino acids for 1963 in the amount of 3,056,000 pounds, it is evident that the hydroxy analog is made in approximately the same amount as methionine itself.

Inasmuch as lysine and methionine are the only amino acids manufactured in quantity, it is possible to make a rough estimate of the amounts

Table I.   Production and Sales of Amino Acids in the United States (24)

Year	Production, 1000 Lb.	Sales, 1000 Lb.	Value, $1000	Value, $ per Lb.
1945	177	189	502	2.66
1950	929	736	1,942	2.65
1955	1,773	2,007	4,901	2.44
1960	5,163	4,214	6,330	1.50
1961	5,946	5,106	7,320	1.43
1962	5,007	5,492	7,210	1.31
1963	3,057	3,283	4,256	1.30
1964	6,049[a]	5,860[a]	6,203[a]	1.06[a]

[a] Preliminary report on methionine and hydroxy analog (24). In previous years the hydroxy analog was included in an "all other" item. In 1964 amino acids other than methionine and glutamic acid are apparently included in an "all other" item. Glutamic acid and monosodium glutamate are shown as an item in the class of flavor and perfume materials.

of each that are sold in the United States on the basis of market quotations and the total value shown in the Tariff Commission report.   In 1963 the price of feed-grade methionine was $1.10 to $1.17 per pound, depending on quantity, and the price of lysine was $3.90 per pound.   Thus the sales at an average price of $1.30 per pound show that probably more than 90% of the production for sale in the United States was feed-grade methionine.

Figures are not available for amino acids production in European countries, Canada, and Japan.   Kinoshita (13) estimates that 3000 to 5000 tons of lysine per year can be produced in Japan, though this rate has not yet been achieved.   The Netherlands does not yet produce amino acids in quantity, but plans have been made to manufacture lysine from caprolactam at the rate of about 3000 tons per year, beginning in 1967 (19).

Statistics on imports into the United States show amino acids as a separate category.   The amounts of the individual amino acids are not shown, but quantities and values such as those given in Table II indicate in some cases which amino acids constitute the bulk of the imports from each country.   At $47.50 per pound the imports from the United Kingdom could only be amino acids other than lysine and methionine.   The small item from Switzerland in the first half of 1965—22 pounds valued at $2932—points to this country also as a source of amino acids that are not yet manufactured in quantity.   Imports from other countries at prices of less than a dollar a pound could be only feed-grade methionine or possibly its hydroxy analog.   No confusion could arise from glutamic acid since monosodium glutamate is reported in a separate category.

Possible Future Demand for Amino Acids

The major prospective use of amino acids is for supplementing the incomplete vegetable proteins in the diets of the peoples of the food-deficient regions of America, Africa, and Asia (*1, 5, 6, 8–11*).   The limiting amino acids to be supplied would be not only lysine and methionine but also threonine, tryptophan, and possibly still others.   The quantities that would be required for effectively upgrading the diet in any one of the protein-deficient regions would be a great many times the present total production.

The widespread interest in supplementation is shown by the large number of papers in American and foreign scientific periodicals on the use of amino acids both for animal feeding and in human nutrition.   The number of patents that are being issued in the major industrial countries on the production of the different essential amino acids gives evidence of commercial interest in the subject.   In the United States the scale and extent of work in progress are shown by the significant imports of the amino acids that are not yet in commercial production.

Table II.   United States Imports of Amino Acids for Consumption (*23*)

Country	1964			January-June 1965		
	Quantity, Lb.	Value, $	Value, $/Lb.	Quantity, Lb.	Value, $	Value, $/Lb.
Canada				5,000	3,494	0.70
Denmark	1,102	2,860	2.60			
United Kingdom	3,824	181,693	47.50	6	1,361	227
Netherlands	111,500	77,984	0.70	97,026	64,978	0.67
France	122,101	112,650	0.92	23,963	22,742	0.95
West Germany	154,477	150,225	0.97	47,259	44,717	0.95
Switzerland	6,458	8,008	1.24	22	2,932	133
Israel		3,695			3,401	
Italy	6,171	11,439	1.86	5,006	10,339	2.05
Japan	117,001	323,364	2.76	76,600	163,595	2.13
Total	522,634	871,918	1.67	254,882	317,559	1.25

The subject of supplementation is no longer of only academic interest. A proposal is under consideration in government circles to add lysine to the wheat that is being sent to developing countries under Public Law 480. This addition would have a twofold advantage.   The lysine would double the efficiency of the 10 to 14% of protein in the wheat and would thereby compensate for a significant part of the deficit in animal protein in the diet of the recipient countries—a deficit that cannot, in the foreseeable future, be supplied as milk, meat, or eggs.   Furthermore, the central control of the wheat would make the addition of lysine a relatively simple matter, assuming that means can be developed for incorporating lysine in wheat in a way that would insure its being carried over without loss into bread and other products made from the wheat.

Incidentally, bread enriched by adding 0.25% of lysine is now made and sold in the United States by a large chain of food stores, notwithstanding the fact that, on the average, there is an abundance of adequate protein from other sources in the American diet.

The shipments of wheat under Public Law 480 in 1964 amounted to 563 million bushels or 33,780 million pounds (16). The addition of 0.25% of lysine, for example, to this quantity of wheat would require 85 million pounds or 38,800 metric tons of lysine, a quantity that is at least 10 to 20 times the present world production. The cost of lysine at the present market price of $3.90 per pound would be $0.58 for each bushel of wheat treated, or about one third of the cost of the wheat. This cost would almost certainly be regarded as prohibitive by administrative officials for other than a pilot operation. If, however, the cost of lysine could be reduced to $1.00 a pound with large scale manufacture, the lysine for treatment of the wheat would cost only $0.15 per bushel, or about 2.5 cents for each pound of protein that would be upgraded. The estimate of $1.00 a pound is based on the usual economies that attend large scale manufacture, with computer-controlled continuous processes. The cost of lysine might be further reduced by using crude lysine from the fermentation, without separation from the vitamins and the other amino acids produced by the fermentation since these substances might prove useful additions to the diet as well as the lysine itself.

The initiation, by national or international action, of a program involving the large scale supplementation of staple foods would present a twofold challenge to the chemical industry. The challenge would be, first, to produce lysine, methionine, threonine, tryptophan, and perhaps other amino acids in an aggregate quantity of one or two million tons a year at prices that would encourage rather than minimize their use; and, second, to develop flavors, odors, colors, and other characteristics in the products serving as carriers of the amino acids that would make supplemented foods eagerly sought after by the recipient peoples.

The chemical industry of the world is fully capable of meeting both challenges. Production of the quantities of the amino acids that would be called for would not tax an industry that produces many items in amounts of over a million tons a year. In the United States alone the production of synthetic organic chemicals amounts to about 34 million metric tons a year. Furthermore, the field of organoleptics has developed to the stage at which the identification and synthesis of substances responsible for the taste and odor of food, if not already accomplished, can be accomplished without major difficulty.

The time is ripe for developing a greatly expanded amino acid industry. The basic raw materials are available. A vast amount of fundamental research is recorded in the literature. In every major industrial country there are manufacturers who have had some experience in making one or more amino acids, and doubtless many firms have new processes awaiting an opportune time for development. In the course of normal commercial operations this development would proceed at a deliberate pace. The production, for example, of the 85 million pounds of lysine a year, which has been suggested for the wheat being shipped to India, might require a lead time of several years and firm commitments for a continuing market. The world food situation today, however, is critical and calls for an emergency program such as that which brought the large and successful synthetic rubber industry into being in two years during World War II. With today's superior resources amino acid production could be expanded manyfold in a short time if accorded the requisite priority, funds, and manpower.

Literature Cited

(1) Altschul, A. M., "Proteins. Their Chemistry and Politics," pp. 130–1, Basic Books, New York, 1965.
(2) Brenner, M., Richenbacher, H. R., *Helv. Chim. Acta* **41**, 181–8 (1958).
(3) Emmick, R. D., U. S. Patent **2,556,907** (June 12, 1951).
(4) Ferris, A. F., et. al., *Chem. Ind. (London)* **1959**, 996.
(5) Flodin, N. W., *J. Agr. Food Chem.* **1**, 222–34 (1953); *Cereal Sci. Today* **4**, 44–8 (1959).
(6) Food and Nutrition Board, Division Biology and Agriculture, Natl. Acad. Sci.–Natl. Research Council, Publ. **711**, (1959).
(7) Hara, Minoru, Togo, Kazushi, Akashi, Takehazu, Japan Patent **28,232** (1964).
(8) Howe, E. E., *Chem. Eng. News*, **40**, 74–82 (July 23, 1962).
(9) Howe, E. E., Gilfillan, E. W., Milner, Max, *Am. J. Clin. Nutr.* **16**, 321–6 (1965).
(10) Howe, E. E., Jansen, G. R., Gilfillan, E. W., *Ibid.*, **16**, 315–20 (1965).
(11) Jansen, G. R., Howe, E. E., *Ibid.*, **15**, 262–74 (1964).
(12) Kinoshita, Shukuo, "Production of Amino Acids by Fermentation Processes," in "Advances in Applied Microbiology I," pp. 201–14, W. W. Umbreit, ed., Academic Press, New York, 1959; "Amino Acids," in "Biochemistry of Industrial Microorganisms," pp. 206–26, C. Rainbow and A. H. Rose, eds., Academic Press, New York, 1963.
(13) Kinoshita, Shukuo, private communication.
(14) Kita, D. A., Huang, T., U. S. Patent **2,841,532** (July 1, 1958).
(15) Meister, Alton "Biochemistry of the Amino Acids," 2nd ed., Vol. II, pp. 928–47, Academic Press, New York, 1965.
(16) Reuter, R. W., "Food for Peace 1964" *Annual Report on Public Law* **480**, p. 15, Supt. of Documents, Washington, D. C., 1965.
(17) Rogers, A. O., U. S. Patent **2,657,230** (Oct. 27, 1953).
(18) *Ibid.*, **2,564,647-8-9** (Aug. 14, 1951).
(19) Royal Netherlands Embassy, Washington, D. C., private communication.
(20) Scott, D., Rogers, A. O., U. S. Patent **2,498,300** (Feb. 21, 1950).
(21) Seto, T. A., *Ibid.*, **3,056,729** (Oct. 2, 1962).
(22) Tuites, D. E., *Ibid.*, **2,934,541** (April 26, 1960).
(23) U. S. Bureau of the Census, "U. S. Imports of Merchandise for Consumption," Report FT 125, (December 1964) and current office records available for consultation by the public.
(24) U. S. Tariff Commission, "Synthetic Organic Chemicals, United States Production and Sales," Annual Reports.

(25) White, H. C., "Practical Routes to the Essential Amino Acids," in "Meeting the Protein Needs of Infants and Children," pp. 489–94, Natl. Acad. Sci.–Natl. Research Council Publ. **843**, (1961).
(26) White, H. C., U. S. Patent **2,859,244** (Nov. 4, 1958).

RECEIVED October 12, 1965.

Cottonseed Protein in Human Foods

RICARDO BRESSANI, LUIZ G. ELÍAS, and EDGAR BRAHAM

Institute of Nutrition of Central America and Panama (INCAP) Guatemala, C. A.

Cottonseed protein has been a recognized human food, used by people of low and high economic resources as supplement to the daily diet, since vegetable protein mixtures were developed at INCAP to eradicate protein malnutrition. Up to 38% has been used to enrich cereal flours, noodles, flaked breakfast foods, sausages, and other foods. The nutritional value, stability, tolerance, acceptability, and shelf life of these foods are good. Information is presented here on the newer and modified older technologies for producing edible cottonseed protein concentrate, and the fate of gossypol after cooking in mixtures containing cottonseed flour in the presence and absence of calcium and ferrous ions, and after ingestion by experimental animals and children.

Cottonseed protein became a recognized food for man 6 years ago, when protein-rich food mixtures containing cottonseed flour began to be commercially produced, distributed, and consumed. Although the number of people using cottonseed protein as food is relatively small at present, the prospects of increasing its use are great. Increased consumption will follow as more knowledge about its industrial preparation is obtained, preserving its nutritive value, keeping its cost low, diversifying its applications in food, and understanding factors which have limited its use.

The developments which led to the use of cottonseed protein concentrate as human food are based on extensive work on the use of cottonseed meal in animal feeding, particularly for monogastric animals. The information obtained from animal feeding studies can be summarized as follows:

The most important factor limiting the use of cottonseed meal was the presence in the meal of the pigment gossypol. This substance, a polyphenol, is toxic to monogastric animals, particularly swine (*40, 51, 77*).

Cottonseed protein is deficient in the amino acid lysine. This deficiency increases as lysine is bound during processing for oil extraction. The pigment gossypol was also partially responsible, since it reacts with the ε-amino group of lysine, making it unavailable. The oil is still economically more important, but the technology is progressing, and both the oil and the protein are being emphasized. The difference in their economic value is becoming smaller (1, 23, 53, 56, 61).

A further drawback was the fact that eggs from hens fed cottonseed meal develop a dark unpleasant color of the yolk and a pink discoloration of the white, and the membrane separating white from yolk becomes more permeable. These effects were due not only to gossypol but also to the presence of sterculic and malvalic acids in the lipid moiety of the seed (36, 55, 65).

The urgent need to develop economic, locally available, and highly nutritive foods for the extremely large number of people, particularly children, suffering protein-calorie malnutrition, moved INCAP to test the possibility of using cottonseed protein for this purpose. Research carried out during the past 8 years at INCAP has resulted in developing several vegetable protein foods containing from 9 to 38% cottonseed protein concentrate, making it possible to use this protein source as a food for many undernourished people of the world.

Table I shows the commercial yearly production of two vegetable protein mixtures (INCAP No. 9 and No. 15), known as Incaparina since 1961. Although their annual production remained essentially the same during the first two years, it doubled in 1963 and increased approximately five-fold in 1964. In 1965 total production reached about 4.0 million pounds. On this basis, in the last 5 years, 800,000 pounds of cottonseed protein have been produced in Central America for Incaparina production and about 700,000 pounds in Colombia.

Table I. Production of Incaparina in Latin America
(Pounds)

Trimester

Year	First	Second	Third	Fourth	Total
1961	—	44,250	100,755	100,731	245,736
1962	68,772	9,568	128,515	—[a]	206,805
1963	63,134	154,464	106,977	163,995	488,570
1964	475,055	237,411	722,844	728,034	2163,344
1965	720,458	832,648			

[a] Not produced because of low availability of cottonseed flour.

Availability of Cottonseed and Cottonseed Protein

Cotton and man have been wedded amicably and profitably since ancient times. The truth of that statement becomes evident on observation of Table II, where production figures in specific countries and the world are shown (76). Total world production for the year 1962 was estimated at 23,390,000 tons, showing continuous increases throughout the years. It was

Table III.   Tentative Chemical Quality of Cottonseed Protein Concentrate for Human Consumption

Moisture, % (maximum)	10.0
Crude fat, % (maximum)	6.0
Protein, % (N × 6.25 minimum)	50.0
Crude fiber, % (maximum)	5.0
Total gossypol, % (maximum)	1.2
Free gossypol, % (maximum)	0.06
Free fatty acids (maximum, as % of oil)	1.8
Available lysine, g./16 g. nitrogen (minimum)	3.6

nitrogen for the cottonseed protein and milk protein tested. A mixture of cottonseed and corn flour fed at 2 to 5 grams of protein per kg. was not adequate for the recovery of the malnourished children studied. At this intake, nitrogen retention as percentage of intake was around 29% for milk, about 18% for cottonseed flour alone, approximately 17% for a mixture of cottonseed flour and rice, and around 30% for a mixture of equal parts of milk and cottonseed flour.

Kaye *et al.* (*49*) reported on nitrogen balance data on three babies fed cottonseed flour alone and cottonseed flour mixtures with rice or wheat protein providing half of the protein from last sources. Retention with milk was significantly greater than with cottonseed, and the cottonseed-rice mixture was superior to the mixture of cottonseed flour and wheat. They concluded that cottonseed flour was a reasonably good protein source.

Table IV.   Amino Acid Composition of Edible Grade Cottonseed Protein Concentrate (*1*)

Amino Acid	G./16 G. N	Amino Acid	G./16 G. N
Lysine	3.30	Aspartic acid	8.01
Leucine	6.46	Glutamic acid	15.99
Isoleucine	2.42	Serine	3.77
Threonine	2.46	Proline	2.68
Valine	3.25	Glycine	2.75
Phenylalanine	4.17	Alanine	4.13
Tryptophan	0.86	Tyrosine	2.53
Methionine	1.40	Histidine	1.98
Cystine	1.45	Arginine	7.15

The results of other workers are summarized in Table VI. DeMaeyer and Vanderborght (*27*, *28*) reported the percentage absorption, biological value (BV), and net protein utilization (NPU) of cottonseed flour in children to be 87, 62, and 54%, respectively. They concluded that cottonseed flour was safe, had a relatively good nutritive value, and was a possible source of protein in the prevention of protein malnutrition. Snyderman,

Boyer, and Holt (72) evaluated cottonseed protein in premature infants, and showed it to have a net protein utilization of 41% when corrected for nitrogen lost in feces. The biological value at protein intakes of 5 and 7 grams per kg. of body weight, was 57 and 46%, respectively. Cow's milk fed at an intake of 5 grams of protein per kg. of body weight had a biological value of 79%.

Table V. Nutritive Value of Human Grade Cottonseed Protein Concentrate on Several Experimental Animals

	Biological Method			
Diet	PER (rat) 10%[a]	NPU (rat) 10%[a]	NBI (dog)	Growth (chick) 20%[a]
Cottonseed protein	2.14	50	0.60	201
Cottonseed protein + lysine	2.40	—	0.72	308
Cottonseed protein + lysine + methionine	—	—	0.85	303
Casein	2.38	72	0.78	—

[a] Protein level.

Methods of Processing. The industrial methods of removing oil from cottonseed are essentially the same as those for processing other oil-containing seeds. Because of the demand for better extraction methods, better quality of oil, and better quality meal, important technological modifications have been developed and introduced and newer and more efficient technologies have evolved. The details have been described (3, 33) and only conditions directly affecting nutritive value are mentioned in this report. The first industrial method for processing cottonseed, hydraulic press processing, is still used in certain underdeveloped areas of the world. Although screw. press processing is the most common method, treatment of the seed by these two processes is essentially the same. The screw press processing method is more efficient for oil extraction than the hydraulic press method, but the latter is less damaging to the protein quality of the seed.

Much work on the utilization of cottonseed protein in the form of meal and on its nutritive value was performed using the by-product of cottonseed obtained by these processes. It was soon found that the nutritional value of the protein of such products was of very low quality, because of excessive temperature, pressure, and time used in processing. Examples of the effect of commercial processing on the nutritive value of the protein of cottonseed meal have been reported by Milligan and Bird (59) using chicks. and by Horn et al. (42) using rats. These investigators reported that the processing conditions caused marked variations in the nutritive value of

Table VI. Nutritive Value of Cottonseed Protein Concentrate in Human Subjects

Protein Source	Protein Intake	% Absorption	Biological Value	NPU	Subjects
Cottonseed protein	28.86 g./day	81.97	62.12	50.83	Children[a]
Cow's milk	30.55 g./day	90.73	82.15	74.50	Children
Cottonseed flour	5 g./kg	71	57	41	Prematures[b]
Cow's milk	5 g./kg	85	79	67	Prematures

[a] (*27, 28*).
[b] (*72*).

different meals. Since the free gossypol levels were below the growth-inhibiting level for chicks, the effects could not be attributed to this pigment. Processing of cottonseed by hydraulic or screw pressing inactivated most of the gossypol but damaged the quality of the protein. This dual nature of the effect of heat on cottonseed protein stimulated re-examination of the nutritional significance of free gossypol and of the nature of the damage to protein quality and resulted in developing processes for reducing or eliminating both disadvantages, as well as increasing the efficiency of oil extraction. The prepress solvent extraction method is now in common use (*3, 33*).

More recently direct solvent extraction has been used. A process developed at the Southern Regional Research Laboratories (SRRL) (*35, 50*) uses a solvent mixture of hexane-acetone-water; the Vaccarino process (*25*) uses only acetone.

Most attention is now being given to the prepress solvent and direct solvent processes for preparing cottonseed flour for human consumption.

The changes in some chemical components taking place in cottonseed meal during screwpress processing are shown in Table VII (*19*). The extreme conditions and the poor quality of the seed resulted in a product of rather low nutritional qualities as judged by a decrease in available lysine from 3.13 to 2.48 grams per 16 grams of nitrogen. In Table VIII are shown the changes in some chemical constituents when cottonseed is processed by the prepress solvent method (*19*). Fat content decreased while total nitrogen increased with respect to the various operations during processing. Free gossypol also decreased significantly, with the greatest change taking place at the expeller level. Most of the rats fed with samples obtained before the conditioning of the seed died within 4 days after initiation of study. On the other hand, the animals grew normally when fed samples obtained on subsequent operations. Weight gain was lower on samples from the solvent extraction tower and from the final product, suggesting a decrease in available lysine during these two operations.

Table VII.   Changes in Fat, Nitrogen, Free-Amino Groups of Lysine and Free and Total Gossypol during Cottonseed Processing by Screw Press

Position in Process[a]	Fat, %	Nitrogen, %	Lysine G./16 G. N	Gossypol[b] Free, mg./100g.	Gossypol[b] Total, G. %
Seed	34.4	5.01	3.13	203	1.94
Cooker	28.0	4.34	3.22	193	1.48
Drier	29.6	4.00	3.52	200	1.46
Conditioner	30.4	4.38	3.12	200	1.49
Expeller	5.2	6.22	2.83	43	1.16
Product[c]	4.7	5.33	2.48	46	1.14

[a] Samples taken after operation.
[b] On fat free basis.
[c] Ground to pass 80 mesh screen.

Table VIII.   Changes in Fat, Nitrogen, Gossypol and Nutritive Value of Cottonseed Processed by Prepress Solvent Extraction

Position in Process[a]	Fat, %	Nitrogen, %	Free Gossypol, Mg./100 G.	Mortality, Start/ Finish	Wt. Gain, G.
Seed	33.3	5.60	930	8/1	—
Cooker	32.8	5.29	951	8/1	—
Dryer	33.0	5.71	933	8/1	—
Conditioner	33.0	5.00	872	8/5	−13
Expeller	10.0	7.09	98	8/8	76
Solvent ext.	2.8	7.85	64	8/8	58
Flour	3.4	8.28	69	8/8	62

[a] Samples taken after operation.

Chemical and biological data for meals prepared by different processing procedures are presented in Table IX. It is evident that the prepress solvent-extracted meals are better than the screw-pressed meals; however, the meals prepared by azeotropic solvent extraction were superior to those prepared by the other methods (57). A better comparison of meals prepared by azeotropic extraction and conventional meals has been reported by Johnston and Watts (47). A further potential advantage is that the mixed solvent extracts aflatoxin from seed with *Aspergillus flavus* (38).

The prepress solvent method yields meals only slightly inferior in quality to that prepared by the mixed solvent process. In contrast, the screw-pressing method significantly damages the protein quality, as indicated by the lower available lysine and protein efficiency ratios (PER) in chicks (57).

Further modifications in present technologies can be introduced to improve nutritional quality. In INCAP studies (19) carried out in a Central American cottonseed oil mill, several variables were tested, with the results shown in Table X. Decreasing the load in the expeller and starting with cottonseed kernels with 18% hulls yielded a product higher in available lysine and lower in free gossypol, after removal of hulls by screening.

Table IX. Evaluation of Cottonseed Meals Prepared by Extraction with Acetone-Hexane-Water Mixture and Other Processes[a]

Process	Gossypol		Available Lysine G./16 G. N	Wt. Gain, G.	PER[b] Wt. Gain/ Protein
	Total	Free			
Aceton-hexane-water (106)[c]	0.37	0.035	3.68	290.33	2.19
Prepress solvent (109)	1.04	0.061	3.37	255.00	1.98
Prepress solvent (111)	1.53	0.093	3.13	224.33	1.91
Prepress solvent (112)	0.90	0.036	3.54	249.00	2.01
Screw press (107)	1.20	0.074	2.97	206.33	1.71
Screw press (108)	1.39	0.056	2.50	165.66	1.46
Screw press (110)	1.38	0.075	2.85	180.66	1.61
SBOM	—	—	—	711.33	3.48

[a] (57).
[b] Chicks.
[c] No. of meal.

Gossypol. The extreme conditions used for cottonseed processing have been responsible for the low protein quality of cottonseed flour, but the problem of gossypol has also limited the use of cottonseed protein. This compound present in the cottonseed in small glands is a very reactive polyphenol (3). During processing, the glands are broken and under the heat and pressure, gossypol reacts with free or ϵ-amino groups of lysine in the protein moiety. Not all gossypol present reacts with lysine since part of it is removed with the oil during pressing and part reacts with other seed constituents. Not all lysine that is unavailable has reacted with gossypol, since carbohydrates are also responsible (58). Binding of lysine by gossypol is, however, an important factor in decreasing the protein quality of cottonseed meal (5, 71). Furthermore, free gossypol is toxic to monogastric animals (3). Therefore, the ideal process for cottonseed would be one which minimizes the inactivation of lysine and reduces or eliminates free gossypol.

Research in this problem is not limited to technologies for conventional seed. Cottonseed varieties have recently been developed which are gland free and, therefore, gossypol free. Flours produced from glandless cottonseed have been shown to have high protein quality (47, 70).

Table X.   Changes in Free Gossypol and On Free Epsilon Amino Groups of Lysine During Processing of Cottonseed under Different Conditions

Condition	Free Gossypol Mg./100 G.	ϵ-NH_2-Lysine, %
Full load[a]	91	1.56
75% load[a]	58	1.74
60% load[a]	47	1.79
Kernels without hulls	92	1.71
Kernels with 18% hulls	68	1.84

[a] Amount of cooked kernels fed to expeller.

Vegetable Protein-Rich Foods Containing Cottonseed Protein

Cottonseed flour as a protein supplement can play an important role in feeding the malnourished and protein-deficient people of underdeveloped areas and the growing populations of the industrial areas as well.   A very practical question is whether a protein-rich product, such as cottonseed flour, should be made available as such, in the hope that it will be used to supplement the proteins in the basic diet, or whether it should be mixed with some other food so as to give a more complete food.   For nutritional and practical reasons it seems best to use the protein-rich foods in combination with other staple foods to form food mixtures of high protein quality and quantity, which can then serve as protein supplement to basic diets or as complete foods.   Ideally, these mixtures should be formulated so that the amino acid patterns of the different food components complement each other for maximum nutritional value.

The purpose is to obtain a food mixture with an essential amino acid pattern as close as possible to that of the higher quality proteins such as milk, meat, or eggs; otherwise the effectiveness of such protein-rich foods is minimized.   When other nutrients such as vitamins and minerals are deficient, these too should be added to the mixture.   Such an approach has been used in vegetable protein mixtures developed at INCAP.

Formulation. VEGETABLE MIXTURE 8.   One of the first formulas containing cottonseed flour to receive extensive testing in experimental animals and human subjects was Vegetable Mixture 8 (*11, 73*), which contained 50% maize flour, 35% sesame flour, 9% cottonseed flour, 3% torula yeast, and 3% dehydrated leaf meal.   This mixture contains 25% crude protein, with a protein score of 67% based on the FAO amino acid reference pattern (*34*).   The amount of cottonseed flour used was small; however, its replacement by skim milk did not significantly improve the protein quality of the mixture.   Even though the results of biological tests in experimental animals indicated that Vegetable Mixture 8 was deficient in lysine when fed at low levels of protein in the diet, children fed the mixture retained as much nitrogen as children fed comparable amounts of protein from milk.

VEGETABLE MIXTURE 9. Biological studies with rats, which indicated that the protein from 38% cottonseed flour constitutes the most efficient amount to complement the protein from the cereal grains, gave rise to Vegetable Mixture 9 (*10, 15*). The experimental formula consists of 28% corn flour, 28% sorghum flour, 38% cottonseed flour, 3% torula yeast, and 3% dehydrated leaf meal. Mixture 9 contains 27.5% crude protein and has a biological value of 72%.

Because the mixture contains 38% cottonseed flour, it was subjected to extensive testing in chicks, rats, dogs, and swine. The studies included short-term protein evaluation tests, effects on carcass, liver, bone, and blood composition, nitrogen balance experiments, growth and toxicity tests in swine, reproduction and lactation studies in rats, as well as multigeneration feeding studies with rats (*13, 14, 20*). Changes during cooking and the stability and shelf life of the dry product were also investigated. The mixture is of good quality, free of adverse physiological effects, and capable of supplementing diets of poor quality (*42*). At physiological levels of protein intake in children, retention of nitrogen was equal to that with equivalent amounts of milk protein (*66*).

Variations of Vegetable Mixture 9. While testing and developing Mixture 9, the several variations shown in Table XI were also studied. Mixtures 9 FF and 9 Casein, 120 contain 3% fish flour or 3% casein, respectively, in place of an equal amount of leaf meal. These two derivatives of Mixture 9 are of a slightly higher protein content and nutritive value, because of the

Table XI. Formulas for INCAP Vegetable Mixture 9 and Variations

Ingredient	VM9 Exptl. %	VM9 FF %	VM9 Casein, %	VM9 Commercial Production, %
Maize[a,b]	28	28	28	29
Sorghum[a,b]	28	28	28	29
Cottonseed protein	38	38	38	38
Dehydrated leaf meal	3	—	—	—
Fish flour	—	3	—	—
Casein	—	—	3	—
Torula yeast	3	3	3	3
Calcium carbonate[c]	—	—	—	1
Vitamin A, I.U.	—	4500	4500	4500

[a] Uncooked or cooked with and without lime. When uncooked or cooked with water 1% $CaCO_3$ is added.
[b] Can be replaced totally or partially by any other common cereal grain.
[c] Calcium hydroxide can be used instead of the carbonate.

relatively larger amounts of lysine present in both animal protein concentrates. These two mixtures have been tested only in experimental animals.

Other variations of Mixture 9 were also studied. In this case, the objective was to combine cottonseed protein with cereal grains other than maize, which are more common or used by other population groups. All of these variations have been tested in experimental animals and most of them have also been tested in children with good results. Mixture 9, made with 58% rice replacing corn, had the highest nutritive value (11, 20).

VEGETABLE MIXTURE 15. Previous results with rats had indicated that mixtures of soybean flour and cottonseed flour, where each provides 50% of the protein, are of higher protein quality than when each ingredient provides 100% of the protein. This finding gave rise to Vegetable Mixture 15, which consists of 56% maize flour, 19% cottonseed flour, 19% soybean flour, 3% torula yeast, 1% calcium phosphate, and 4500 I.U. of vitamin A. Mixture 15 contains 27% crude protein and has a biological value of 75% (17).

Other vegetable protein mixtures containing cottonseed flour. From food composition data and information of the nutritive value of certain vegetable seeds and cottonseed flour, Bradfield (6), in Peru, formulated two protein supplements, I and II. No. I consisted of 30% cottonseed flour, 10% quinua flour, 10% Vicia faba flour, 10% Amaranthus caudatus flour, 2% alfalfa leaf meal, 2% torula yeast, and 35% wheat flour. It contained 25.7% crude protein and 352 calories per 100 grams. No. II contained 35% cottonseed flour, 20% quinua flour, 3% alfalfa leaf meal, 2% torula yeast, and 40% wheat flour. The protein and calorie contents were 26.3% and 353 per 100 grams, respectively. The nutritive values of these mixtures were found by Graham (39) sufficiently good to consolidate the cure of children with severe protein malnutrition.

At INCAP, full-fat peanut flour enriched with cottonseed flour has been tested in experimental animals (12). The data of Table XII indicate that the addition of 10 to 20% cottonseed flour improved the protein value of whole roasted peanuts. Addition of peanut flour to supply protein equal in amount to that derived from the levels of cottonseed flour used did not alter the PER.

Table XII.   Supplementation of Full Fat Roasted Peanuts[a] with Cottonseed Protein Concentrate

Supplement Added	% Added	Protein in Diet, %	PER
Peanut protein[b]	10.0	16.2	0.82
Cottonseed protein	10.0	17.6	0.91
Peanut Protein	20.0	20.0	0.89
Cottonseed protein	20.0	24.5	1.10

[a] Amount of full fat peanut in diet, 50%.
[b] Screw press processed peanut protein concentrate.

Attention has also been given to mixtures of cottonseed flour and cooked bean flour (*Phaseolus vulgaris*) (*9*). These two products combine well from the nutritive value point of view when cottonseed provides 70% of the protein and bean flour 30% (Table XIII). Besides increasing the protein value of beans, it significantly increased the total amount of protein. From these combinations, Formula 17 was developed, consisting of 35% cottonseed flour, 37% bean flour, 24% cereal grain, 3% yeast, and 1% calcium phosphate, with a protein concentration of about 28%. Similar combinations have been prepared with cottonseed flour and other legumes generally with a higher PER than the nutritive value of either of the two components. None has yet been fed to human subjects.

Table XIII. Combination between Dehydrated Black Bean Flour and Cottonseed Protein Concentrate

Black Bean Flour	Cottonseed Protein, %	Average Wt. Gain, G.[a]	PER[b]
46.7	—	42	1.59
37.3	3.8	55	1.85
28.0	7.6	69	2.15
23.4	9.5	79	2.08
18.7	11.4	92	2.34
9.3	15.2	86	2.32
—	19.0	65	1.94

[a] Average initial weight, 42 g.
[b] Protein in diets, 10%.

Chemical and Biological Observations on Food Mixtures Containing Cottonseed Flour

Free gossypol content has been one of the factors limiting the utilization of cottonseed flour. Since gossypol is toxic to monogastric animals, the significance of its presence in protein-rich foods for human feeding becomes of much importance. The standard adapted by the WHO/FAO/UNICEF Protein Advisory Committee specifies that edible grade cottonseed flour should not contain more than 0.060% free gossypol. This figure is diluted when cottonseed flour is incorporated in food mixtures. Still, it was of interest to learn more about the fate of this substance when mixtures are prepared for consumption and after ingestion of the food.

Effect of Cooking. The results of several cooking experiments with Vegetable Mixture 9 in the presence and absence of calcium and ferrous ions are summarized in Table XIV. For these studies, Vegetable Mixture 9 without calcium carbonate was prepared with 38% cottonseed flour, containing from 32 to 96 mg. of free gossypol. The mixture was cooked as

**Table XIV. Effect of Cooking on Free and Total Gossypol Content
of Vegetable Mixture 9 in Absence and Presence of Calcium
and Ferrous Ions**

GOSSYPOL

Addition to VM9[a]	Free Mg./100 G.		% Loss	Total G./100 G.		% Loss
	Initial	Final		Initial	Final	
None	22.4	10.8	51.7	0.34	0.35	—
$CaCO_3$	17.9	7.6	57.5	0.41	0.40	—
$Ca(OH)_2$	17.9	5.5	69.2	0.33	0.33	—
$FeSO_4 \cdot 7\ H_2O$	16.8	10.1	40.0	0.34	0.33	2.9
$FeSO_4 \cdot 7\ H_2O$ pH 9.15	22.1	0	100.0	0.41	0.38	7.3
None pH 9.18	31.5	3.1	90.1	0.43	0.42	2.3
$Ca\ (OH)_2 + FeSO_4 \cdot 7H_2O$	10.9	2.9	73.4	0.31	0.25	19.3

[a] 1% Ca CO_3, 1% Ca $(OH)_2$, 0.1% $FeSO_4 \cdot 7H_2O$.

recommended for human consumption and freeze-dried. Free gossypol
decreased about 52% when the mixture was cooked in water alone. The
presence of 1% calcium carbonate or calcium hydroxide in the mixture
decreased free gossypol level to 57 and 69%, respectively. The addition
of 0.1% ferrous sulfate ($7H_2O$) and cooking reduced free gossypol only 40%,
which is less than the decrease when cooked in water alone. The presence
of calcium and ferrous ions during cooking caused a decrease of up to 73%.
Cooking at pH 9 in the majority of cases caused a complete disappearance
of free gossypol (*18*). Available lysine content has not been affected. The
representative results shown in Table XV indicate that even after 25
minutes of cooking Mixture 9 with and without additional compounds,
lysine remained essentially the same. Nitrogen balance studies provided
further evidence that protein quality of the mixture is not impaired by
cooking (Table XV).

Cooking is not necessary to decrease free gossypol levels in the mixture,
if sufficient calcium and ferrous ions are present. Calcium and ferrous ions
each protected swine from gossypol toxicity, although not completely.
When both were present, full protection was achieved. The animals gained
weight and appeared as well as those fed soybean oil meal (*46*).

The disappearance or destruction of gossypol upon wetting and
cooking with calcium and ferrous ions is still not understood. A possible
explanation is that the gossypol is converted to compounds such as gossy-
purpurin, which decompose under the conditions of treatment. Since
available lysine and nutritive value remain essentially the same, it can,
therefore, be assumed that the decrease in gossypol occurs in a different
manner than when free gossypol is decreased by binding with lysine during
processing for oil extraction.

Fate of Ingested Gossypol. To learn more about the fate of gossypol ingested by experimental animals or human subjects fed Mixture 9, studies were carried out to determine if the pigment was present in the feces (*16*). Representative results obtained in dogs (Table XVI.) indicate that all total gossypol fed in the mixture appeared in the feces while free gossypol in the feces was about 3.4 times higher than that ingested. Since total gossypol includes free gossypol, and good recoveries were obtained for total gossypol in the feces, it would seem that the higher fecal free gossypol was due to liberation of the bound gossypol in the intestinal tract (*16*).

Table XV. Effect of Cooking of Vegetable Mixture 9 on Available Lysine and on Nitrogen Balance in Dogs

Addition to VM9[a]	Available Lysine Mg./100 G.		Nitrogen Retention, % of Intake[b]	
	Initial[c]	Final[d]	Initial[c]	Final[d]
None	1049	1098	—	—
1% Ca CO₃ + 0.1% FeSO₄·7H₂O	1025	1019	—	—
1% CaCO₃	—	—	17.5	16.3

[a] VM9 contained 1% starch instead of 1% CaCO₃.
[b] Initial and final intake of nitrogen 844 and 865 mg./kg./day, respectively.
[c] No cooking.
[d] 25 min. cooking with water.

Similar studies were carried out in children fed Mixture 9. Representative results are shown in Table XVII. As with dogs, acceptable recoveries in some cases are obtained from total gossypol values; however, free gossypol levels are higher than expected. Although these results are not comparable to the dog data, for technical reasons, they indicate that the gossypol ingested is being excreted in feces. When the children were no longer fed cottonseed flour, free and total gossypol disappeared from feces (*44*).

Protein Quality of Cottonseed Flour Samples Prepared by Two Industrial Processes. It was desirable, for practical purposes, to find out if flours prepared by modified prepress solvent extraction methods were inferior to flour prepared by azeotropic solvent extraction, which has been reported to yield flours of high quality. The two types of flours were used to prepare Mixture 9 and fed to children at two levels of nitrogen intake. The results shown in Table XVIII indicate that the protein quality of the two samples is essentially the same at intakes of 2 and 1 grams of protein per kg. of body weight per day, and lower than that of skim milk protein only at the lower level of dietary protein. Protein digestibility was lower in both than for milk, but greater in the sample prepared by azeotropic solvent extraction than for the prepress solvent-extracted flour.

The children in this study were fed cottonseed flour for approximately 60 days without changes in hemoglobin or hematocrit values (21). Swine receiving relatively large levels of free gossypol in the ration showed decrease in hemoglobin and hematocrit values (46).

Table XVI.   Gossypol Intake and Fecal Excretion of Dogs Fed a Cottonseed Flour-Corn Mixture Cooked for Several Periods of Time[a] (13)

Gossypol[b]	Cooking Time, Minutes				
	0	8	16	24	0
Intake[c]					
Free (A)	31	30	26	22	34
Total	709	689	704	715	780
Fecal[c]					
Free (B)	108	91	86	83	103
Total	703	687	757	735	805
Ratio free B/A	3.5	3.0	3.3	3.8	3.0

[a] Average 3 dogs.
[b] Mg./dog/day.
[c] 7 day/cooking period.

Long Feeding Tests. During the nutritional testing of Mixture 9, using the nitrogen balance technique, children were fed high, intermediate, and low levels of protein from Mixture 9, which contains 38% cottonseed flour, 20 mg. of free gossypol, and 400 mg. of total gossypol per 100 grams.

Table XVII.   Intake and Fecal Gossypol of Children Fed INCAP Vegetable Mixture 9 Made with Two Different Samples of Cottonseed Protein Concentrate

Case No.	Total Gossypol[a], Mg.		Total Gossypol[b], Mg.	
	Intake	Output	Intake	Output
PC-120	655	786	3591	2817
PC-125	596	592	3107	2456
PC-126	518	531	2792	2164
PC-135	561	464	2260	2183
PC-136	482	813	2039	1998
VV- 25	838	776	4219	2263

[a] Cottonseed flour used in VM9 contained 25 mg. free and 209 mg. total gossypol per 100 g.
[b] Cottonseed flour used in VM9 contained 57 mg. free and 881 mg. total gossypol per 100 g.

It is evident from Table XIX that at protein intake of 2 grams per kg. of body weight and above, nitrogen retention of the children is comparable to that with milk protein feeding. When protein intake is 1 gram per kg. per day or below, nitrogen retention from Mixture 9 is somewhat lower than with milk, because Mixture 9 has a minor deficiency of lysine, which becomes apparent at low protein intakes (*66, 67*). Although these tests lasted about 3 weeks, children have been fed the mixture for much longer times. Representative results of weight changes up to 90 days are shown in Figure 2. All the children gained weight as normally as with milk. No adverse effects of any kind were noted. A much longer experience is available. In an experimental program in a highland Indian village in Guatemala, all children under 5 years of age have been offered a supplement of 27 grams of Incaparina per day (7.5 grams of protein) made up in milk (7.5 grams of protein). Twenty-five children have received the supplement at least two thirds (50% and over) of the possible days for over 4 years, and ten for 5 years. No adverse reactions have been reported, and children receiving the supplement have grown and developed well by village standards (*68*).

Table XVIII.   Nitrogen Balance of Children Fed Skim Milk and Two Cottonseed Flours Prepared by Different Processes

Test Protein	Intake, Mg./Kg./Day	Nitrogen Absorbed, Mg./Kg./Day	Nitrogen Retained, Mg./Kg./Day
Skim milk	305	255	82
CSF B[a]	302	218	72
CSF CF21[b]	303	237	77
Skim milk	164	128	51
CSF B	161	109	24
CSF CF21	163	117	18

[a] Cottonseed flour B prepress solvent extracted flour.
[b] Cottonseed flour CF21 azeotropic solvent extracted flour.

Table XIX.   Nitrogen Balance of Children Fed Skim Milk and INCAP Mixture 9 at Different Levels of Protein Intake

Protein Intake, G./Kg./day	No. of Children	No. of Balances	Milk Nitrogen		VM9 Nitrogen	
			Absorption %	Retention of Intake	Absorption %	Retention of Intake
> 4.0	1	2	84.4	22.0	66.1	24.1
3.0–3.9	4	11	84.9	17.1	70.2	16.8
2.0–2.9	9	48	82.6	16.3	68.9	17.8
1.0–1.9	4	13	78.1	24.9	66.2	15.5
< 1.0	2	2	67.2	8.1	59.1	4.5

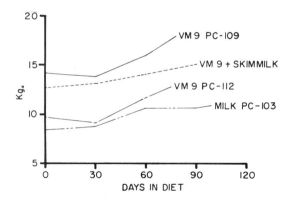

Figure 2. Weight of children fed Mixture 9

Tolerance and Acceptability. Vegetable protein mixtures containing cottonseed flour have been tested for acceptability and tolerance by different rural population groups in several Latin American countries. In all these trials, the mixtures were highly acceptable, indicating that cottonseed flour is of good nutritive value, palatable, and free of toxic effects. Furthermore, these findings indicate acceptability of the food in spite of the color of the product.

Other Characteristics of Cottonseed Protein-Containing Foods. Some of the physical characteristics of food products containing cottonseed flour have been mentioned. In others, such as maize or wheat flours supplemented with cottonseed protein concentrate, the principal visual characteristic is the color. This is yellow light brown, which upon cooking or baking becomes darker. In our experience, color has not caused any serious acceptability problems. The color is masked when chocolate is added, as in some acceptability tests in Central America and Mexico.

The taste of the foods containing cottonseed flour is either bland or slightly nutty. Some flavor concentrates are usually added, such as vanilla, cinnamon, or anise, as well as sugar. When sweetened, this food is a filling and satisfying drink.

The mixtures for child feeding are usually consumed as gruels. A possible disadvantage is that they become thick, because of the starch from the cereal grains. The problem can be solved by adding from 0.1 to 0.3% of amylolytic enzymes, which liquefy the gruel upon cooking. If it is cooked mildly with small amounts of water and allowed to cool, it becomes a gel which can be consumed as a pudding and, with proper flavoring, is very tasty.

The keeping quality of cereal mixtures containing cottonseed flour is satisfactory, as measured by fat acidity and biological tests with experimental animals. INCAP studies showed that the products kept very well up to 6 months even under tropical conditions; the major problem was infestation by insects. If the packaging material allows moisture to penetrate, the mixture eventually becomes darker and nutritive value decreases significantly.

The mixtures discussed are now marketed as powder passing an 80-mesh sieve. Several types of food preparations could be marketed, such as cakes, cookies, bread, and other baked goods. Flavor and structure can be improved by precooking followed by drum drying; however, drying must be carefully controlled to conserve nutritive value. Many kinds of food preparations have been made from the mixture. They can be used as substitutes for part of the cereal flour or starch in the preparation and cooking of many foods.

Other Food Uses

Besides the important use of cottonseed flour in protein-rich foods it is being used as an additive in bakery products, a filler in meat-like food products, and a protein supplement to cereal grain flours.

Additive. Cottonseed protein in the form of flour is used to prepare a few bakery products such as cookies, crackers, doughnuts, and other foods of a similar nature in amounts varying between 1 and 6%. The cottonseed flour reduces dough stickiness, binds water, benefits machining properties, reduces fat absorption, and increases shelf life because of antioxidant properties. Doughnuts absorb 2 to 3% less fat when cottonseed flour is included in the formula. Overman (*62*) reported that 3 to 10% cottonseed flour delayed the development of organoleptic rancidity in raw food mixes and to a lesser extent in baked pastry. This property has been attributed to the tocopherols present in cottonseed flour; it might also be due to the small amounts of free gossypol present since it is an antioxidant and a polymerization inhibitor (*3, 4*).

Filler. The use of cottonseed flour in ground meat products such as sausages, meat loaves, hamburger patties, frankfurters, and baby meats has not been studied very extensively.

Duckworth and Woodham (*29*) have described the preparation and nutritive value of frankfurters made of 34.5% lean beef, 10% lard, and 14% cottonseed flour. The raw sausage mixture contained 14.2% protein and was cured for 30 minutes at 85° to 88°C. The nutritive value of the sausage was as good as that of sausages made with 14% milk replacing cottonseed flour. Furthermore, the cottonseed flour frankfurters supplemented cereal diets; this work represents a step forward in utilizing cottonseed flour for this purpose.

Protein Supplement Besides serving as a major protein constituent in protein-rich foods, described above, cottonseed flour can be used as a supplement to the diet, and as a supplement to cereal grain flours.

Supplement to poor-quality diets. The approach of using cottonseed protein as such to supplement diets low in protein quality was first studied by Kuppuswamy et al. (54) in India. Their results indicate that 10% cottonseed protein improved the quality of South Indian diets by supplying some of the deficient amino acids as well as additional protein. Subrahmanyan et al. (74) and Krishnamurthy et al. (52), using 10% of cottonseed flour prepared from cottonseed kernels extracted with alcohol, investigated its supplementary value to wheat and ragi diets in India. Both supplemented diets were significantly better than the unsupplemented ones.

Supplement to cereal grain flours. Properly prepared cottonseed flour contains protein of high nutritive value and offers an excellent means of supplying dietary proteins to extend and partially replace protein foods of animal origin. Cottonseed flour was first used for enriching wheat flour by Jones and Divine (48). They found that the addition of as little as 5 parts of cottonseed flour to 95 parts of wheat flour produced mixtures containing 16 to 19% more protein than wheat flour alone and a protein combination superior in its growth-promoting value to isonitrogenous quantities of wheat flour.

Womack et al. (78) reported that bread made from 10 parts of cottonseed flour to 100 parts of white wheat flour gave greater gains than equal amounts of bread without cottonseed flour. Bread made with 4 parts of nonfat milk solids and 8 parts of cottonseed flour to 100 parts of white wheat flour gave greater gains in weight than equal amounts of bread made with milk solids but without cottonseed flour. However, NER's were not significantly different at the 10% protein level. Jarquín and Bressani (45) also found that addition of 8 to 10% cottonseed flour improved the protein quantity and quality of wheat flour and white wheat flour, as measured by weight gain and protein efficiency ratio (PER) in growing rats. The bread made from it was acceptable to rural workers in Guatemala.

El Katib (32) reported that the protein quantity and quality of maize flour could be improved by adding 4 to 10% cottonseed flour. Bressani and Marenco (22) described the improvement of lime-treated maize flour with several vegetable and animal protein concentrates. Significant improvement in weight gain and PER was obtained by adding 10% cottonseed flour to lime-treated maize flour. The protein content increased from about 9% in the "masa" flour to about 14% in the enriched product. "Tortillas" made from this mixture did not differ greatly in flavor and color from tortillas made from yellow maize.

Results of baking experiments using a wholesome cottonseed flour in all types of baked foods were reported by Summers, Mead, and Thurber (75). These baked foods were offered for sale over an 18 month period with no evidence of allergies or other disturbances. Baked foods with and without added cottonseed flour were equally acceptable.

Similar results have been found by Elías *et al.* (*31*) for enriching rice flour with protein. Although the increase in nutritive value is less than observed with other cereal grains, protein quantity and quality are both improved.

These studies indicate that cottonseed flour has a definite place in enriching cereal grains. An advantage of this method of enrichment is that the protein-enriched food can be maintained in the common physical form in which it is customarily eaten. For example, in Mexico, Central America, and other Latin American countries, maize is consumed in the form of tortillas.

Conclusion

Vegetable protein mixtures containing cottonseed protein in the form of cottonseed flour have already found a successful market in several countries in Latin America.

Among the countries now producing commercial foods containing cottonseed flour is Guatemala, where current production of Vegetable Mixture 9 (Incaparina) amounts to 120,000 pounds per month. Surveys have indicated that there are now a wide knowledge and acceptance of the product and its nutritional value among consumers. As high as 90% of the people in most areas of the country hear about Incaparina, and more than 40% of these are using the product either occasionally or regularly. In Colombia, where Mixture 15 is being produced, commercial production has reached about 200,000 pounds per month after 2 years. Recently, Venezuela has started market testing of Formula 9 and the first reports indicate that it should be successful.

The extensive research carried out at INCAP on foods containing variable amounts of cottonseed flour has proved that as a human food it is safe, nutritious, inexpensive, and palatable. The Incaparina program and the increased world production and consumption of foods with cottonseed protein have had a significant impact in many parts of the world, and reports on new technologies for the preparation and use of cottonseed flour for human consumption are being published from India, Brazil, Peru, the United States, and Guatemala (*25*). Not only are new technologies for better cottonseed flour production being developed, but it is almost certain that cottonseed protein will find many new uses in foods for man in the near future.

Summary

Cottonseed protein has been a recognized human food ever since vegetable protein mixtures were developed at INCAP to eradicate protein malnutrition. People of low and high economic resources are using such mixtures as regular supplements to their daily diet. Since 1961, 1,083,637 pounds of cottonseed in the form of flour (50% protein) have been produced for human consumption in Latin America. Cottonseed protein has also been used for enriching cereal flours, and in preparing noodles, flaked breakfast foods, sausages, and other foods. Amounts used vary up to 38%. The nutritional value, stability, tolerance, acceptability, and shelf life of these foods have been good. The production of cottonseed protein for human use has been limited by inadequate technologies. Research has shown, however, that changes in the prepress solvent process yield a product of as good a quality as that from newer technologies. Furthermore, in vitro and in vivo studies indicate that moist cooking in the presence of small amounts of calcium and ferrous ions eliminates gossypol toxicity. Gossypol is excreted in feces to a very large extent. The color of cottonseed flour has met with some objections, but chemical treatment gives a product of a light color with no changes in nutritive quality.

Literature Cited

(1) Adriaens, E. L., Bigwood, E. J., *Bull. Soc. Chim. Biol.* **36**, 579–83 (1954).
(2) Allison, J. B., Wannemacher, R. W., Jr., McCoy, J. R., "Determination of Nutritive Value of Cottonseed Flour," in "Cottonseed Protein for Animal and Man," Proceedings of a conference, November 1960, New Orleans, La., p. 1–6.
(3) Altschul, A. M., Lyman, C. M., Thurber, F. H., "Cottonseed Meal," in "Processed Plant Protein Foodstuffs," A. M. Altschul, ed., p. 469–534, Academic Press, New York, 1958.
(4) Bailey, A. E., ed., "Cottonseed and Cottonseed Products, Their Chemistry and Chemical Technology," Interscience, New York, 1948.
(5) Baliga, B. P., Lyman, C. M., *J. Am. Oil Chemists Soc.* **34**, 21–4 (1957).
(6) Bradfield, R. B., "Development of a Low-Cost High Nutritive Value Food Supplement for Peruvian Children," in "Cottonseed Protein for Animal and Man," Proceedings of conference. November 14–16, 1960, New Orleans, La., p. 22–9.
(7) Braham, J. E., Bressani, R., Zaghi, S. de, Flores, M., *J. Agr. Food Chem.*, **13**, 594 (1965).
(8) Braham, J. E., Elías, L. G., Bressani, R., *J. Food Sci.* **30**, 531–37 (1965).
(9) Bressani, R., *Food Technol.* **19**, 97–9 (1965).
(10) Bressani, R., Aguirre, A., Elías, L. G., Arroyave, R., Jarquín, R., Scrimshaw, N. S., *J. Nutr.* **74**, 209–16 (1961).
(11) Bressani, R., Aguirre, A., Scrimshaw, N. S., *Ibid.*, **69**, 351–5 (1959).
(12) Bressani, R., Béhar, M., "Use of Plant Protein Foods in Preventing Malnutrition," in "Proceedings of the Sixth International Congress of Nutrition," Edinburgh, August 1963, p. 181–206, E. & S. Livingstone, Edinburgh, 1964.
(13) Bressani, R., Braham, J. E., Elías, L. G., Zaghi, S. de, *Can. J. Biochem.* **42**, 631–9 (1964).
(14) Bressani, R., Braham, J. E., Jarquín, R., Elías, L. G., *Arch. Venezolanos Nutr.* **12**, 229–44 (1962).
(15) Bressani, R., Elías, L. G., Aguirre, A., Scrimshaw, N. S., *J. Nutr.* **74**, 201–8 (1961).
(16) Bressani, R., Elías, L. G., Braham, J. E., *Ibid.*, **83**, 209–17 (1964).

(17) Bressani, R., Elías, L. G., Braham, J. E., Erales, M., unpublished manuscript.
(18) Bressani, R., Elías, L. G., Jarquín, R., Braham, J. E., *Food Technol.* **18**, 95–9 (1964).
(19) Bressani, R., Elías, L. G., Jarquín, R., Braham, J. E., unpublished.
(20) Bressani, R., Elías, L. G., Scrimshaw, N. S., *J. Food Sci.* **27**, 203–9 (1962).
(21) Bressani, R., Elías, L. G., Zaghi, S. de, Mosovich, L., Viteri, F., unpublished manuscript.
(22) Bressani, R., Marenco, E., *J. Agr. Food Chem.* **11**, 517–22 (1963).
(23) Clark, E. P., *J. Biol. Chem.* **76**, 229–35 (1928).
(24) Conference on Cottonseed Protein for Animal and Man, New Orleans, La., April 1962, (ARS 72–24).
(25) Conference on Cottonseed Protein Concentrates, New Orleans, La., Jan. 15–17, 1964, U. S. Dept. Agr. Agricultural Research Service, April 1965 (ARS-72–38).
(26) Cravioto, J., Solano, Y., Morales, M., Ramos Galván, R., Pérez Navarrete, J. L., *Bol. Ofic. Sanit. Panam.* **52**, 122–9 (1962).
(27) DeMaeyer, E. M., Vanderborght, H. L., Natl. Acad. Sci.—Natl. Res. Council, Publ. **843**, 143–55 (1961).
(28) DeMaeyer, E. M., Vanderborght, H., *J. Nutr.* **65**, 335–52 (1958).
(29) Duckworth, J., Woodham, A. A., *Arch. Venezolonos Nutr.* **11**, 239–52 (1961).
(30) Dyer, I. A., Harrison, J. T., Nicholson, W. S., Jr., Cullison, A. E., *J. Animal Sci.* **11**, 465–73 (1952).
(31) Elías, L. G., Bressani, R., Jarquín, R., Braham, E., unpublished manuscript.
(32) El Katib, M. M. T., *Nature* **159**, 716 (1947).
(33) Fincher, H. D., "Processing of Oilseeds," in "Processed Plant Protein Food-stuffs," A. M. Altschul, ed., p. 67–78, Academic Press, New York, 1958.
(34) Food and Agricultural Organization, United Nations, "Protein Requirements," Report of FAO Committee, Rome, Italy, October 1955, FAO Nutritional Studies No. 16, 1957.
(35) Frampton, V. L., *Oil Mill Gaz.* **65**, 33, August 1961.
(36) Frampton, V. L., Carter, F. L., Piccolo, B., Heywang, B. W., *J. Agr. Food Chem.* **10**, 46–8 (1962).
(37) Frenk, S., Natl. Acad. Sci.—Natl. Res. Council, Publ. **843**, 21–33 (1961).
(38) Goldblatt, L. A., "Mycotoxins in Foodstuffs," G. N. Wogan, ed., p.261, MIT Press, Cambridge, 1965.
(39) Graham, G. G., Cordano, A., Baertl, J. M., *J. Nutr.* **84**, 71–6 (1964).
(40) Hale, F., Lyman, C. M., Smith, H. A.,Texas Agri. Expt. Sta. Bull. **898** (1958).
(41) Heywang, B. W., Bird, H. R., *Poultry Sci.* **29**, 486–95 (1950).
(42) Horn, M. J., Blum, A. E., Womack, M., Gersdorff, C. E. F., *J. Nutr.* **48**, 231–41 (1952).
(43) Institute of Nutrition of Central America and Panama, "Incaparina, The Fourth Year," report to WHO/UNICEF/FAO Protein Advisory Group, July 1965.
(44) Institute of Nutrition of Central America and Panama, unpublished data.
(45) Jarquín, R., Bressani, R., unpublished manuscript.
(46) Jarquín, R., Bressani, R., Elías, L. G., Tejada, C., González, M., Braham, J. E., *J. Agr. Food Chem.* **14**, 275 (1966).
(47) Johnson, Charles, Watts, A. B., *Poultry Sci.* **43**, 957–63 (1964).
(48) Jones, D. B., Divine, J. P., *J. Nutr.* **28**, 41–9 (1944).
(49) Kaye, R., Barness, L. A., Valyasevi, A., Knapp, J., Natl. Acad. Sci.—Natl. Res. Council, Publ. **843**, 297–312 (1961).

(50) King, W. H., Kuck, J. C., Frampton, V. L., *J. Am. Oil Chemists Soc.* **38**, 19–21 (1961).

(51) Kornegay, E. T., Clawson, A. J., Smith, F. H., Barrick, E. R., *J. Animal Sci.* **20**, 597–602 (1961).

(52) Krishnamurthy, K., Pantalu, A. J., Narayana Rao, M., Swaminathan, M. Raghunatha Rao, Y. K., Subrahmanyan, V., *Indian J. Physiol. Allied Sci.* **13**, 20–4 (1959).

(53) Kuiken, K. A., Lyman, C. M. *J. Nutr.* **36**, 359–68 (1948).

(54) Kuppuswamy, S., Giri, K. V., Subrahmanyan, V., *Indian J. Med. Res.* **37**, 41–50 (1949).

(55) Lorenz, F. W., *Poultry Sci.* **18**, 295–300 (1939).

(56) Lyman, C. M., Baliga, B. P., Slay, M. W., *Arch. Biochem. Biophys.* **84**, 486–97 (1959).

(57) Mann, G. E., Carter, F. L., Frampton, V. L., Watts, A. B., Johnson, C., *J. Am. Oil. Chemists Soc.* **39**, 86–90 (1962).

(58) Martínez, W. H., Frampton, V. L., Cabell, C. A., *J. Agr. Food Chem.* **9**, 64–6 (1961).

(59) Milligan, J. L., Bird, H. R., *Poultry Sci.* **30**, 651–7 (1951).

(60) Milligan, J. L., Machlin, L. J., Bird, H. R., Heywang, B. W., *Ibid.*, **30**, 578–86 (1951).

(61) Miner, J. J., Clower, W. B., Noland, P. R., Stephenson, E. L., *J. Animal Sci.* **14**, 24–9 (1955).

(62) Overman, A., *Food Res.* **16**, 39–42 (1951).

(63) Protein Advisory Group, WHO/UNICEF/FAO, "Tentative Quality and Processing Guide, Cottonseed Protein Concentrate for Human Conusmption," July 1965.

(64) Richardson, L. R., Blaylock, L. G., *Poultry Sci.* **29**, 651–5 (1950).

(65) Schaible, P. J., Moore, L. A., Moore, J. M., *Ibid.*, **12**, 334 (1933).

(66) Scrimshaw, N. S., Béhar, M., Wilson, D., Viteri, F., Arroyave, G., Bressani, R., *Am. J. Clin. Nutr.* **9**, 196–205 (1961).

(67) Scrimshaw, N. S., Bressani, R., Wilson, D., Béhar, M., *Am. J. Clin. Nutr.* **11**, 537–42 (1962).

(68) Scrimshaw, N. S., Salomon, J. B., Bruch, H. A., Gordon, J. E., *Am. J. Trop. Med. Hyg.*, (submitted for publication).

(69) Sherwood, R. M., Couch, J. R., *Poultry Sci.* **29**, 501–7 (1950).

(70) Smith, F. H., Rhyne, C. L., Smart, V. M., *J. Agr. Food Chem.* **9**, 82–4 (1961).

(71) Smith, F. H., Young, C. T., Sherwood, F. W., *J. Nutr.* **66**, 393–409 (1958).

(72) Snyderman, S. E., Boyer, A., Holt, L. E., Jr., Natl. Acad. Sci.—Natl. Res. Council, Publ. **843**, 331–42 (1961).

(73) Squibb, R. L., Wyld, M. K., Scrimshaw, N. S., Bressani, R., *J. Nutr.* **69**, 343–50 (1959).

(74) Subrahmanyan, V., Krishnamurthy, K., Swaminathan, M., Bathia, D. S., Raghunatha Rao, Y. K., *Bull. Central Food Technol. Res. Inst. Mysore (India)* **3**, 225–6 (1954).

(75) Summers, J. C., Mead, B., Thurber, F. H., Oklahoma Agricultural & Mechanical College, School of Technical Training, Okmulgee, Oklahoma Bull., 1953.

(76) U. S. Department of Agriculture, Economic Research Service, "Agricultural Statistics," p. 119, 1963.

(77) Withers, W. A., Carruth, F. E., *J. Agr. Res.* **5**, 261–81 (1915).

(78) Womack, M., Marshall, M. W., Summers, J. C., *J. Agr. Food Chem.* **2**, 138–40 (1954).

RECEIVED October 12, 1965.

Full-Fat Soybean Flours
by Continuous Extrusion Cooking

GUS C. MUSTAKAS, EDWARD L. GRIFFIN, JR., and VIRGIL E. SOHNS

Northern Regional Research Laboratory, Peoria, Ill. 61604

Extrusion processing, a method continuing to find new and wider applications in the food industry, is adaptable to the production of full-fat soybean flour, and can produce an edible flour of good flavor, oxidative stability, and high nutritional value. Experimentally produced flours were evaluated by chemical analyses, biological assays, available lysine content, vitamin assays, organoleptic tests, oxidative-stability storage tests, and clinical testing with infants up to 12 months old. The future potential of this process for soybeans seems promising, owing to unique characteristics which lend themselves to modern high-production, low-cost techniques that can yield a high-quality product.

A deficiency in protein is one of the important dietary problems encountered in many of the developing countries of the world. Although animal products are a desirable protein source, their high cost and limited availability restrict their use. Consequently, there is a large and growing need for high-quality, low-cost plant proteins. The protein-deficiency problem is particularly serious with infants and preschool children, especially in tropical and subtropical areas of the world. Although powdered milk has been of major importance in feeding programs, its supply is limited, and there is a great need for additional sources of food protein.

UNICEF nutritionists have observed that deficiencies in the diet of both children and adults in newly emerging countries are not just from a lack of protein; they arise from a shortage of both proteins and calories. If calories are limited, proteins are consumed for the necessary energy and, therefore, are not available for body building. Full-fat soybean flours would serve both purposes because soybeans contain an oil high in calories and because flour from them can be formulated easily with indigenous foods. Since these flours would contain all the dehulled soybean, they represent a concentrated form of food and a most economical source of protein as well.   For use of the flour in beverages, the natural lecithin in soybeans lends emulsifying properties to give a powder easily and rapidly mixed with water to produce an instant dispersion.

Introduction of foods of an unfamiliar type can be expected to take time for acceptance.   We cannot expect people in need of protein supplementation to like the kind of foods we do.   Instead, the protein must be incorporated into the traditional foods of these populations.   For the broadest use of soybean flours, the mild, but characteristic, flavor of soybeans must become acceptable to those not familiar with it.   Extrusion cooking has good potential for making desirable forms of soybeans economically available to developing countries.   Extrusion is now widely applied by the American food industry for shaping new products and simplifying production of older ones.   Some new food areas where extrusion processing is being used are pet foods, breakfast cereals, confections, bakery goods, dough processing, cheese, macaroni, sausage, and the many crispy snack tems.

Extrusion Cooking of Soybeans

In developing a system for cooking whole-fat soybeans, the objectives are to achieve a cooked soybean flour product with a high nutritional value, to cook the beans adequately to control the growth inhibitors in soybeans, and to produce a bland and palatable product substantially free from unpleasant bitterness or "beany" taste and with adequate shelf life without refrigeration.

Studies were previously carried out and reported (1, 2) jointly by our laboratory, UNICEF, and the Wenger Mixer Manufacturing Co. on a new method for producing full-fat soybean flour based on extrusion cooking.   Flours of high nutritive value, stability, and flavor acceptance were produced during the experimental program.

The process for full-fat extrusion cooking is carried out as shown in Figure 1.   The soybeans are first cracked, dehulled, and flaked, although the flaking step is optional.   The material is then preconditioned in two stages with both direct and indirect steam to add water and heat, mixed, extrusion-cooked, cooled, dried, and milled to a flour.

Flakes or grits initially have an average of 9 to 12% moisture and the preconditioner adds additional moisture as steam, bringing the product up to approximately 20% moisture on extrusion.   Retention time in the preconditioner and mixer is approximately 3 minutes.

The extruder-cooker has the configuration shown in Figure 1.   It consists of at least three sections separated by back-pressure dies (perforated plates). The unit shown is a production model of that used in our cooperative work with Wenger.   Throughput is approximately 70 pounds per minute.

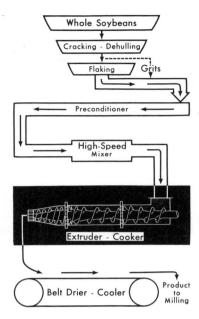

Figure 1. Continuous extrusion-cooking process for producing full-fat soybean flour

During passage through the various sections, the material is subjected to increased pressure and temperature. Pressure is increased by pitched screws separated by the perforated plates that create back-pressure and prevent feedback of oil through the feed inlet, which is at atmospheric pressure. Finally, the maximum pressure is created in the last tapered-screw or cone-nose section. The first two segments are steam-jacketed, but heating is accomplished primarily by mechanical friction of the screw on the material, particularly in the final segment. Retention time in the extruder is 1 minute. During extrusion, oil is expelled and freed from the cells, but as the material extrudes from the final die plate, the oil is immediately reabsorbed in the meal. Freeing the oil from the cells should make it readily available for digestion.

Figure 2 shows a time-temperature profile of the cooking process.

Extrusion-cooking should offer many unique features that will enable it to grow in importance as a process for converting soybeans to food products. By this process, the beans are held at elevated temperatures for only a few minutes, in contrast to commercial soybean meal toasting at about 212° F. for 30 to 45 minutes. Thus, almost instant cooking is achieved under continuous operation, which results in a minimum of damage to heat-sensitive, nutritional factors. Temperature of the meal in the final high-pressure section reaches values above atmospheric boiling;

however, moisture is not lost, and the extruder section acts as a continuous pressure cooker.

Diversified applications, flexibility, and simple control are valuable features of the extrusion process that appeal to the food industry. The character of a product can be controlled by altering extrusion temperatures, pressures, or both, to change product viscosity, taste, moisture content, water absorption, and protein solubility. Extrusion-cooking of cereal products can pregelatinize starches. By incorporating other chemicals one can modify the product chemically on a continuous basis. Physical shapes and bulk densities of the product can be controlled by using dies in various forms, shapes, and thicknesses. These and other possible variations in processing make extrusion-cooking a highly flexible operation.

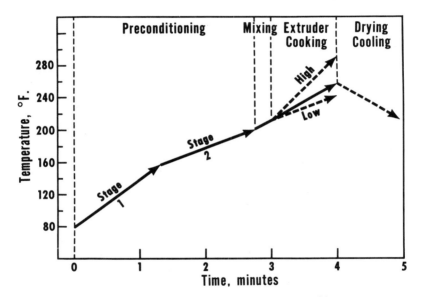

Figure 2. Time-temperature profile of extrusion-cooking process

Discussion

Removal of Growth Inhibitors. The short cook time with extrusion minimizes damage to nutritional properties but still adequately removes growth inhibitors. This removal is demonstrated by low assays for trypsin inhibitor and urease activity. Representative products analyze 95% or better destruction of trypsin inhibitor and have low to zero urease activity.

Proximate Analyses of Flours The soybean protein contains a good balance of the amino acids essential to human nutrition and, in this respect, tends to be comparable to animal proteins. It is a good source of lysine, more or less lacking in cereal proteins. The extrusion-cooked products average 5.3% available lysine. Table I gives a proximate analysis of extrusion-cooked flours; these values compare favorably with commercial flours.

In most cooking processes, the percentage of water-soluble protein, as measured by the nitrogen solubility index (NSI), generally reflects the degree of heat treatment received by the product. Extruded flours are cooked to values ranging from 13 to 21. Protein solubility correlates inversely with processing temperature. The higher the maximum temperature, the lower the protein solubility.

In commercial processing of soybeans, the heat treatment generally reduces their vitamin content. Soybeans are outstanding as a source of thiamine, but this vitamin is heat-sensitive and generally heat treatments so necessary to prepare soybeans for animal and human consumption result in destroying thiamine. Assays for thiamine, riboflavin, and niacin on the extruded products indicate no significant loss of original vitamin content during processing.

Table I. Proximate Analysis of Extruded Soybean Flours

Protein, %	44
Crude fat, %	20
Crude fiber, %	<3
Ash, %	5
Acid-insoluble ash, %	0.02
Available lysine, % of protein	5.3
Peroxide value, meq./1000 g. extracted oil	0.40
Free fatty acid, % in extracted oil	0.50
Granulation	95+% through 100 mesh

Animal Feeding Tests   The results of protein efficiency ratio (PER) tests (*1*) in rat feeding indicate that the experimentally extruded products are of the same general value as commercially prepared full-fat and defatted soybean flours.

Feeding tests with broiler chicks (*1*) at the University of Maryland for 4.5 weeks showed that for both growth promotion and efficiency of feed conversion the extruded product about equaled a good quality commerical full-fat soybean flour and a defatted flour reconstituted with soybean oil. In these tests, 1400 broiler chicks were maintained in floor pens and fed rations containing identical levels of protein and fat from the three products. Supplementation with methionine gave about equal improvement in each case.

Flavor Evaluation and Stability.   In organoleptic evaluations (*1*) at the Northern Laboratory by our taste panel, the extrusion-cooked flours scored relatively high in blandness of flavor; they were neither beany nor rancid. They compared most favorably with a commercial soybean flour. Accelerated storage tests (1) were conducted at 100° and 113° F. up to 9 months. At the higher temperatures, good stability was exhibited through the first 9 weeks. At 100° F. good stability was maintained throughout the entire 9-month period as determined by odor, taste, free fatty acid, and peroxide value test. Extrapolation of these data by previous experience to 70° F. storage indicates that the extruded flours should have good stability for 1 to 2 years.

The Food Quality Laboratory of the ARS Human Nutrition Research Division, U.S. Department Agriculture, Beltsville, Md., has been studying the use of the extruded full-fat flour in various food products. The Beltsville workers report that they are pleased with their preliminary test products, which include biscuits, cookies, noodles, tortillas, yeast bread, and unleavened bread.

Clinical Testing with Infants. UNICEF has sent approximately a ton of the full-fat flour (1) from the cooperative processing trials to Taiwan, where it has been utilized for acceptability testing, clinically supervised in infant feeding programs at the University of Taiwan. In these tests, it was formulated with sugar and supplementary vitamins and fed to children from 4 to 12 months of age in comparison with milk and other soybean products, including an infant food and a conventional full-fat soybean product. The latest reports (3) from Dr. Tung in Taiwan indicated that the extrusion-processed full-fat soybean flour supports excellent growth and development in infants as young as 4 months and that these gains are virtually comparable to those observed in babies fed cow's milk.

Table II. Estimated Processing Costs for Extrusion-Cooking Plants Producing Full-Fat Soybean Flour from Dehulled Soybeans

Whole beans processed:						
per day, tons	14	30	48	28	60	96
per hour, tons	2	2	2	4	4	4
Shifts of operation per day[a]	1	2	3	1	2	3
Processing costs, cents per lb. of flour[b]	0.63	0.50	0.45	0.50	0.40	0.36
With classifying[b]	0.76	0.58	0.51	0.63	0.48	0.42

[a] Operation 250 days per year, 7 hours production for 1 shift per day, 15 hours for 2 shifts, 24 hours for 3 shifts.
[b] About 88 pounds of flour obtained from 100 pounds of whole beans.

Cost Study Preliminary cost estimates have been prepared for the production of full-fat soybean flour by the continuous extrusion-cooking method for dehulled soybeans. Processing costs are reported in Table II for flour produced by fine-grinding the meats obtained from the extrusion-cooking operation and then classifying the finely ground material, as well as for a system that omits the classifying step. Whether classifying is required may well depend upon the specifications of the final product.

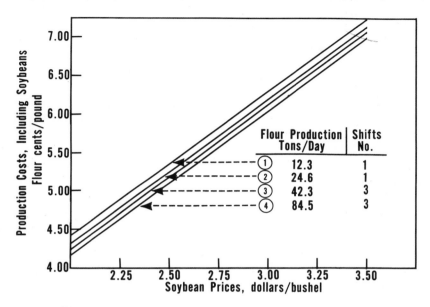

Figure 3. Production costs of full-fat soybean flour at various soybean prices

Soybean costs are not included as part of the processing costs but only utilities, labor and supervision, maintenance, and fixed charges.

It has been assumed that soybean flour production will be conducted as part of an existing soybean processing plant; under such circumstances, such facilities as storage and equipment for unloading, cleaning, cracking, and dehulling the beans which are a part of the usual soybean processing plant can be used for flour production. The cost of such items, therefore, is not included in the estimated fixed capital investment of a flour plant. Estimated fixed capital investment for a plant processing 2 tons of beans per hour is $68,000 if classification is not required for acceptable flour production; if classification is required, the estimated fixed capital investment is $101,000. Estimated fixed capital investments if 4 tons of beans are processed per hour are $107,000 without classification equipment and $173,000 for installations with such equipment. Estimated production costs for full-fat soybean flour at various soybean prices are given in Figure 3. The curves show that the price of soybeans contributes the greatest share of the flour cost and that relatively small fluctuations in market cost of soybeans can more than equal plant production costs.

Conclusion

The extrusion-cooking process can produce a full-fat soybean flour of high nutritive value, mild flavor, and good oxidative stability. Growth inhibitors are effectively destroyed while the heat-labile lysine, vitamins, and other nutrients are preserved. The process largely removes objectionable taste characteristics, as shown by taste panel acceptance scores. Good acceptability and excellent growth development for infants were shown in clinical tests.

The cost of soybeans is by far the largest single cost item in the over-all process and under some conditions it may be more than 90% of the cost of making full-fat soybean flour. The versatility and effectiveness of extruders for rapid continuous cooking should result in their rapid acceptance for processing soybeans into many valuable food products.

Acknowledgment

We are indebted to Max Milner of UNICEF, United Nations, New York, for furnishing the reports of Dr. Wu and Dr. Tung of the University of Taipei, Taiwan, on the clinically supervised acceptability studies. Estimates of costs of machinery for the cost study were furnished by Wenger Mixer Manufacturing, Sabetha, Kan., and the Alpine American Corp., Natick, Mass.

Literature Cited

(1) Mustakas, G. C., Griffin, E. L., Jr., Allen, L. E., Smith, O. B., *J. Am. Oil Chemists' Soc.* **41** (9), 607 (1964).
(2) Mustakas, G. C., Mayberry, D. H., *Food Eng.* **36** (10), 52 (1964).
(3) WHO/FAO/UNICEF Protein-Rich Foods Program, News Bull. **5**. (April 1965)

RECEIVED OCTOBER 12, 1965.

Discussion

Oak B. Smith*: The process reported so well by Mr. Mustakas is a short time/high temperature method of continuous extrusion cooking. It was developed originally for gelatinizing cereals and was later adapted to cooking mixtures of cereals and oilseed proteins.

The period of maximum temperature in this short time/high temperature cook varies from 12 to 17 seconds. Prior to this short time cook, steam is applied at atmospheric pressures to a carefully limited degree as a moisturizing agent in a preconditioning zone. The temperature

* Wenger Mixer Manufacturing Co., Sabetha, Kan.

Table I.   Distribution of World's Population and Food Supplies, by Regions (8) (1957-1959)

Regions	% of Population	% of Food Supplies		
		Total	Animal	Crops
Far East (incl. China, mainland)	52.9	27.8	18.5	44.2
Near East	4.4	4.2	2.8	5.5
Africa	7.1	4.3	2.8	6.3
Latin America	6.9	6.4	6.7	6.5
Europe (incl. USSR)	21.6	34.2	38.4	26.2
North America	6.6	21.8	29.2	10.4
Oceania	0.5	1.3	1.6	0.9
World	100.0	100.0	100.0	100.0

The strikingly low levels of food production per unit of land as well as the low output of foods of animal origin in the less developed areas (Table II) are due to a variety of factors, the more important being small farm holdings, backwardness in agricultural practice and animal husbandry, low soil fertility, and the lack of incentive to expand production.   Losses through infestation and diseases of food crops are also heavy.   In India rodent and insect pests destroy as much as 20% of the standing crops and 10 to 15% of the stored grains, amounting to more than 20 million tons of food per year.   There is no doubt that by applying modern science and technology to farming practices, increasing use of fertilizers, and preventing infestation, the availability of food supplies could be increased substantially.   However, in actual practice this task is beset with many difficulties in an underdeveloped socioeconomic situation, and the increase in food production in these areas continues to fall short of expectations.

Table II.   Average Yields of Major Crops and Cattle Products by Groups of Regions (8) (1957-60)

Commodity	Less Developed Regions	Developed Regions	World
Crops, 100 kg/ha.			
Wheat	9.4	13.3	11.9
Rice, paddy	19.1	38.4	19.2
Other cereals	9.0	18.0	13.3
Starches	74.5	122.2	97.1
Pulses	6.1	6.5	6.2
Cattle products[a]			
100 kg./head of cattle	2.6	13.9	6.5

[a] Meat and milk in terms of milk equivalent, taking 1 unit of meat as equal to 10 units of milk. Averages for 1958–60.

The disparities in the available food supplies in turn have an influence on the nutritive value of the diets in terms of both calories and protein content. The per capita consumption in the less developed regions averages between 2000 and 2200 calories with a daily supply of 58 grams of proteins while the corresponding figures for the developed regions average over 3000 and 90, respectively (15). The estimated consumption of protein per capita in India is approximately 50 grams. Taking into consideration the variations in the economic levels of the consumers, the lower income groups get as low as 30 to 35 grams of protein per day. The distribution of protein in the diet is very uneven. The adults get larger quantities of protein while the children, who need most, get less. The disparities are even more glaring in respect to animal proteins in the diets of the two regions, being 6 and 44 grams per capita per day respectively (Table III).

The diets of the people in the less developed areas consist predominantly of cereals and tubers and include only negligible quantities of

Table III.   Current Consumption Levels For India, Group I Countries, Group II Countries, and the World as a Whole (15)

	India	Group I, excl. India	Group I[a]	Group II[b]	World
		Grams per Person per Day at Retail Level			
Cereals	375	393	389	328	370
Starchy roots	30	229	189	316	227
Sugar	45	26	29	88	47
Pulses and nuts	65	50	53	16	42
Fruits and vegetables	80	191	169	362	227
Meat	4	37	30	152	67
Fish	7	28	24	34	27
Eggs	1	5	4	33	12
Milks and milk products (excl. butter)	140	64	79	573	228
Fats and oils	11	12	12	47	22
Calories	1,970	2,190	2,150	3,060	2,420
Animal protein, g.	6	10	9	44	20
Total protein, g.	51	60	58	90	68
Fats, g.	27	36	34	106	56
Calcium, mg.	446	293	324	1,099	557
Iron, mg.	15	13	14	17	15
Vitamin A, IU	1,432	2,945	2,642	5,555	3,516
Thiamin, mg.	1.3	1.6	1.5	2	2
Riboflavin, mg.	0.6	0.7	0.7	2	1
Niacin, mg.	7	14	14	19	15
Ascorbic acid, mg.	26	83	72	116	85

[a] Far East, Near East, Africa, and Latin America, excluding River Plate countries.
[b] Europe, North America, Ocenia, and River Plate countries.

protective and protein-rich foods such as milk, eggs, meat, and fish. The consumption of other types of protective foods like fresh vegetables and fruits is also very inadequate. The consequences of dietary deficiencies in calories, proteins, minerals, and vitamins are seen strikingly in the vulnerable groups of the population, as evidenced by high mortality rates among infants and children, widespread prevalence of specific deficiency diseases, and the short life span of the people. Protein malnutrition stands out as the most serious of the nutritional deficiencies in many of the underdeveloped countries of the world (*16*).

The current consumption levels of the main categories of food in India generally reflect the pattern that exists in many of the less developed countries (Table IV). Cereals form the staple food of the people and contribute nearly 70% of the calories and 60% of the total proteins in the diet. The principal food crops are rice, wheat, and millets. Grain legumes (pulses), which constitute an important adjunct to cereals, provide 14 grams per capita daily of proteins and 27% of the total dietary proteins. The daily per capita supply of animal proteins is as low as 6 grams or 12% of the total proteins in the diet and much of this (5 grams per capita per day) is derived from milk and milk products. Milk supplies only 5 grams of protein per capita in India while its availability in other countries of the region is much lower.

With a population of nearly 480 million people, India has livestock numbering 336 million, consisting of cattle, buffaloes, sheep, goats, horses, ponies, etc., and a poultry population estimated at 117 million. Cattle are primarily used as work animals and occupy an important place in the agricultural economy of the country. The heavy pressure of large human and livestock populations on the available land resources has led to an acute competition between man and beast for its produce. The livestock have of necessity to subsist on agricultural wastes like straws and other low energy foods. In the absence of nutritious fodder, grasses, and food concentrates, it is obviously extremely difficult to increase the availability of animal foods for the use of people. The maintenance of unproductive animals adds to the problem of feed requirements. With an average production of eight eggs per person per year, the link between low productivity and the inadequate supply of cheap nutritious poultry feeds in the country is clearly seen.

With a coast line of over 3000 miles and over 17,000 miles of rivers and canals, there is a great potential for increasing the production of marine and fresh water fish. The present annual catch of fish is only 1.4 million tons as against 6.9 million tons in Japan. The development of fisheries is, therefore, receiving considerable encouragement and support. Its success will depend, to an extent, on raising the living standards (*11*).

The contribution made by animal foods to nutrition in India is comparatively minor because of their low availability and high cost in

Table IV.   Per Capita Protein Supplies

Country	Total Protein	Animal Protein	Grains	Starchy Roots
Ceylon				
Grams per day	45	9	27	1
% of total protein		20	60	2
China (Taiwan)				
Grams per day	57	14	31	3
% of total protein		25	54	5
India				
Grams per day	51	6	30	—
% of total protein		12	59	—
Japan				
Grams per day	67	17	31	2
% of total protein		26	46	3
Pakistan				
Grams per day	46	7	33	—
% of total protein		16	72	—
Philippines				
Grams per day	47	13	26	2
% of total protein		28	55	4

relation to the income.   Though a majority of the people (over 70%) are nonvegetarians, they cannot afford to buy flesh foods regularly and the frequency of consumption varies from once a week to a few times a year.   With an average per capita income of only $63 per year, the expenditure on food is as high as $36, 60% of which is spent on cereals.   Only about 5% of Indian households have annual incomes exceeding $600 and can afford to have a somewhat balanced diet.

Available Protein Resources

Legumes and Pulses   The importance of plant protein foodstuffs. in the existing dietary patterns of the country is thus evident.   Grain legumes (pulses) are widely used in the Indian diet and contribute significantly to its nutritional quality.   The levels of production and consumption of pulses in India are possibly the highest in the world (Table V) and their contribution to the over-all protein intake is nearly three times that derived from milk.   The commonly available pulses are red gram (*Cajanus cajan*), Bengal gram or chick pea (*Cicer arietinum*), green gram (*Phaseolus radiatus*), black gram (*Phaseolus mungo*), lentil (*Lens esculanta*), pea (*Pisum sativum*), cow pea (*Vigna catjang*), and field bean (*Dolichos lablab*) and these are consumed regularly in varying

in Countries of Far East (7)

Pulses, Oilseeds, and Nuts	Vegetables	Fruit	Meat and Poultry	Eggs	Fish	Milk and Products
7	2	—	1	—	6	2
16	4	—	2	—	13	4
7	2	—	6	—	7	1
12	4	—	11	—	12	2
14	1	—	1	—	—	5
27	2	—	2	—	—	10
13	4	—	3	1	12	1
19	6	—	5	1	18	1
4	1	—	1	—	1	5
9	2	—	2	—	2	11
2	3	1	4	1	7	1
4	6	2	9	2	15	2

amounts as part of the diet. The most common method of using pulses is to cook them until soft and prepare a seasoned soup with added vegetables. Fermented mixtures of black gram and rice are popularly used in South India for steam-cooked or fritter-like fried preparations. Roasted or parched Bengal gram and dried peas are popular products and Bengal gram flour is widely used for preparing sweets and snacks.

The demand for pulses is widespread and there has been a steep rise in their prices in recent times. Intensive efforts are being made to increase their cultivation and supply, as these crops not only increase protein supplies and enhance soil fertility, but also provide valuable livestock fodder. Increased availability of pulses in India will reduce their cost and qualitatively improve the diet of low income groups. As pulses have a traditional place in the diet of even the poorest, increased consumption would be assured. Much could be done to increase the production and supply through measures such as varietal selection, genetic improvement of local stocks, supply of high quality seeds, and improved methods of cultivation and storage. These measures have been given top priority in the agricultural research and extension plans of the country. Work on the milling characteristics of pulses to increase their yield, methods of processing to improve their nutritional value, and development of weaning foods for children based on legumes are in progress at the Central

**Table V.   Estimated Production and Availability of Legumes
for Human Consumption in Different Countries**[a] **(12)**

Country	Total Production Thousand Metric Tons	Grams per Day per Capita
Argentina	82	8.9
Australia	14	4.7
Austria	5	1.4
Belgium-Luxembourg	38	5.2
Canada	66	6.0
Ceylon	4	13.1
Denmark	36	11.2
Egypt	305	24.7
Finland	12	4.6
Germany, Federal Republic	15	4.8
Greece	107	30.1
Honduras	201	30.2
India	10,617	60.8
Ireland	2	2.7
Israel	2.6	8.8
Italy	850	16.2
Netherlands	105	7.7
New Zealand	24	5.2
Norway	1	7.1
Pakistan	900	20.5
Philippines	40	5.3
Portugal	55	17.3
Switzerland	—	5.8
Sweden	38	4.1
Turkey	282	26.3
Union of South Africa	58	5.3
United Kingdom	62	11.0
United States of America	914	10.6
Uruguay	3.7	5.0

[a] Exclusive of peanut and soybean.

Food Technological Research Institute, Mysore.   The introduction of economically and nutritionally important legumes such as the soybean (*Glycine max*) is also being explored in selected areas.

Oilseeds.   Abundant supplies of oilseeds in the protein-deficient countries have led to an increasing realization of their importance as sources of supplementary protein for human feeding.   India is one of the major oilseed-producing countries in the world and has the largest production of peanut and sesame.   It also has substantial quantities of cotton-seed and coconut.   While most of the peanut and sesame are processed for oil, over 70% of cottonseed is fed to cattle.   Coconut is used extensively throughout the country, and about 50% of copra has to be imported to produce oil for edible and industrial uses.   The production of the major oilseeds and coconuts and the potential availability of protein from these sources are given in Tables VI and VII.

Peanut. Of the total production of 4.8 million tons of peanut in the shell, only 5 to 6% is used for edible purposes and over 80% for the recovery of oil. Approximately 1.6 million tons of press cake and extracted meal with 50% protein content are made available every year and the commercial meal fetches only a fifth of the value of the oil per ton. The resultant commercial meal is unfit for human consumption because of poor handling and processing.

Before India's independence, large quantities of peanuts were exported. With the growing domestic demand for fats and oils and the development of large and medium scale oil crushing and solvent extraction units during the last two decades, increasing quantities of solvent-extracted meals are now exported. During 1963–64, the exports of peanut

Table VI   Production of Major Oilseeds and Chick Pea in India and Some Regions and Selected Countries of the World (*6*)

(1000 metric tons per annum during 1961–62)

Region or Country	Peanut (in Shell)	Cotton-seed	Sesame	Copra	Chick Pea	Soya-bean
World production (excluding USSR)	14,100	20,600	1,500	3,600	7,600	31,000
North America	790	5,420	4	—	—	18,730
Latin America	—	2,800	205	255	140	310
Near East	230	1,940	225	—	145	5
Far East	5,990	2,940	530	2,960	7,010	1,290
Africa	3,900	460	140	110	140	30
India	4,757	1,600	501	254	6,324	—
Indonesia	400	2	—	876	—	425
Mexico	90	766	115	188	136	—
Nigeria	1,245	56	12	3	—	15
Brazil	581[a]	1,152	—	—	—	—

[a] For 1960–61.

Table VII.   Oilseeds and Oilseed Meals as Sources of Protein in India (*6*)

Commodity	Annual Production, 1000 Metric Tons	Yield of Meal, 1000 Metric Tons	Average Protein Content of Meal, %	Available Protein, 1000 Metric Tons
Peanut (kernels)	3,330	1,984	50.0	992.0
Cottonseed (kernels)	800	640	47.0	300.0
Sesame seed	501	420	33.3	140.0
Copra	234	127	21.0	26.7

meal amounted to over 800,000 tons and the remaining nearly equal quantity of press cake was used locally for livestock feeding and as fertilizer.

Much valuable work on peanut processing to upgrade meal quality has been done at the Central Food Technological Research Institute, and a process for preparing a low-fat edible quality peanut flour, free from adventitious toxic factors such as aflatoxins, has been developed. The flour has been successfully used to develop a variety of inexpensive nutritious foods suitable for different groups of the population. UNICEF is actively assisting the Government of India to establish two large scale production units for peanut flour. The status of technology in respect to peanut protein isolate has also reached the stage of commercial exploitation, and this again is due to the pioneering work carried out at the Mysore Institute. It has been possible to expand the research program on vegetable proteins with financial assistance from the National Institutes of Health, using the PL 480 funds available in India.

Cottonseed. The present production of cottonseed in India is about 1.6 million tons, and this could provide 600,000 tons of edible quality flour containing 50% protein if modern methods of processing are adopted. A pilot plant with a capacity of 10 tons per day has now been established with UNICEF assistance at the Regional Research Laboratory, Hyderabad, and the Central Food Technological Research Institute is actively collaborating in developing food formulations suitable for child feeding.

Sesame. The available supply of sesame seed in India is about 500,000 tons, the second largest in the world. It is a rich source of methionine and tryptophan and could be advantageously used along with peanut and chick pea flours to prepare protein-rich foods. The main obstacle in the extended use of sesame meal in protein blends is, however, the presence of hulls which impart a slight bitterness and dark color to products. Much of the calcium in sesame is in the form of calcium oxalate, found in the hulls. Recent work at the Central Food Technological Research Institute has shown the possibilities of decuticling the seed by short-period lye treatment. Pilot plant studies on the project are now in progress.

Coconut. India produces 44.8 million coconuts (254,000 metric tons of copra), 64% of which are consumed as such for culinary purposes or as tender coconut. The rest is milled for oil, 60% used as human foodstuff and the remaining 40% used to manufacture soaps and cosmetics. In addition, India is importing about 85,000 tons of copra. The copra cake is not used for human consumption, because of its high fiber content and poor grade of raw material. Recently several methods have been developed for processing the ripe coconut kernel instead of copra and utilizing the proteins in human foods (3). CFTRI has modified the Krauss-Maffei process in which the ripe coconut kernels are milled and oil and protein are obtained.   Methods for using this protein in infant foods and foods for weaned children have been developed (*4*).

Processed Foods Based on Peanut Flour.   India   produces   over 4.8 million tons of peanuts, which could supply 1.6 million tons of high protein flour for human consumption   A considerable amount of work has been done on developing different types of products utilizing peanut flour and protein isolate   A detailed account of this was given at the International Conference on Prevention of Malnutrition in the Preschool Child in December 1964, Washington D C. (*10*)   The various products which have been developed for large-scale utilization are classified in four groups:

High protein supplementary foods containing 40% protein such as Indian Multipurpose Food.
Bulk foods containing 12 to 14% protein, such as tapioca macaroni, Mysore flour, and *Paushtik attá*.
Weaning foods containing 30% protein, such as balanced malt food and precooked weaning food.
Specialty foods containing 17 to 20% protein, such as enriched macaroni and Nutro biscuits.

Microatomization technique   (below 200-mesh) has demonstrated the possibility of using some of these blends in foods for infants, as by this process it is possible to disperse the food in hot water into a milk-like emulsion for feeding infants and children.

In developing these foods great care has been taken to blend the constituents so that they supplement each other in amino acids and give a final product of better biological value.   Apart from the laboratory trials and clinical evaluation, acceptability trials and extension work have been carried out with most of the products developed.   Widespread public acceptance of tapioca macaroni in the state of Kerala was accomplished through such techniques.   Mysore flour (tapioca flour and peanut flour 3 to 1) has been used with success in distressed areas of Madras and Mysore states.   Consumer acceptability trials with *Paushtik attá'* (wheat flour, peanut flour, and tapioca flour 75:8:17) in Uttar Pradesh have shown that the majority of people generally prefer this product to atta or flour.   Nutro biscuits are now being made by one of the large manufacturers as a regular product.

Indian Multipurpose Food is now recognized as one of the most suitable supplements to cereal-based, low-protein diets.   CFTRI's pilot plant produces half a ton of this product per day, which is being utilized for experiments and demonstration work.   It is also distributed by various organizations, including the American Meals for Millions Foundation in community and school feeding programs and other social service organizations.   Municipal and government schools in Madras and Mysore states have begun or will soon begin to use this supplement in midday school feeding programs. One industrial unit in Coimbatore has begun producing the MPF supplement. The West Bengal Government is also starting a plant to manufacture this product for use in its school feeding program.

Recent Developments in Protein Foods

Peanut Protein Isolate and Products Based on It. The isolation of protein from peanut has been standardized at the institute and recent investigations have shown that it can be used to prepare protein foods for feeding children and also for treating protein malnutrition (2). Animal experiments have established that isolation of the peanut protein has not lowered the nutritive value of the protein present in the raw material (1). The protein efficiency ratio (PER) of the isolated peanut protein was found to be 1.4 and that of the peanut flour 1.47. This process has now been given to one of the leading industrial concerns in India for exploitation. The plant has been set up in Bombay in collaboration with the institute and the National Research Development Corp. It is expected to start production early in 1966. It has a capacity of 2.5 tons of protein per day.

Milk Substitutes. Recent investigations have shown the feasibil.ty of using nutritious milk substitutes made from peanut or soybean to supplement the diets of infants and children. One pound of peanut kernel yields 7 to 8 pounds of mi k substitute and is palatable to children. When fortified with calcium and vitamins, t has a good nutritive value (9). The "milk" by itself has a noticeable peanut flavor which meets with some consumer resistance from children and adults, but when subjected to lact c fermentation the peanut flavor is largely masked and the resultant yoghurt is acceptable to the users. The institute, for 10 years now, has been manufacturing this product for its staff as well as the general public.

Spray-Dried Infant Foods. The production of spray-dried milk substitutes for feeding infants is an important feature of the research program of the institute. Several blends based on peanut and soybean have been standardized, but major emphasis has been on developing an infant food based on peanut protein isolate and milk (14). This blend contains about 22 to 26% protein, $\frac{2}{3}$ of which is obtained from peanut and $\frac{1}{3}$ from milk. The spray-dried powder reconstitutes easily in warm water and can be bottle-fed to infants. The composition of the product as well as the flow sheet (Table VIII and Figure 1) for the production are given. It has been estimated that the cost of this product on an ex-factory basis will work out to about Rs. 4.75 per kg. ($ 1.00).

New Infant Food Based on Peanut Flour, Malt Extract, and But-termilk Solids. Infant food described earlier depends on the production of protein isolate by a separate factory. Besides, the whey solids from the production of protein isolate from peanut are not utilized. To over-

Table VIII.   Chemical Composition of Infant Food Based on Peanut Protein Isolate

(Values per 100 G.)

Moisture, g.	2.8	Vitamin A, IU	1500
Protein, g.	26.2	Vitamin D, IU	400
Fat, g.	18.4	Vitamin E, mg.	5.0
Minerals, g.	5.3	Thiamin, mg.	0.9
Carbohydrates, g. (by difference)	47.3	Riboflavin, mg.	1.5
Calcium, g.	0.95	Niacin, mg.	6.0
Phosphorus, g.	0.73	Pyridoxine, mg.	3.8

come these disadvantages, research is now being concentrated on producing an infant food using peanut flour in place of the protein isolate. The main steps in the production of this infant food are:

Hydrolysis of gelatinized wheat with barley malt to produce malt extract.

Blending of the malt extract, along with the enzyme it contains, with cooked peanut flour in order to hydrolyze the starch content of the peanut flour.

Extraction of the protein in the peanut by adjusting the pH.

Centrifugation and removal of the nonextractable fibrous portions of the peanut.

Blending of the centrifugate with skim milk powder or buttermilk powder and hydrogenated vegetable fat.

Homogenization.

Drying. The spray-dried powder is fortified with vitamins by dry mixing (Figure 2).

The composition of the product is given in Table IX. The protein content of the product is 25% (54% is from peanut protein, 36% from milk proteins, and 10% from cereal proteins). The amino acid composition of the product is given in Table X. Animal experiments have shown that the protein efficiency ratio (PER) of this product is 2.5 as such and 2.8 when fortified with methionine (Table XII). Infant feeding trials for this product will be carried out shortly at the Christian Medical College and Hospital, Vellore.

Studies on the shelf life and packaging of the product are in progress. This product will go a long way to stretch the limited milk supplies in India.

Foods for Weaned Children.   In India and other developing countries, infants are weaned from milk to gruels and other starch based foods, very low in protein. This results in protein malnutrition, and many cases of kwashiorkor are admitted to the hospitals (*13*). There is an acute milk shortage in all these countries, and any foods based on milk or milk protein are normally beyond the reach of the majority. It is absolutely necessary, therefore, to develop and manufacture foods for weaned children mainly based on vegetable proteins blended in such a way that their amino acids supplement one another.

The institute has formulated some precooked foods having a fairly high content of protein which could be fed to weaned infants as gruels or porridge. One blend containing peanut flour, green gram flour (*Phaseolus radiatus*), pea flour (*Pisum sativum*), and Bengal gram flour (*Cicer arietinum*), has been standardized. The PER of this product when supplemented with methionine is 2.5 as compared with 3.0 of milk (Table XII). The process for preparing this product is shown in Figure 3. It consists

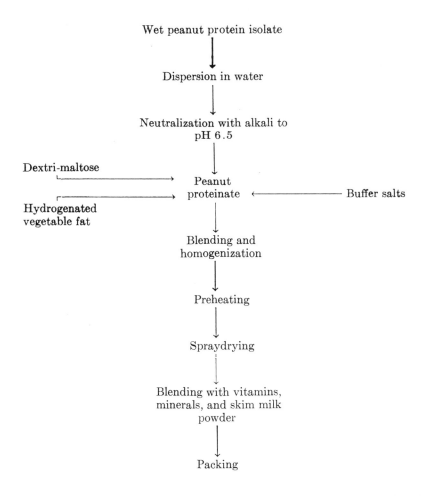

Figure 1. Flowsheet of process for preparation of an infant food based on peanut protein isolate and skim milk powder

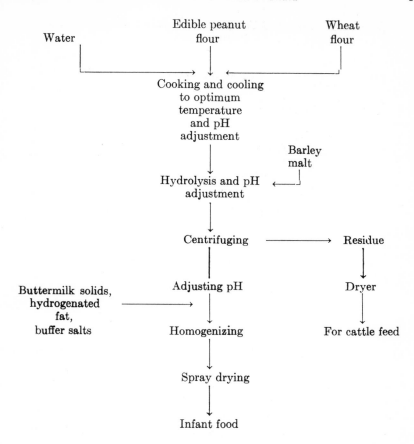

Figure 2. Flowsheet for production of infant food based on peanut flour and buttermilk solids

mainly of cooking the various ingredients, extruding into vermicelli-like strands, cutting, and flaking.

The product has a fairly high acceptability as it has a pleasant taste and can easily be made into a porridge. Studies have shown that its shelf life is satisfactory. The composition of the product is given in Table XI. It is expected to cost about Rs. 2.50 ($ 0.50) per kg. exfactory when packed in polyethylene bags.

Toned Vegetable Milk (Lac-Tone). The annual production of milk in India is about 22 million tons and, in spite of the vigorous measures taken by the Dairy Development Department, may not go beyond 25 million tons at the end of the Fourth Plan. The reason for this is the low yield of the cattle population and inadequate fodder. In India cattle are meant both for milk and draught. Hence, adequate stress is not

Table IX.   Chemical Composition of Infant Food Based on Peanut Flour

(Values per 100 G.)

Moisture, g.	3.0
Protein, g.[a]	25.0
Fat, g.	18.0
Minerals, g.	5.0
Carbohydrate, g. (by diff.)	49.0
Calcium, g.	1.0
Phosphorus, g.	1.0
Iron, mg.	6.0
Vitamins (added)	
Vitamin A, IU	1500
Vitamin D, IU	400
Vitamin E, mg.	2
Vitamin C, mg.	30
Thiamine, mg.	0.6
Riboflavin, mg.	1.0
Pyridoxin, mg.	0.3
Niacin, mg.	6.0
Calcium pantothenate, mg.	3.8
Vitamin B_{12}, μg.	2.2

[a] 13.5 parts of peanut protein, 9.0 parts of milk protein, and 2.5 parts of cereal protein.

laid on milk production. Many of the urban milk supply schemes are unable to cope with the demand for milk in the cities. The milk supplies are stretched to some extent by producing what is generally known as toned milk—i.e., buffalo milk, the fat of which has been toned down to about 3% by mixing with reconstituted skim milk solids.

The program, though initially successful in meeting the needs of a larger population, is now faced with the shortage of skim milk powder both through world organizations like UNICEF and in the open market. Many of the dairies are unable to meet even the demand for toned milk in the cities. To overcome this difficulty, the institute has been experimenting with the use of peanut protein isolate in place of skim milk protein for preparing toned milk. The process for making the product is shown in Figure 4. The main steps are: reconstitution of the peanut protein isolate at optimum pH in water, addition of liquid glucose to make up total solids, and addition of salts and vitamins for fortification and buffering.

This reconstituted emulsion is mixed with buffalo milk, so that the protein content of the blended milk is 3.5%, fat content 3.0% and, the solids not fat 9.0%. This blend is homoginized, pasteurized, and bottled. The institute produces about 100 liters of this product (Lac -Tone) per day and sells it to the staff members at Rs. 0.50 per liter ($ 0.10). It is proposed in the near future to produce this milk in a dairy unit in one of the large cities.   The nutritive value of the milk has also been determined by animal experiments and found satisfactory (Table XII).

Relative Costs of Processed Protein Foods.   Table XIII gives the protein content, ex-factory cost estimate, and protein value cost index (PVCI) (*10*) of the protein foods developed in this laboratory.   Protein foods based on blends of oilseed meals require comparatively little processing and can be manufactured in a relatively simple manner without costly equipment.   At a cost of Rs. 0.05 ($ 0.01) to 0.10 ($ 0.02), a supplement of 20 grams of protein can be provided, but when more processing is involved, as in the case of precooked weaning foods or spray-dried infant food, the cost of production is much higher.   Though less processing is needed to prepare Lac-Tone, its cost is fairly high because protein isolate is used in its production.

The consumption of milk-based infant foods has greatly increased recently, and the production is proposed to be raised from 3000 to 6000 tons per annum.   The production targets under the Fourth Five-Year Plan have been fixed at 25,000 tons per annum.   There is an acute shortage of this type of infant food in the country at present.   In India, milk has

Table X.   Calculated Amino Acid Composition of Infant Food Based on Peanut Flour
(G./16 G. nitrogen)

Amino Acids	Infant Food[a]	FAO Reference Pattern
Tryptophan	1.2	2.4
Threonine	3.5	2.8
Isoleucine	4.4	4.2
Leucine	7.6	4.8
Lysine	5.1	4.2
Methionine	1.6	2.2
Total sulfur acids	3.1	4.2
Phenylalanine	4.7	2.8
Valine	5.4	4.2
Arginine	7.4	—
Histidine	2.2	—

[a] To be fortified with methionine and lysine.

Table XI.   Composition of Weaning Food Based on Peanut Flour and Pulses
(Values per 100 G.)

Moisture, g.	2.7	Riboflavin, mg.	1.8
Protein, g.	35.0	Vitamin A, IU	3000
Fat, g.	4.0	Vitamin D, IU	300
Calcium, g.	0.9	Vitamin C, mg.	30
Thiamin, mg.	1.1		

Table XII. Protein Efficiency Ratio of Infant Food Based on Peanut Flour, Precooked Weaning Food, and Toned Vegetable Milk (Lac-Tone)

Dietary Sources of Protein	PER[a]
Infant food (based on peanut flour)	2.5
+ methionine	2.8
Precooked weaning food	1.8
+ methionine	2.5
Toned vegetable milk (Lac-Tone)	2.3
Skim milk powder (control)	3.0

[a] Mean values for 10 male rats; level of protein in diet 10%; duration of experiment 4 weeks.

been an important part of infant diets.   Milk and milk products provide almost one tenth of the total protein consumed by the people (Table IV). Generally parents are prepared to make significant sacrifices for their children if they are convinced of the value of what they are getting.   In view of this, there seems to be a good potential for the production of infant foods based on vegetable proteins and blends of vegetable proteins and milk.

The scope for the production of toned vegetable milk (Lac-Tone) is also considerable since skim milk powder is both costly and scarce.

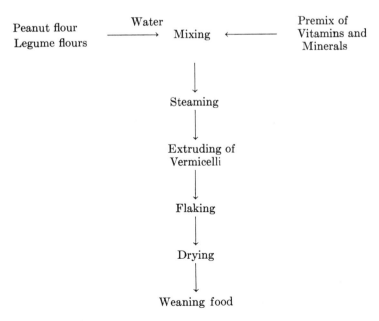

Figure 3. Flowsheet for preparation of precooked weaning food

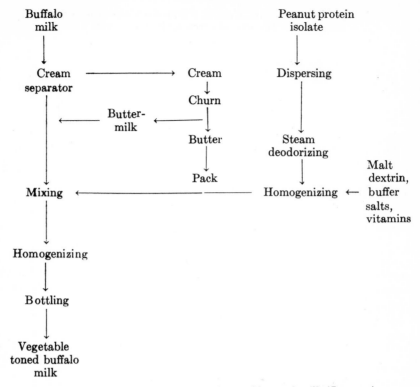

Figure 4. Flowsheet for production of vegetable toned milk (Lac-tone)

Measures to enhance the present supply of milk by using vegetable proteins deserve urgent consideration.

High protein weaning foods to supplement the starchy diets of pre-school children should receive high priority. Such foods developed at the institute are based entirely on vegetable proteins and do not involve the use of milk powder. The cost per unit of this weaning food is lower and well within the means of most of the people.

Conclusions

The principal sources of protein in the diet of the Indian people are cereals and legumes; the former supply 59% and the latter 27% of protein. Out of the total of 50 grams of protein which an average Indian gets daily, only 6 grams or 12% come from animal foods. Other important available sources of protein are the oilseeds, of which India produces 10 million tons annually. Out of these, peanuts alone account for 5 million tons and could supply 1.6 million tons of meal with 50% protein.

Table XIII. Relative Cost and Protein Contents of Some Processed Protein Foods

Protein Food	Cost per kg.		Protein, %	Cost per 20 g. Protein		PER	PVCI[a]
	Indian Rs.	US $		Indian paise	US cents		
Fortified peanut flour	1.20	0.22	50.1	5	1.0	1.6	36.4
Indian MPF	1.60	0.32	41.9	8	1.5	1.8	23.6
Infant food (protein isolate and skim milk powder)	4.00	0.80	26.0	31	6.2	2.3	7.5
Weaning food (pulses and peanut flour)	2.50	0.50	34.0	15	3.0	1.8	12.2
+ methionine	2.60	0.52	34.0	15	3.0	2.5	16.3
Infant food (peanut flour and buttermilk solids)	4.50	0.90	25.0	36	7.0	2.5	7.0
Infant food + methionine	4.60	0.92	25.0	36	7.0	2.8	7.6
Lac-Tone	0.50	0.10	3.5	30	6.0	2.3	8.1
Buffalo milk	0.85	0.17	3.5	51	10.2	3.0[b]	6.2

[a] $PVCI = \dfrac{\text{protein per 100 g.}}{\text{cost per 100 g. in cents}} \times PER$

[b] PER of sample of buffalo skim milk powder included as control food.

Efforts have been concentrated on developing protein foods based on edible grade peanut flour, peanut protein isolate, and legumes with or without inclusion of milk protein. The main objective is to fix the ingredients in such a manner as to provide a fairly good balance of amino acids and make the final product of sufficiently high biological value. Products have, therefore, been developed with a view to stretching the meager milk supplies and introducing new weaning foods as well as other high protein foods which would have PER equivalent to milk. Some of the products have found good consumer acceptance and offer possibility of commercial exploitation in the near future.

India has no alternative but to concentrate on low cost vegetable proteins because of the low standard of living, the per capita income being only $63 per year. Due attention has been given to sociological factors in developing the products which would fit into the existing dietary pattern as substitutes and supplements.

Protein isolate from peanut flour has been used to treat kwashiorkor in the form of microatomized flour and also as a constituent of processed foods like spray-dried infant food and Lac-Tone. A new process for using peanut flour in place of protein isolate has been developed, whereby all the fractions of peanut flour, excluding the fiber and insoluble carbohydrates, are utilized. The process does not depend on an external supply of protein isolate, and malt extract is utilized in the process as a source of enzyme for hydrolyzing starch as well as to supply some protein. Toned vegetable milk using protein isolate has considerable scope in the country. Experiments to investigate the possibilities of preparing toned vegetable milk from peanut flour instead of protein isolate are in progress. Infant feeding trials on these various foods are being conducted, and animal experiments, already completed, indicate the possibility that these foods could be used successfully.

Acknowledgment

The authors acknowledge with thanks the valuable help given by M. Swaminathan and M. R. Chandrasekhara in going through the manuscript and making useful suggestions.

Literature Cited

(1) Anantharaman, K., Subramanian, N., Bhatia, D. S., Swaminathan, M., Sreenivasan, A., Subrahmanyan, V., *Food Sci.* **11** (1), 1 (1962).
(2) Bhatia, D. S., Kalbag, S. S., Subramanian, N., Anantharaman, K., Eapen, K. E., Sreenivasan A., Subrahmanyan, V., "Technology of Peanut Protein Isolate," 1st International Congress of Food Science and Technology, London, Sept. 18–21, 1962.
(3) CFTRI, Report on "Use of Coconut Preparations as a Protein Supplement in Child Feeding: Prospects" PAG-WHO/UNICEF Meeting, Geneva, August 1963.
(4) Chandrasekhara, M. R., Ramanatham, G., Rama Rao, G., Bhatia, D. S., Swaminathan, M., Sreenivasan, A., Subrahmanyan, V., *J. Sci. Food Agr.* **15** (12), 839 (1964).
(5) Food and Agriculture Organization, United Nations, "Food Balance Sheet," 1955.
(6) Food and Agriculture Organization, United Nations, "Production Yearbook," Vol. 16, 1962.
(7) Food and Agriculture Organization, United Nations, Rome, "Protein—at the Heart of the World Food Problem," 1964.
(8) Food and Agriculture Organization, Rome, "Third World Food Survey," Basic Study **11** (1963).
(9) Indian Council of Medical Research, New Delhi, "Milk Substitutes of Vegetable Origin," Spec. Rept. Ser. **31** (1955).

(10) Parpia, H. A. B., "Development of Food Mixes for Preschool Children in India," International Conference on Prevention of Malnutrition in the Preschool Child, Washington, D. C., Dec. 7–11, 1964.

(11) Parpia, H. A. B., Dastur, K. M., Amla, B. L., "Science and Technology in Conservation of Food Resources in India," Symposium on Science and the Nation during the 3rd Five Year Plan, New Delhi, July 28, 1964.

(12) Patwardhan, V. N., *Am. J. Clin. Nutr.* **11,** 12 (1962).

(13) Someswara Rao, K., Swaminathan, M. C., Swarup, S., Patwardhan, V. N., *Bull World Health Org.* **20,** 603 (1959).

(14) Subrahmanyan, V., Chandrasekhara, M. R., Subramanian, N., Korula, S., Bhatia, D. S., Sreenivasan, A., Swaminathan, M., *Food Sci.* **11** (1), 9 (1962).

(15) Sukhatme, P. V., "Feeding India's Growing Millions," Asia Publishing House, Bombay, 1965.

(16) World Health Organization, Geneva, "Malnutrition and Disease," Basic Study **13** (1963).

RECEIVED October 12, 1965.

Table II.   Amino Acid Composition of Some Seed Proteins
(G. per 16g. N)

	Peanut (*Lypro*)	Coconut Protein	Cottonseed Protein	Target Amino Acid Levels (*10*)
Lysine	3.0	3.6	3.9	5.3
Methionine	1.1	1.9	1.7	4.2
Cystine	1.4	1.3	1.6	4.2
Leucine	7.6	7.3	6.7	6.4
Isoleucine	3.8	4.8	3.9	5.3
Valine	4.7	6.5	6.0	5.3
Threonine	2.0	3.0	3.6	4.3
Phenylalanine	5.2	5.7	6.3	6.9[a]
Tryptophan	1.0	1.2	1.3	1.0
Histidine	2.5	2.5	2.5	8.5
Arginine	11.6	12.8	7.4	1.8
Total essential amino acids	43.9	50.6	44.9	
NPU	40–45	63	50	92
Digestibility	95–100	95–100	75	
Biological value	40–47	63–65	60	
Aspartic acid	11.8	7.0	9.8	
Serine	4.5	4.8	5.0	
Glumatic acid	17.2	15.9	18.5	
Proline	3.9	2.9	3.4	
Glycine	4.2	4.6	4.7	
Alanine	3.6	4.2	4.8	
Tyrosine	3.7	2.2	3.3	
NH$_3$	2.1	1.6	1.9	
Total non-essential amino acids	51.0	43.2	51.4	
Total amino acids	94.9	93.8	95.3	

[a] Phal + tyr.

TRYPSIN INHIBITOR. In common with many leguminous seeds, the peanut contains a trypsin inhibitor (*1*). In producing *Lypro* about one half of the trypsin inhibitor acitivity originally in the peanuts is found in the wet lipid-protein paste, but this residual activity is destroyed in the final stages of sterilization and spray-drying, and *Lypro* is free from trypsin inhibitor.

ANTIHEMOPHILIC FACTOR. There is increasing evidence that hemophilics can achieve hemostasis by eating raw peanuts (*2*). Several patients have found that peanuts can be replaced by an equivalent amount of *Lypro*, which is a convenient source of the factor This suggests that the factor goes mainly into the *Lypro* fraction.

PROPERTIES OF *Lypro* IN RELATION TO FOOD USES.   For use as a food *Lypro* can be dispersed in water without further additions to give a bland milk-like drink, which may be sweetened or given various flavors.   For specialized uses such as in pediatrics or geriatrics, other proteins—for example, casein—may be added to give a better essential amino acid balance.   A logical extension is to adapt these drink recipes for freezing to "sorbets," and the physicochemical properties of *Lypro* prevent crystallization and ensure a good "overrun" in addition to increasing the nutritional value.

There is some evidence that lipid-protein water complexes exert control on the properties of bread (8).   Waldt *et al.* (17) have investigated the extent to which the physicochemical properties of *Lypro* can be utilized to replace traditional lipo-proteins in cooking and food technology. In baking, part of the egg in standard recipes could be replaced by *Lypro* with no loss of quality.   In comminuted meat processing they found that it controlled hydration and fat migration more effectively than added milk proteins.   Rosen (15) has also discussed uses of *Lypro* in the food industry as a protein fortifier and an improver of texture and shelf life.

Coconut Kernels

Recognition is growing that coconut protein could be used to supplement the diets of infants and children in areas where protein malnutrition is prevalent; in these areas coconut is frequently available in large quantities.   Traditionally coconuts are processed only for the oil, which is released by milling or expelling copra, the sun- or oven-dried nut.   The oil cake thus obtained is not fit for human consumption; it has a high fiber content, is generally infected, and the protein moiety has a low biological value.   Sreenivasan (16) has discussed problems associated with making coconut protein available for child feeding, and he reviews some of the currently available protein-extraction processes, including the Chayen impulse process.

In our hands, the impulse process has proved a most elegant tool for separating protein from the coconut kernel as the lipid-protein complex. The flow diagram for impulse-rendering coconut kernels is given in Figure 2. The fresh kernels, with shells removed, but not comminuted, are fed into the impulse renderer with ten times their weight of 0.15% sodium hydroxide solution.   The carbohydrate-fiber fraction is removed on a vibrating screen and the liquor passing forward is centrifuged to separate the free oil from the lipid-protein complex.   The oil and the complex are recovered by methods similar to those used in peanut processing.   A balance for oil and protein recoveries, obtained in a typical coconut kernel impulse-rendering trial, is given in Table III.

The free oil, which accounts for more than three quarters of the total lipid of the kernels, after one washing only, separates as an almost colorless solid of low free fatty acid content and with a faint odor of coconut. About three quarters of the nitrogen of the original kernels is recovered as protein in the lipid-protein complex. The dried complex, comprising 60% protein and 35% lipid, is an almost odorless and tasteless, free-flowing brown powder of pleasing appearance. Table II gives the amino acid composition of the protein moiety of the complex. Miller (*10*) found a mean NPU of 63 for carefully prepared coconut protein concentrates.

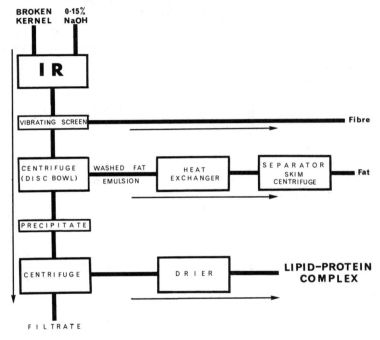

Figure 2. Diagram of impulse process plant for coconut

Cottonseed

Chayen and Webb (*6*) have recently studied the application of the impulse process to the processing of undelintered cottonseed for animal feeding. Table IV summarizes the results obtained in a typical experiment in which, by impulse rendering in water, 100 parts of undelintered cottonseed were sharply resolved into 60 parts of a meal fraction and 40 parts of a cotton-hull fraction. Most of the protein and oil contained in the original cottonseed was carried forward in the meal, which was only slightly contaminated with hulls. The moist meal fraction was cooked at 100° C, to inactivate the gossypol and improve its nutritional value. It was then either dried, or partly dried and, while still hot, squeezed in a normal oil expeller to remove about three quarters of the total oil.

Nutritional Value of Lipid-Protein Fraction   Fed to rats at a 10% protein level, these meals gave NPU values of about 50, with a digestibility of 75%, corresponding to a biological value of about 60. These meals have also been successfully fed at a 10% level to laying hens as part of the protein ration.

Table III.   Composition of Coconut Kernel and Fractions Derived by Impulse Rendering

		Composition	Recovery from Dry Kernel
		%	%
Original coconut kernel	Moisture	43.0	
	Total solid	57.0	
	Protein (N × 6.25)	8.0	
	Lipid	65.0	
	Carbohydrate (by difference)	18.0	
	Fiber	6.0	
	Ash	2.0	
Lipid-protein complex	Protein (N × 6.25)	60.0	70.0
	Lipid	35.0	4.0
	Carbohydrate (by difference)	2.5	2.0
	Ash	2.5	
Carbohydrate meal	Protein (N × 6.25)	1.5	4.0
	Lipid	20.0	10.0
	Carbohydrate fiber	75.0	90.0
	Ash	3.3	
Protein effluent	Protein (N × 6.25)	—	25.0
Free oil	Lipid	100.0	80.0
	Free fatty acid	0.28	—
	Color (transmission in 5¼ inch cell) 1.0 Red		
	4.5 Yellow		

Leaves

Chibnall (7), in his classic book on protein metabolism in the plant, considered the essential amino acid composition of leaf proteins and concluded that "the excellent nutritive value of leaf proteins is clearly evident." In England there are now two processes for the extraction of protein concentrates from green leaves, that of Pirie (13) and the Chayen impulse process. Since 1964 an impulse process unit has been operating under license in Haifa, Israel, for making alfalfa leaf lipid protein. As most leaves behave in a similar way, it is convenient to describe the results obtained with alfalfa in detail.

Alfalfa

A flow diagram for the impulse processing of alfalfa is given in Figure 3. Fresh alfalfa is fed into the impulse renderer at the rate of 1 ton per hour with dilute alkali. The alkali contains an antioxidant (Santoquin) to prevent oxidative losses of carotenoids during processing. Fiber is removed from the emerging liquor and is washed, dewatered, and dried. The lipid-protein complex is precipitated in line by pH adjustment and is thickened to a paste containing up to 50% solids by centrifugation. The paste may be spray-dried; or it may be air-dried, either after extruding to form "noodles" or spreading on a carrier of ground cereal.

Table IV.   Composition of Undelintered Cottonseed and Fractions Derived by Impulse Rendering

		Composition	Distribution between Fractions
		%	%
Original	Meats	50	—
undelintered	Hull	40	—
cottonseed,	Cotton	10	—
100 parts			
	Protein	23	—
	Oil	18	—
	Fiber	22	—
	Carbohydrate	37	—
	Gossypol (total)	1.1	—
Fractions recovered			
Cotton hull,	Protein (N × 6.25)	7	15
40 parts	Oil	3	7
	Fiber	45	88
	Carbohydrate	45	51
Protein meal,	Protein (N × 6.25)	33	85
60 parts	Oil	32	93
	Fiber	5	12
	Carbohydrate	30	49
	Gossypol (total)	0.6	
	(free)	0.02	
Squeezed protein	Protein (N × 6.25)	43	
meal	Oil	10	
	Fiber	7	
	Carbohydrate	40	
	Gossypol (free)	0.03	

Table V gives the material balance obtained in a continuous manu-facturing run with fresh alfalfa tops.

Fiber Fraction.   About one quarter of the original nitrogen of the leaf remains with the washed fiber fraction.   Part of this nitrogen is associated with a few leaf cells which escape breakage in the process; but part seems to be associated with the leaf structural tissue elements (5). A disproportionate amount of energy would be needed to liberate this residual nitrogen, which for practical purposes is best utilized by feeding the meal to cattle.

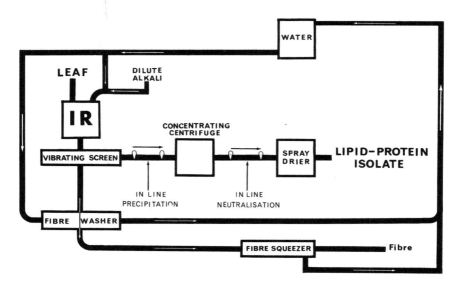

Figure 3.   Diagram of impulse process plant for alfalfa

Lipid-Protein Isolate.   More than half of the original nitrogen and most of the lipids and pigments of the leaf are recovered in the lipid-protein fraction.   The spray-dried product is an intensely green fine powder with a characteristic grassy odor.   The "noodled" isolates are dried to a granular product which is more convenient to handle.

AMINO ACID COMPOSITION AND BIOLOGICAL VALUE.   An analysis of the protein moiety of typical alfalfa isolate is given in Table VI.

Methionine-cystine is the first limiting amino acid in this protein, giving a chemical score of 62 which agrees with the biological value of 59 (NPU 44, digestibility 74%) found in the rat, and with the biological value of 60 (NPU 60, digestibility 95 to 100%) obtained by feeding an equivalent "synthetic" mixture of L-amino acids.

Methionine supplements of 1.5% of protein weight gave optimal effects, increasing the biological value to 72 (NPU 56, digestibility 77%), which compares with the value of 67 obtained by feeding the equivalent L-amino acid mixture.

DIGESTIBILITY.   Only about 75% digestibility is found for leaf proteins in rats (monogastrics), which means that a quarter of the amino acid potential is not utilized. This low digestibility is not associated with the processing or drying conditions, because similar values are obtained with freeze-dried complexes and even with undried pastes prepared in the laboratory by mild extraction methods. Neither is it associated with the presence of a saponin "bloat" factor of the kind found by Cowlishaw *et al.* (*9*) in alfalfa leaf preparations. There is no increase in digestibility or NPU after hot water and alcohol washing to remove this putative saponin, or on addition of 0.5% of cholesterol to the diet as a steroid competitor. From this evidence and from animal feeding studies we conclude that saponin bloat factors are removed in the impulse processing of alfalfa.

Fractionation of the lipid-protein liquor into a "chloroplastic" fraction and a soluble "cytoplasmic" fraction showed that the nitrogen was about equally distributed between them. When tested in vitro with pepsin and trypsin, the digestibility of the chloroplastic fraction was about 60 to 70%, whereas the digestibility of the soluble cytoplasmic fraction was 95 to 100%. The amino acid composition of the two fractions is similar (Table VI).

Table V.   Composition of Alfalfa and Fractions Derived by Impulse Rendering

		Composition	Yield
		%	%
Alfalfa,	Total solid	20.0[a]	
20 parts	Crude protein (N × 6.25)	4.4[a]	
	Acetone-solubles	2.0[a]	
Lipid-protein,	Protein (N × 6.25)	61.0	55
4 parts	Fiber	0.7	
	Carbohydrates	12.5	
	Acetone-solubles	17.0	
Fiber, 10 parts	Protein (N × 6.25)	11.5	25
	Fiber	34.0	
	Carbohydrate	35.0	
	Acetone-solubles	2.0	
Protein effluent, 6 parts	Crude protein (N × 6.25)	0.01[a]	20

[a] All other results calculated to dry basis.

Table VI. Amino Acid Composition of Proteins
(*G. per 16g. N*)

	Alfalfa Leaf Protein	Alfalfa Leaf Cytoplasmic Fraction	Alfalfa Leaf Chloroplast Fraction	Target Amino Acid Levels (10)
Lysine	6.3	6.2	6.5	5.3
Methionine	1.8	1.6	1.8	4.2
Cystine	0.8	1.1	0.9	4.2
Leucine	9.6	7.0	10.3	6.4
Isoleucine	5.3	5.0	5.0	5.3
Valine	5.8	5.7	5.6	5.3
Threonine	5.0	4.9	5.2	4.3
Phenylalanine	6.1	6.5	6.5	6.9[a]
Tryptophan	2.0	1.6	1.2	1.0
Histidine	2.0	3.0	1.9	3.5
Arginine	7.3	8.1	6.6	1.8
Total essential amino acids	52.0	50.7	51.5	
Chemical score	57	65	54	100
NPU	44			92
Digestibility	75	95–100[b]	60–70[b]	
Biological value	59			
Aspartic acid	9.7	9.4	9.1	
Serine	4.5	4.8	4.2	
Glutamic acid	10.6	10.0	10.4	
Proline	4.5	4.4	4.9	
Glycine	4.7	4.8	5.6	
Alanine	5.8	5.7	6.0	
Tyrosine	5.0	4.8	4.9	
NH$_3$	1.4	1.6	1.6	
Total non-essential amino acid	46.2	45.5	46.7	
Total	98.2	96.2	98.2	

[a] Phal + tyr.
[b] Test in vitro.

Exhaustive extraction of the chloroplast fraction with polar, nonpolar solvent mixtures, in an attempt to break the lipid-protein associations which stabilize the structure of the chloroplast, gave no significant increase in digestibility. We therefore conclude that the incomplete digestion by the nonruminant is associated with fragments of structural elements which are present in the fraction.

CAROTENOID PIGMENTS. Provided suitable antioxidants are used, the leaf pigments xanthophyll and carotene are recovered in high yield in the lipid-protein fraction.

USES FOR LIPID-PROTEIN ISOLATE. For animal rations the green lipid-protein isolate may be used, replacing dried alfalfa and other sources of protein. This replacement is especially useful in starter rations for animals which cannot tolerate high proportions of fiber. Experience has shown that animals are less prone to bloat when the lipid-protein isolate replaces dried alfalfa in their ration. As a poultry ration component, the alfalfa isolate provides, in addition to protein, carotenoid needed for flesh and egg pigmentation.

Pirie (14) has advocated using green protein concentrates from leaves for human feeding. While it may be possible to conceal small amounts of the green lipid-protein complex in certain highly flavored dishes, we feel that for most human feeding purposes the strongly flavored pigments must first be removed. This may be done by azeotropically drying the moist paste or by solvent-extracting the air- or spray-dried isolate. The bland grayish powder thus obtained may then be incorporated as a protein supplement into most traditional "native" carbohydrate-rich dishes. The mixture of pigments and lipids obtained from this extraction (Table VII) are separated and the components sold, for example, to the pharmaceutical and animal feeding industries.

Table VII. Analysis of Acetone-Solubles from Alfalfa Lipid-Protein Isolate

	Mg./Gm.	*Mg./Lb.*
Copper chlorophyllin	110	50,000
Crude wax	25	11,000
Sterols	10	4,540
Xanthophylls	5.5	2,500
Carotene	3.3	1,500

Other Leaves

We have made lipid-protein isolates from many other green leaves, including domestic grasses, Bermuda grass, maize, sugar beet tops, and cassava. The isolate from cassava is free of cyanide, which is present in high concentration in the original leaf. Industrially, Bermuda grass would be processed for the valuable fiber fraction; the small lipid-protein fraction could then be isolated as a cheap animal food.

In leaf processing it is generally possible to vary the composition of the carbohydrate-fiber and lipid-protein fractions by modifying the impulse-processing conditions. Thus, for example, if a fiber fraction of higher protein content were needed for a specific feeding purpose, this could be produced by impulse-rendering in weaker alkali solution, or even in water.

Discussion

The economics of the impulse process for extracting protein foods from vegetable material may be vitally influenced by two considerations; the size of the operation and the ability to utilize all the separated products effectively. For most applications, the optimal size of plant would be one with an impulse unit of 4 tons per hour capacity. The free oil recovered on impulse processing oilseeds is of good quality and may fetch high prices, even without further refining. The carbohydrate-meal fraction is also a valuable product which has many possible uses in modern food technology. Thus, by effectively selling these by-products, the lipid-protein isolate may be made more cheaply available for human feeding requirements.

In the extreme example of the coconut, which contains much oil and a little high-quality protein, proceeds from the sale of the very high quality oil separated by impulse processing might subsidize recovery of the protein and its distribution to the needy. At present some 3 million tons of coconut are annually converted to copra for oil production, with, as far as human nutrition is concerned, the virtual destruction of the protein present. The oil thus obtained is yellow, and even after refining does not compare in color with that separated in the impulse process.

Commercial evaluation of the pigments, waxes, and fats extracted from leaf lipid-protein isolates is now being pursued in Israel and in England. In this fraction lies an enormous potential for the chemical and pharmaceutical industries; and in its proper exploitation may lie the true key to the provision of cheap protein for human feeding.

Acknowledgment

I am indebted to I. H. Chayen, managing director, British Glues and Chemicals, Ltd., for his stimulating help and for his generosity in allowing me to use as much of his unpublished work as I wished.

I also thank T. Webb for allowing me to incorporate so many of his results in this paper, D. S. Miller for much nutritional advice and help, and G. Zimmermann for the analysis of alfalfa lipids.

I cannot end without thanking M. L. Anson for the unique friendship, help, and encouragement which I have now enjoyed for many years.

Literature Cited

(1) Borchers, R., Ackerson, C. W., *Arch. Biochem.* **13,** 291 (1947).
(2) Boudreaux, H. B., Frampton, V. L., IXth World Congress, International Society for Rehabilitation of Disabled, Copenhagen, 1963.
(3) Chayen, I. H., U. S. Patent **2,928,821** (March 15, 1960).
(4) Chayen, I. H., Ashworth, D. R., *J. Appl. Chem.* **3,** 529 (1953).

(5) Chayen, I. H., Smith, R. H., Tristam, G. R., Thirknell, D., Webb, T., *J. Sci. Food Agr.* **7,** 502 (1961).
(6) Chayen, I. H., Webb, T., private communication, 1965.
(7) Chibnall, A. C., "Nitrogen Metabolism in the Plant," Yale University Press, New Haven, Conn., 1939.
(8) Cookson, M. A., Ritchie, M. L., Coppock, J. B. M., *J. Sci. Food Agr.* **8,** 105 (1957).
(9) Cowlishaw, S. J., Eyles, D. E., Raymond, W. F., Tilley, J. M. A., *Ibid.,* **7,** 768, 775 (1956).
(10) Miller, D. S., private communication, 1965.
(11) Miller, D. S., Bender, A. E., *Brit. J. Nutr.* **9,** 382 (1955).
(12) Miller, D. S., Payne, P. R., *Ibid.,* **13,** 501 (1959).
(13) Morrison, J. E., Pirie, N. W., *J. Sci. Food Agr.* **12,** 1 (1961).
(14) Morrison, J. E., Pirie, N. W., *Nutrition* **14,** 7 (1960).
(15) Rosen, G. D., *Cereal Sci. Today* **10,** 68, 100, 208 (1965).
(16) Sreenivasan, A., Nutrition Document R9/Add 5 PAG (WHO/FAO/UNICEF), Geneva, August 1963.
(17) Waldt, L. M., Debreczeni, E. J., Schwarcz, M., O'Keefe, T., *Food Technol.* **17,** 107 (1963).

RECEIVED October 12, 1965.

11

Major Seed Proteins and the Concept of Aleurins

J. M. DECHARY and A. M. ALTSCHUL

Seed Protein Pioneering Research Laboratory, New Orleans, La.

Aleurone grains are subcellular particles of seeds which contain the major proteins. "Aleurins" has been suggested as a name to distinguish proteins in aleurone grains from cytoplasmic proteins. Solubility properties of the major seed proteins are described, and the solubility classification system is discussed. The aleurins of wheat and the globulins of soybeans, peanuts, peas, and hempseed are examined with respect to particle size and association-dissociation properties.

The purpose of this paper is to provide background on the properties of the major proteins of seeds, their common characteristics, and their uniqueness, if any.

Seeds vary widely in protein content from a low of around 5% to as high as 60% (Table I). Of those with a naturally high protein content, the soybean is perhaps the best example of one widely utilized. Even for seeds of lower protein content, such as other oilseeds which contain perhaps 20% protein, the removal of the lipids elevates the protein content of the remainder to over 40%. Hence, the nonlipid portion of the seed has a high protein content.

Subcellular Location of Major Seed Proteins

One might ask whether there is a special location for most of the protein or is it scattered throughout the seed cytoplasm. That seed proteins are in specific locations called aleurone grains has been known for over 100 years. In recent years with the advent of electron microscopy, this problem has been investigated anew, and it has been shown definitely that these protein bodies exist and some morphological characteristics have been determined. Some idea of the aleurone grains of oilseeds is given in the electron micrograph of a cottonseed section (Figure 1). It is possible that aleurone grains exist in other seed tissue. Bils and Howell (5) prepared electron micrographs of germinated soybean cotyledon tissue and observed densely stained bodies, and Varner and Schidlovsky (24) observed protein bodies in electron micrographs of germinated pea cotyledon tissue. The light micrograph studies made by Duvick (9) of the developing corn endosperm showed the presence of protein granules containing mostly zein.

Altschul *et al.* (4) by the use of Carbowax showed that 75% of the proteins of peanuts are in particulates. In general, it might be concluded that the major proteins of seeds are in the aleurone grains and these are the unique proteins of seeds. Altschul *et al.* (3) suggested that they be named "aleurins" to distinguish them from the minor proteins of seeds which exist in the cytoplasm. It is not suggested that all of the proteins in aleurone grains are the so-called storage or ergastic proteins, which exist primarily for furnishing amino acids or nitrogen for the germinating seeds. Enzymes may be associated with them in small quantities. But it is suggested that by far the large proportion of the proteins in the aleurone grains are ergastic proteins.

Classification and Solubility

Since they are present as a large component of the protein part and are easily crystallized and separated by fractional precipitation, the major

Table I.   Protein Content of Some Seeds (1, 23)

Common Name	Botanical Name	Protein Content[a]
Cereals		
Wheat	*Triticum aestivum*	12–14
Corn	*Zea mays*	7–9
Rice	*Oryza sativa*	7.5–9
Legumes		
Soybean	*Glycine max*	32–42
Groundnut (peanut)	*Arachis hypogaea*	25–28
Chick pea	*Cicer arietinum*	20–28
Lentil	*Lens esculenta*	23–27
	Onobrychis vulgaris	41
	Tephrosia leiocarpa	44
Oilseeds		
Cottonseed	*Gossypium hirsutum*	17–21
Sesame seed	*Sesamum indicum*	25
Sunflower seed	*Helianthus annus*	27
Walnut	*Juglans regia*	15–21
Others		
Lauraceae	*Avocado* (Persian species)	5
Gramineae	*Fingerhuthia sesleriaeformis*	33
Liliaceae	*Dasylirion wheeleri*	50
Rosacaea	*Rhodotypos tetrapetala*	49

[a] Nitrogen multiplied by 6.25.

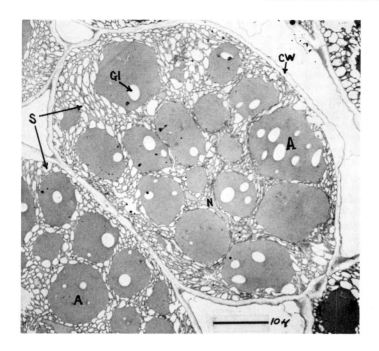

*Figure 1.   Electron micrograph of cottonseed cotyledon showing
aleurone grains*

A. *Aleurone grain*
C W. *Cell wall*
Gl. *Globoid*
N. *Nucleus*
S. *Spherosome*

seed proteins have been often considered pure and unique species: Indeed,
many show one component in the ultracentrifuge and cannot be separated
into many components by free electrophoresis.   This was the state of
affairs before the advent of modern techniques of protein separation such as
chromatography, gel electrophoresis, and gel filtration.

For most seeds, with the exception of many of the cereals, the major
proteins are globulins.   These are soluble in dilute salt solution, are precipitated by moderate salt concentrations, and are soluble at alkaline pH
and at pH below 4.   There existed a nomenclature of globulins unique for
each seed: edestin from hempseed, arachin and conarachin from peanuts,
glycinin from soybean, amandin from almonds, and legumin from peas, to
mention a few.   Attempts were made to find common properties of these
globulins on the basis of molecular size and amino acid composition, and
indeed there are many similarities.   Table II gives the particle sizes of some
major seed proteins.   They all have large molecular weight; many associate
and dissociate into various molecular sizes depending on the pH and ionic

strength of the medium; they are high in arginine and carboxylic amino acids and in amide nitrogen. In recent years it has been shown by chromatography and electrophoresis that the classical seed proteins are not monodisperse and some of the properties attributed to these proteins as supposedly unique species must be reconsidered in light of this evidence.

The cereal proteins are considered to have two classes of major seed proteins in their storage tissues: the alcohol-soluble prolamins and alkali- or acid-soluble glutelins. There are also globulins in the embryo, but since the embryo is such a small proportion of the seed, the corresponding proportion of globulin is usually small.

The classification of major seed proteins on the basis of solubility has the advantage of simplicity and is the most universally used one. But the questions still remain: Are these solely reserve proteins? Are they associated with other reserve material? Are any enzymes associated with the major proteins in the seed? Is there the possibility that some of the proteins are artifacts of grinding the entire tissue in extraction of these fractions? Since the major proteins do not have any obvious biological values, the question of artifact cannot be answered so readily.

Table II.   Particle Size of Some Major Seed Proteins

Protein	Solvent	pH	$S°20,w$	M.W.[a]	Ref.
α-Conarachin	$\mu = 0.06$, phosphate buffer	7.8	12.6	295,000 (estimated) (S)	(11)
	$\mu = 0.5$, phosphate buffer	7.8	7.8	142,000 (estimated) (S)	(11)
Arachin	$\mu = 0.1$	7.9	14.6	330,000 (S)	(14)
	$\mu = 0.1$	7.9	9.0	180,000 (S)	(14)
Arachin (isolated as aleurin)	$\mu = 0.06$, phosphate buffer	7.8	9.0		(3)
Peanut protein	$\mu = 0.1$, phosphate buffer, 7M urea	8.8	2		(10)
Amandin (almonds)	0.1M NaCl, Tris buffer	8.4		330,000 (L)	(17)
	6.7M urea			30,300 (S)	(25)
Soybean protein, 11 S fraction	$\mu = 0.5$, phosphate buffer + NaCl	7.6	11.8–12.2	363,000 (S) 345,000 (L)	(27) (13)
Soybean protein 7 S fraction	$\mu = 0.5$, phosphate buffer	7.6	8.0	330,000 (S)	(18)
Cottonseed protein	0.5M NaCl	7.0	9.2	180,000 (L)	(19)
γ-Gliadin	Aluminum lactate buffer	3.1		50,000 (S)	(28)
	4M guanidine hydrochloride	3.1		26,000 (S)	(28)

[a] (S) by sedimentation; (L) by light scattering.

Aleurins of Wheat

One of the most extensive studies of the protein bodies in seeds is that of the late R. K. Morton and his colleagues on the developing wheat endosperm. Graham *et al.* (*12*) showed osmiophilic bodies within a lipoprotein membrane. Because of their fragility the bodies were difficult to isolate, but good preparations were obtained which contained about 85% protein. Starch gel electrophoresis of the proteins from the isolated bodies showed that they have the patterns resembling the acetic acid–soluble fraction. Since they increase in size and number during development and acetic acid–soluble proteins increase rapidly during maturation of the endosperm, there is good evidence that these bodies contain the storage proteins of the wheat endosperm.

Globulins

Soybean. The mature soybean contains more than 40% protein on a dry weight basis, and the soybean globulins can be isolated by extracting defatted soybean meal with 10% sodium chloride and collecting the fraction which precipitates upon dialysis against water. This fraction was originally considered a homogeneous protein and was called glycinin, but it is now evident that glycinin is heterogeneous when examined by ultracentrifugation and by electrophoresis. It consists of at least four fractions which have been designated 4, 7, 11, and 15 S on the basis of their sedimentation pattern. The 11 S fraction is present to the greatest extent, and the 11 and 7 S components account for 70% of the protein. When a concentrated, aqueous solution of soybean protein is cooled, a cold-insoluble fraction is obtained which is primarily 11 S protein.

Attempts to understand the relationship between the various fractions observed in the ultracentrifuge are complicated by the fact that the protein can form complexes with other materials in the seed; phytin-protein complexes have been found (*20*). When the phytic acid has been removed by treatment with the anion exchange resin Dowex 1-x10, the solubility of the protein increases, particularly on the acid side of the point of minimum solubility. Secondly, the 7 and 11 S components are capable of forming disulfide-linked polymers during manipulation of the protein solutions. The disulfide interchange reaction can be eliminated by adding mercaptoethanol routinely to the pH 7.6 buffer containing added NaCl. This gives the simplest ultracentrifuge patterns because association is suppressed by high ionic strength and because disulfide polymerization is prevented by the reducing conditions. The so-called cold-insoluble fraction—the 11 S fraction—was purified to the extent of about 90% by extraction of the acid-precipitated protein with sodium chloride of graded ionic strengths. A particle weight of 363,000 by sedimentation diffusion and 345,000 by light scattering was obtained; this compares to the reported molecular weight of 380,000 for the 11 S fraction obtained by ammonium sulfate fractionation (*26*).   Further purification was achieved by Hasegawa *et al.* (*13, 16*) by means of Sephadex G-200.   The impurity was the 7 S fraction and this could be removed by chromatography on calcium phosphate gel.   The purified 11 S component is homogeneous by sedimentation analysis, but no information is available on its purity by gel electrophoresis.

Roberts and Briggs (*18*) purified the 7 S component by gel filtration on Sephadex G-100.   It contains only a trace of the 11 S component.   The 7 S component will associate when the electrolyte concentration is lowered from 0.5 to 0.1 ionic strength to give a 9 S form.   Both forms have a concentration dependence of molecular weight; extrapolated to zero concentration, the molecular weight of the 9 S component is 650,000 and of the 7 S is 330,000.   The amino acid composition of the 7 S component is somewhat comparable to the whole globulin, but the 7 S component has 5.9% carbohydrate compared with 1.5% for a relatively pure 11 S component.   Two moles each of serine and glutamic acid and one mole each of glycine, valine, and leucine are the *N*-terminal amino acids per 300,000 molecular weight.   This would indicate a minimum of seven peptide chains.   Both the 7 S and 11 S components will associate, depending on the ionic strength, but there is no interconversion of the 11 S to the 7 S component once the 11 S component has been obtained pure.

There are no data to show whether the glycinin fraction is within particles in the soybean cotyledon and might properly be called an aleurin.   That the proteins in cotyledons are in subcellular particles was suggested by Bils and Howell (*5*), who studied the changes in the developing soybean cotyledon.   The protein particles are fragile and do not survive solvents which are satisfactory for the isolation of mitochondria, microsomes, and chloroplasts.

Peanuts.   About 90% of the proteins of peanut cotyledons are soluble in a dilute neutral buffer or 5% sodium chloride solution.   The classical fractionation of the salt-soluble protein is by precipitation with ammonium sulfate.   That fraction precipitating at 40% saturation was called "arachin" and the fraction precipitating in the range of 40 to 85% was called conarachin.   Neither of these fractions is pure, as noted from its ultracentrifuge pattern.   Their solutions give complex patterns on diethylaminoethyl-cellulose (*6*) and many components by polyacrylamide gel electrophoresis (*11*).   The major protein of the conarachin fraction was isolated by repeated chromatography on DEAE cellulose until homogeneous by chromatography, sedimentation, and almost pure (about 85%) by electrophoresis on polyacrylamide gel.   This fraction, named alpha-conarachin, associates and dissociates on the basis of ionic strength of the medium at pH 7.9.   At an ionic strength of 0.03 it has a sedimentation coefficient of 13.1 S; at an ionic strength of 0.5 it has a sedimentation coefficient of 7.8 S.   These give the approximate particle weights of 295,000 at low ionic strength and 142,000 at high ionic strength.

Dieckert *et al.* (*7*) homogenized cotyledonary tissue of the peanut in nonaqueous medium to prevent the rupture of protein bodies and isolated two fractions which contain 11 and 13% nitrogen, respectively. Although these fractions have similar protein composition as seen by chromatography on diethylaminoethylcellulose, one of them contains practically all the phytic acid. Electron micrographs of the isolated protein bodies are similar in appearance to those of sections of the tissue itself (*2*).

The protein bodies of the peanut are fragile and dissolve in 0.5*M* sucrose in buffer at pH 7.0. When unbuffered 0.25*M* sucrose was used one could isolate the protein body fraction. Protein bodies were obtained by macerating the peanut cotyledon in 0.05*M* citrate buffer at pH 5, and 0.25*M* in sucrose and 0.05*M* in sodium (ethylenedinitrilo) tetraacetic acid (*3*). A second particulate fraction was obtained by exposing the lighter particle to pH 6 for 18 hours at 4° C. The two fractions differed in their original patterns on diethylaminoethylcellulose and in their lipid content (the heavy fraction contained 8% lipid, whereas the pH 6 stable particle had 45% lipid); both particulate fractions contained 56% protein.

The protein obtained by this particulate method of separation was identical with the arachin fraction, except that the arachin ordinarily obtained by ammonium sulfate fractionation was the dimer; this particular method of isolation produced predominantly the monomer. Recently Tombs suggested that arachin exists in two variant forms (*22*).

The classical arachin fraction can be classified as an aleurin. The presence of two aleurin fractions might suggest that there are at least two different kinds of particles and several aleurins in the peanut. Alpha-conarachin, which is a major fraction of the peanut proteins and comprises approximately 25 to 30% of the total fraction, has not been isolated in particulate fractions.

Pea Protein. It has been known for some time that the major pea proteins are globulins. Varner and Schidlovsky (*24*) observed a large number of spherical bodies averaging 2 microns in diameter scattered throughout the cytoplasm of pea cotyledon in the early stages of germination. They designated these as protein bodies and observed that at various stages of development of the pea, the appearance of these bodies follows the course of globulin synthesis.

Hempseed. Edestin, the protein of hempseed (*Cannabis sativus*), was one of the first proteins to be isolated, since it is easily crystallized. Edestin is prepared by extracting defatted hempseed flour at 40° to 50° C. and then cooling the extract to 0° C. It has long been considered homogeneous, but obviously it is no purer than any of the other proteins mentioned.

One recent approach to its purification was by Stockwell *et al.* (*21*), who chromatographed edestin on DEAE cellulose at 50° C. and were able to obtain a fraction which shows an elution pattern of one peak upon rechromatography.   At relatively high ionic strength this protein has a sedimentation value of 13.4 S; this would approximate to a particle weight of 300,000.   The amino acid composition of edestin is given in Table III.

Table III.   Amino Acid Composition of Edestin

(G. of anhydro acid per 100 g. of protein)

Aspartic acid	11.02(*21*)	11.43(*15*)
Threonine	2.81	3.15
Serine	4.41	4.85
Glutamic acid	14.19	18.67
Proline	3.31	3.19
Glycine	3.33	3.81
Alanine	3.51	4.10
1/2 cystine	0.86	1.04
Valine	3.87	5.40
Methionine	1.60	2.14
Isoleucine	2.88	4.74
Leucine	4.78	6.78
Tyrosine	3.28	4.38
Tryptophan	1.46	1.12
Phenylalanine	3.97	5.64
Lysine	2.18	2.54
Histidine	2.57	2.54
Ammonia	2.54	2.53
		(amide N)
Arginine	14.29	15.48
Total	86.9	101.0

Another approach to purification was by Dlouhá *et al.* (*8*), who purified edestin by chromatography on diethylaminoethylcellulose in $6M$ urea at pH 6.9.   Their purified sample showed one elution peak by this technique and gave a molecular weight of 300,000.   They were able to effect further purification of this material by reductive cleavage according to the method of Swan, which yields S-sulfoedestin.   It gave two spots by electrophoresis on starch gel in urea buffer at pH 8.7: One component (A) moved to the anode and the other (B) to the cathode.   The two components were separated by chromatography on DEAE cellulose in urea-phosphate buffer of pH 9.   A high content of arginine, glutamic acid, and aspartic acid is characteristic of component A; much less of these are in component B. Neither contains any sugars.   On the basis of sedimentation they obtained molecular weights of 27,000 for A and 23,000 for B.   The A chain does not yield an N-terminal group and the B chain yields one mole of N-terminal glycine per mole of protein.   These authors believe that the edestin molecule is a unit of 300,000 molecular weight, which in turn is composed of six subunits, each of 50,000 molecular weight.   Each subunit in turn is composed of two polypeptide chains of molecular weights approximately 27,000 and 23,000 and connected by disulfide bonds.

Typical Major Seed Proteins

Eventually, it should be possible to relate proteins to certain biochemical functions and to classify proteins of seeds on the basis of their function. The first approach in that direction is to classify seed proteins on the basis of their association with subcellular structures and to divide the seed proteins into two classes: those within protein bodies, which can be separated as particulates, and those in the cytoplasmic matrix. At the moment, only a few proteins have definitely been shown to be aleurins. If for the sake of simplification, we equate the major proteins of seeds to the aleurins and take whatever information is now available about aleurins, we can present two prototypes of proteins that would represent the aleurins of seeds and their major proteins. One of these is the major protein of cereals as typified by gliadin of wheat and zein of corn. The other would be like the arachin of peanut or any of the major proteins of seeds other than the cereals.

No pure major protein has been isolated—that is, no seed protein has been isolated which shows homogeneity by three criteria simultaneously:

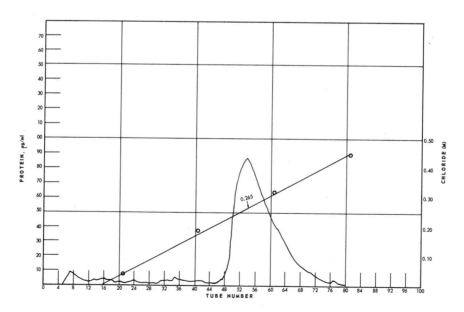

Figure 2. Chromatography of purified arachin fraction on diethylaminoethylcellulose Protein eluted with linear NaCl gradient, 0 to 0.6M, in phosphate buffer, pH 7.9, μ = 0.03

where ND-p Cals % = % net dietary protein calories

$$P = \% \text{ protein calories}$$

$$Pm = 400/\text{protein score}$$

The validity of Miller and Donoso's prediction equation is based upon a number of assumptions, one of which is that the amino acids in foods are available to the body. That this assumption may not always be valid is indicated by the studies of Miller and Carpenter (45), who reported that for a series of seven fish, meat, and whale meals, there was no correlation between the sulfur content and net protein utilization for rats, although the quality of the protein was limited by the sulfur amino acids. Cystine and methionine accounted for less than two thirds of the sulfur found in five of the seven samples. The digestibility of sulfur ranged from 53 to 90% and the product of sulfur amino acid content and sulfur digestibility correlated closely ($r = 0.93$) with values for NPU.

The studies of Miller and Carpenter (45) illustrate a principle which is becoming increasingly apparent—that the nutritional value of processed proteins cannot be predicted accurately from data on amino acid composi-

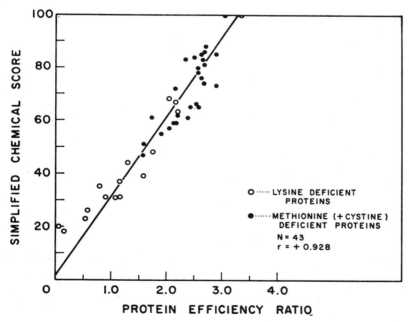

Figure 2.   Correlation between SCS and PER for 43 foods after adjustment of (methionine plus cystine) scores

Courtesy Canadian Journal Biochemistry

tion. It now is well established that, during processing, the amino acids of foods may be made partially unavailable to the body, with the result that the amounts of amino acids available for metabolic functions may represent only a small percentage of those present in the food protein. Continued population pressure on conventional food resources indicates that man will be forced to make ever-increasing use of highly processed protein foods, many of which now are used largely for fertilizer or animal feeds. In preparing such foods, careful attention must be paid to factors which influence the availability of the amino acids. It is not surprising, therefore, that many investigators have devoted considerable time and effort to develop procedures for measuring amino acid availability. This report summarizes available information on this important subject. No attempt has been made to provide an encyclopedic coverage of the literature. The scope of the paper has been restricted to a discussion of recent papers which illustrate important principles.

Table I.   Prediction of ND-p Cals % from Chemical Score Data for Canadian Meals

Meal	Protein Cal., %	Simplified Chemical Score	Limiting Amino Acids	ND-p Cals %		
					Calculated	
				Found	M^a	M & P^b
1	16.0	52	L	5.8	5.2	6.8
2	16.1	80	M + C	8.4	8.1	9.9
3	21.4	79	M + C	9.0	9.1	11.3
4	18.7	60	M + C	6.9	7.2	8.4
5	18.1	83	L	8.3	8.8	11.0
6	22.6	72	Tr	8.4	8.8	10.6

[a] (51).
[b] (49).

Evaluation of Amino Acid Availability

Chemical Methods. Perhaps the most useful chemical method developed thus far to measure amino acid availability is the procedure of Carpenter and Ellinger (7), which employs Sanger's reagent (61). It is based on the reaction of dinitrofluorobenzene (DNFB) with free amino groups in proteins. The ϵ-dinitrophenyllysine (ϵ-DNP lysine) released after subsequent hydrolysis is measured spectrophotometrically.

This simple procedure proved useful for estimating available lysine in a range of animal materials (6), but was affected significantly by interference from α-dinitrophenylarginine when applied to autolyzed materials and from dinitrophenol arising from the breakdown of excess DNFB if carbohydrates were present (10). Furthermore, vegetable foods may give rise to colors which interfere with the procedure. This interference was avoided by a modification (*4*) in which methoxycarbonyl chloride was used, but treatment with this reagent led to the unexpected development of a colored histidine derivative (*8*).

Conkerton and Frampton (*10*) took advantage of differences in the absorbance of dinitrophenol at 360 mμ in acid and alkaline media to correct for the dinitrophenol present in protein hydrolyzates. Other yellow substances such as dinitroaniline also may occur in the hydrolyzates of some dinitrophenylated proteins and introduce errors in colorimetric estimation of available lysine (*21*). The water-soluble imidazole-DNP histidine and *O*-DNP-tyrosine, which are colorless but absorb slightly at 360 mμ, are also likely to be found in dinitrophenylated protein hydrolyzates. In addition, the brown human pigments that occur in acid hydrolyzates of proteins may contribute to the error in estimating available lysine by the DNFB procedure.

Interference in the DNFB procedure from a colored histidine derivative was reduced by a modification of the method (*6*) which involved removal with diethyl ether of the lysine–methoxycarbonyl chloride reaction product, and use of the resultant "blank" value to correct for interference due to histidine. Suitable corrections were applied to allow for losses of DNP-lysine during the acid hydrolysis, by making use of the recovery of an internal standard of DNP-lysine added to the samples prior to hydrolysis. Handwerck *et al.* (*21*) observed that the conditions of the chemical procedure partly protected DNP-lysine from the destructive effect of acid hydrolysis in the presence of sugars. The protection was less effective with starch, in the presence of which the recovery of added DNP-lysine was only 74%, compared with a mean recovery of 92% obtained with animal products essentially free of carbohydrates (*6*).

In an attempt to overcome errors in the colorimetric estimation caused by interfering materials, Baliga *et al.* (*2*) resorted to a chromatographic separation of ϵ-DNP-lysine, followed by colorimetric estimation. The ϵ-DNP-lysine was separated from the other water-soluble DNP-amino acids on filter paper, using butanol–acetic acid–water (4:1:1) for irrigation. The ϵ-DNP-lysine, which separates as a heavy band with an R_f value of 0.6, was eluted with 1N HCl, the color density determined at 363 mμ, and the value read from a standard curve. The reaction with DNFB was carried out at 40°C. as recommended by Sanger (*61*). Attempts to use higher temperatures in hope of shortening the reaction time gave lower values, probably due to slow destruction of the DNP derivative.

Raghavendar Rao *et al.* (*60*) successfully used ion-exchange resin chromatography for separating ϵ-DNP-lysine quantitatively from other yellow and brown components in protein hydrolyzates. The column was developed with a mixture of methyl ethyl ketone and 3N aqueous HCl. Calculations of available lysine were made from measurement of absorbance at 435 mμ. The authors claim that the method lends itself to routine analysis, since one operator can carry out eight determinations simultaneously.

Carpenter's procedure using Sanger's reagent has been widely used by various workers for estimating available lysine in vegetable and animal products. There is a need for further modifications of the procedure for use with foods rich in carbohydrates to reduce their destructive effect on DNP-lysine during acid hydrolysis.

More recently, Mauron and Bujard (41) suggested guanidation as an alternative approach for determining available lysine in foods. Guanidation with o-methylisourea transforms lysine molecules with a free ϵ-amino group into homoarginine, which is stable during acid hydrolysis. The sample containing the protein is made to react with o-methylisourea, and the guanidinated proteins are precipitated with trichloroacetic acid and hydrolyzed with 6N HCl. The homoarginine present then is estimated by column chromatography. In lyophilized and spray-dried skim milk powder, about 95% of total lysine was converted to homoarginine and was therefore considered "available." In peanut flour, the homoarginine value was slightly lower than the corresponding ϵ-DNP-lysine value, but in soybean flour it was higher. From the limited data reported by Mauron, it is difficult to appraise the method fully, except to indicate that it appears promising.

Moran et al. (50) used the reaction of the dye Orange G with basic amino acids (16) to determine the availability of free amino, imidazole, and guanidyl groups of proteins. They noted that the dye-binding capacities of soybean meals heated for varying lengths of time were closely related to the growth of chicks fed the meals. Ascarelli and Gestetner (1) also found that the dye-binding capacity of soybean meal was a good measure of its biological value. In other studies, however, we could find no correlation between the ability of Canadian meals to bind Orange G and the nutritional value of the protein contained therein, as determined in the growing rat (51).

Suitable chemical procedures to evaluate the availability of sulfur amino acids have not been developed, although the need for them is obvious. It is possible that advantage may be taken of the reaction between CNBr and the free terminal methionine residues in a peptide chain (18). Cyanogen bromide can cleave methionine peptide bonds in proteins, producing cyanosulfonium derivatives of methionine, which under acidic conditions yield homoserine lactone. This substance can be determined colorimetrically. It is conceivable these reactions may serve as the basis for a rapid chemical procedure for determining available methionine.

Enzymatic Methods. In vitro enzymatic studies have demonstrated clearly that amino acid availability and amino acid content of foods may differ markedly. Comparative measurements of the enzymatic and chemical liberation of a number of amino acids have been made by numerous investigators, including Evans and Butts (*14*) using soybean protein and Hankes *et al.* (*22*) using casein. Evans and Butts (*14*) demonstrated that autoclaving soybean protein with sucrose for 4 hours did not seriously affect the in vitro enzymatic release of phenylalanine, threonine, leucine, isoleucine, and valine. Under the same test conditions, however, 84% of the lysine and 41% of the methionine were not released by enzymatic digestion of the protein-sucrose mixture. Approximately half of the loss of lysine was attributed to destruction and half to the formation of bonds within the protein molecule which resisted attack by proteolytic enzymes. The deterioration of methionine appeared to be caused by the formation of enzyme-resistant linkages within the protein molecule. In the study of Hankes *et al.* (*22*), casein was autoclaved for 20 hours in the absence of carbohydrates. The rate of release of lysine by enzymes was markedly reduced by the heat treatment, whereas other amino acids were not so severely affected.

In vitro analytical procedures for determining amino acid availability based on enzymatic release of amino acids from proteins have been deveoped by Sheffner *et al.* (*64*) and Mauron *et al.* (*43*).

Sheffner *et al.* (*64*) studied the relationship between the pattern of amino acids released by digestive enzymes and the biological value of food proteins. An amino acid index was described which attempts to take into account the physiological availability of amino acids during digestion. The index combines the pattern of essential amino acids released by in vitro pepsin digestion with the amino acid pattern of the pepsin-resistant residue to produce an integrated index termed the pepsin digest residue (PDR) amino acid index. PDR index values were closely correlated with NPU values for a variety of proteins. Division of the PDR index by the digestibility coefficient of the respective proteins yielded values which accurately predicted the biological value of the proteins studied, as determined by nitrogen balance techniques in the rat.

The conditions established by Sheffner *et al.* (*64*) for obtaining in vitro pepsin digests were determined from feeding experiments with rats, which indicated that approximately 30% of ingested egg protein nitrogen is absorbed before the chyme has reached the area of the intestine where tryptic activity is significant. The quantity of pepsin used and the duration of incubation in the in vitro procedure therefore were adjusted to produce approximately 30% release of microbiologically available essential amino acids from egg protein. With pepsin of the proper activity the conditions are such that small variations in time, temperature, and quantity of enzyme did not appear to cause significant variation in the results.

Although Sheffner's procedure appears to give results which agree with those found in the rat, the amount of work involved in the method renders it unacceptable for routine evaluation of available amino acids in foodstuffs.

The procedure of Mauron *et al.* (*43*) is concerned with measurement of only three essential amino acids—lysine, methionine, and tryptophan— the amino acids which are most likely to be limiting in foodstuffs. Briefly, the method is as follows:

The sample is first dialyzed against tap water to eliminate substances of low molecular weight and then digested in the dialysis bag with pepsin at 37° at pH 2. After 15 hours of pepsin digestion the sample is digested for 24 hours with pancreatin at 50° and pH 7 to 7.5. The dialyzed fractions containing the amino acids are siphoned every hour and analyzed by appropriate procedures. Tryptophan and methionine are determined colorimetrically, lysine with a specific decarboxylase, and amino nitrogen gasometrically.

This method has been extensively used by Mauron *et al.* (*42, 43*) for determining the availability of amino acids in processed foods of vegetable and animal origin and appears to provide useful information.

In Vivo Methods. Although in vitro results are of value in providing information on the release of amino acids, they obviously cannot be used directly as an index of availability in the intact animal. As a result, many investigators have used in vivo procedures to measure the availability of amino acids in foods. Schweigert and Guthneck (*20, 62, 63*) used the growth of protein-depleted rats and fecal excretion of amino acids to determine the availability of lysine and methionine in foods. Purified rations containing oxidized casein or sesame meal plus diammonium citrate and amino acids were used as basal diets deficient in methionine or lysine, respectively. The weight gains of protein-depleted rats receiving the basal rations plus graded levels of pure lysine and methionine were compared with those of animals given equivalent amounts of these amino acids in foods to provide an estimate of the availability of the protein-bound amino acid. The reproducibility of results obtained with different levels of the test product indicated that this procedure could be used to study the utilization or availability of amino acids from foods. Since Schweigert's early studies, growth procedures using rats or chicks have been used by many investigators to determine the availability of amino acids in foods. Factors influencing availability values obtained from growth studies have been reviewed by Harper and de Muelenaere (*23*), and are therefore not described here in detail.

Kuiken and Lyman (*27*) estimated the availability of the ten essential amino acids in different foods by measuring the excretion of amino acids in the feces. The amounts of endogenous amino acids in the feces were calculated from control periods during which the animals received a low-protein diet containing small amount of egg protein. Using this technique, Kuiken (*26*) later demonstrated effects of processing on the availability of essential amino acids in cottonseed meal. Watts *et al.* (*67, 68, 69*) evaluated amino acid availability in human subjects following a procedure similar to that of Kuiken and Lyman (*27*).

The interpretation of any study involving the amino acid content of feces is limited by the inability to measure the extent of degradation and synthesis of amino acids by intestinal bacteria. Intestinal microorganisms may alter the amino acid distribution in food residues as they pass through the intestine. Furthermore, endogenous losses of amino acids by subjects receiving a low-protein diet may be markedly different from those of the same subjects receiving an adequate diet. The problems of relating availability to fecal excretion of amino acids are even more difficult in coprophagic animals, such as the rat, where fecal amino acids may be recycled through the animal.

The availability of an amino acid in foods also can be determined by measuring nitrogen balance during alternate periods of feeding a basal diet supplemented with equivalent amounts of the amino acid in free or protein-bound form (*34*). Using this technique, Linkswiler *et al.* (*31, 32, 33*) showed that valine, threonine, and isoleucine in corn are fully available to man. The nitrogen balance method is time-consuming and expensive since large quantities of pure essential amino acids are required. At the same time, it suffers from the defects usually associated with a nitrogen balance study. Specifically, it may be questioned whether the nitrogen balance technique is sufficiently sensitive to detect relatively small changes in availability since a number of rat growth studies indicate isoleucine to be partially unavailable in corn (*11*).

Plasma Amino Acid Methods. Early studies by Wheeler and Morgan (*70*) and Guggenheim *et al.* (*19*) indicated that the levels of free amino acids in the plasma after a test meal may provide information on the in vivo availability of the dietary amino acids. Investigations carried out in our laboratory (*38*) on adult humans showed that peak plasma lysine and methionine levels were much higher after a meal of alcohol-extracted fish solids, than after a meal of fish extracted with 1,2-dichloroethane. The latter sample was known from other studies to contain unavailable amino acids (*52, 54*). Smith and Scott (*65, 66*) reported that chicks fed overheated fish meal had lower plasma concentrations of lysine and threonine than those receiving unheated fish meal. In other studies with rats, McLaughlan (*39*) observed a high degree of correlation between plasma levels of lysine, methionine, tryptophan, leucine, isoleucine, and phenylalanine and the amounts of these amino acids in a test meal. Data which illustrate those findings are summarized in Figure 3. From the preliminary information available, therefore, it appears that measurement of plasma amino acid levels may provide a very useful index of the availability of amino acids in vivo.

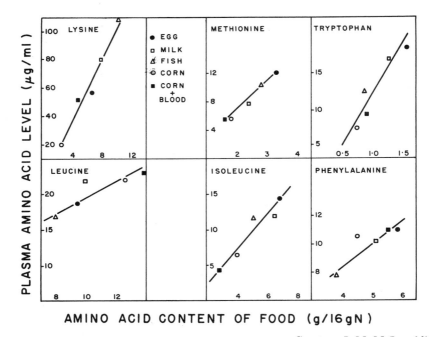

Courtesy J. M. McLaughlin

Figure 3. Relation between plasma amino acid level and amino acid content of foods

Microbiological Methods. *Streptococcus symogenes* NCDO592, a vigorously proteolytic micro-organism, was used by Ford (*15*) to measure the biological availability of methionine, histidine, leucine, isoleucine, arginine, tryptophan, and valine in different food proteins. The foods were hydrolyzed with papain before assay with the microorganism. Ford (*15*) recommended use of 1 ml. of 1% solution of crude papain for each 100 mg. of nitrogen in the sample. Values obtained for available amino acids in 12 samples of whale meal correlated closely with each other, with NPU values, and with available lysine values obtained for the same materials by Bunyan and Price (*5*).

A number of workers (*9, 57*) have noted that the extent of hydrolysis of the test protein by papain exerts a profound effect on the amount of available methionine as determined by Ford's procedure. In order to obtain consistent results, therefore, it is necessary to define closely the conditions of papain predigestion and to use that amount which gives results correlating closely with available methionine values determined from studies in higher animals. For example, Miller *et al.* (*46*) noted that estimation of available methionine by treatment with 0.09% crude papain followed by *Strep. zymogenes* assay significantly underestimated the chick

value for available methionine by 28%.   The values obtained after treatment with 0.36% papain, however, were not significantly different from
those found in the chick.   The close correlation between the microbiological
and chick values for available methionine is shown in Figure 4, taken
from the paper of Miller *et al.* (*46*).   These results show that assay of
available methionine with *Strep. zymogenes* following papain predigestion
can provide useful information on the availability to the growing animal
of methionine in highly processed animal feeds.   Nevertheless, because
of the danger in extrapolating from results obtained with microorganisms
to those found with higher animals, it is necessary to check microbiological
values against those found in animal assays for the products in question.

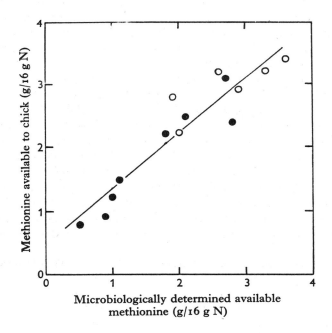

Courtesy British Journal of Nutrition

*Figure 4.   Relation between values obtained biologically (chick)
and microbiologically (Streptococcus zymogenes) for available
methionine in protein concentrates*

*Response metameter for calculating results of chick assays was food conversion efficiency.
Microbiological values obtained by assays with Strep. zymogenes after predigestion with
0.36% crude papain.*
   ○ *Laboratory preparation of cod muscle.*
   ● *Commercial meat, fish, and whale meals.*
   *Least squares regression line, chick value = 0.49 + 0.87 (microbiological value), also
shown.*

Some Recent Problems

Effects of Solvents. Although it is well established that excessive heating during processing may reduce the availability of amino acids in foods, relatively little attention has been paid to the effects of other processing variables on the nutritional value of proteins. It is becoming increasingly apparent, however, that careful attention must also be paid to the effects of other conditions of processing on the biological availability of amino acids in foods. This is illustrated by recent studies on fish protein concentrate (FPC), a highly processed food which represents a potentially important source of high quality protein for use in underdeveloped areas of the world. Many investigators (44, 53) have observed marked variability in nutritional quality of the protein in samples of FPC produced by various procedures from different species of fish. Morrison and Sabry (55) reported that measurements of net protein ratio and PER indicated marked variability in the nutritional value of the protein in eight samples of FPC. The availability of lysine in the samples was examined by in vitro digestion studies, animal growth assays, and Carpenter's DNFB procedure (6) (Table II). One sample (Sample S) which from its color appeared to have been damaged by excessive heating during processing, contained unavailable lysine, as shown by the DNFB procedure, reduced release of lysine during enzymic digestion of the sample, and rat bioassay results. Another sample (Sample Z) also showed a relatively low content of available lysine as determined by the DNFB procedure. The ratio of available lysine to total lysine in this sample was not reduced, however, and rat studies using two bioassay procedures did not indicate reduction in lysine availability. These findings illustrate the obvious fact that reduced values for available lysine obtained with the DNFB procedure may not necessarily indicate a reduction in avail-

Table II. Content and Availability of Lysine in Fish Flours

Sample	Acid hydrolysis	Enzyme hydrolysis	DNFB	% Availability by Bioassay	Gross Protein Value
	Method				
	Lysine Content, G./16 G. N				
X	8.7	5.8	7.4	88	$5.99 + 0.44^a (101)^b$
Y	7.1	4.7	6.5	95	$5.72 + 0.70$ (97)
Z	6.7	4.6	6.0	92	$4.28 + 0.29$ (72)
S	7.0	2.9	5.3	61	$2.85 + 0.66$ (48)
T	8.8	5.0	7.1	83	$5.72 + 0.48$ (97)
U	8.9	5.4	6.9	85	$5.97 + 0.48$ (101)
V	9.1	5.5	7.1	94	$5.41 + 0.34$ (92)
W	8.7	5.2	7.0	100	$5.97 + 0.54$ (101)

[a] Standard error.
[b] Percentage of value for casein.

ability of lysine but merely a reduction in total amount of lysine present in the sample.

Morrison and Sabry (*55*) also examined the availability of the sulfur amino acids in the eight samples of FPC mentioned above. The results (Table III) showed that total methionine values varied from 2.5 grams per 16 grams of nitrogen (samples Z and S) to 3.2 grams per 16 grams of nitrogen (sample V) where as cystine levels varied from 0.6 to 1.0 gram per 16 grams of nitrogen.   The amount of methionine released by enzymatic digestion of Sample S was less than that from the other samples.   The procedure used involved treatment with the triple enzyme system of Wooley and Sebrell (*71*), followed by assay with a proteolytic strain of *Strep. zymogenes*.   The in vitro results gave no indication that Sample X contained unavailable sulfur amino acids.   Gross protein values determined on a methionine-deficient basal diet, however, indicated that Samples S and X contained unavailable sulfur amino acids.   Furthermore, total methionine plus cystine values correlated closely with PER values for all samples except S and X.   The in vitro procedure used, therefore, gave a misleading impression as to the biological availability of the amino acids in Sample X.   They indicate that microbiological procedures for available methionine may not reflect the availability of this amino acid to the animal and should be used with caution, unless a correlation with animal results has been established for the particular products being tested.

Table III.   Methionine and Cystine in Fish Flours

	(G./16 G. N)		
Sample	Methionine		Cystine
	Acid Hydrolysis	Enzyme Hydrolysis	Acid Hydrolysis
X	3.0	3.0	1.0
Y	2.8	2.3	0.8
Z	2.5	2.1	0.7
S	2.5	1.4	0.6
T	3.1	2.8	1.0
U	3.0	2.6	0.8
V	3.2	3.0	1.0
W	3.0	2.8	1.0

In subsequent studies (*52, 54*), it was observed that the weight gains of rats fed FPC Sample X were markedly increased by adding histidine and methionine to the diet.   The amounts of methionine and histidine released during in vitro digestion with pancreatin were much less for Sample X than for a sample of FPC which was of high nutritional value (Table IV).   Steaming Sample X for 30 minutes significantly increased its gross protein value determined in a methionine-deficient diet.

Table IV.   Histidine and Methionine in Fish Flours X and CFF

Sample	Methionine, G./16 G. N		Histidine, G /16 G. N	
	Acid	Enzyme	Acid	Enzyme
X	3.30	1.48	1.60	0.49
CFF	3.34	2.07	2.10	1.15

Although relatively little information was available on the processing history of Sample X, it was known that the material had been prepared in a pilot plant by azeotropic extraction with 1, 2-dichloroethane. It is well established that alkyl halides can react with sulfhydryl groups of reduced wool (*17*, *59*), cysteine, and glutathione (*36*), to produce thioethers. *S*-(Dichlorovinyl)-L-cysteine, prepared by reaction of trichloroethylene with the disodium salt of L-cysteine in liquid ammonia, produces an aplastic anemia in calves and has been implicated as the toxic factor in trichloroethylene-extracted soybean meal (*37*). Studies were conducted, therefore, to determine whether 1,2-dichloroethane or other solvents can react with the protein of fish solids during production of FPC (*54*). As shown in Table V, extraction of freeze-dried cod fillets with 1,2-dichloroethane resulted in destroying cystine and histidine and interfering with the release of cystine, histidine, and methionine by pancreatic digestion. Hexane, ethanol, and isopropyl alcohol had no effects on the amino acids in fish solids. The reaction was pH—dependent, occuring most readily under slightly alkaline conditions. The thioether *S,S'*-ethylenebiscysteine was synthesized by reaction of cysteine and 1,2-dichloroethane. The reaction involved apparently takes place as follows:

$$2(\text{R-SH}) + (\text{Cl-CH}_2)_2 \rightarrow \text{R-S-CH}_2\text{-CH}_2\text{-S-R} + 2\,\text{HCl}$$

$$\text{where R} = \text{CH}_2\text{-CH(NH}_2)\text{-COOH}$$

Alkylation of reduced wool or fish solids, and subsequent hydrolysis, yielded a sulfur-containing compound with the same R_f value as the synthetic thioether. The thioether appeared devoid of biological activity for *L. mesenteroides* P–60, *Tetrahymena pyriformis* W, and the rat. It was cleaved by autoclaving but stable to acid hydrolysis.

These studies suggest that sulfhydryl groups of protein can be alkylated by 1,2-dichloroethane to produce thioether linkages, which resist hydrolysis by proteolytic enzymes. Although relatively little is known concerning the actual mechanisms by which enzymes attach to protein substrates, it is possible that the reduced susceptibility to hydrolysis may be related, in part, to a reduction in the number of substrate sulfhydryl groups available as points of attachment for enzyme molecules. Furthermore, if thioether bridges are established between adjacent peptide chains, it is conceivable that the susceptibility of these peptides to proteolytic attack may be lessened.

The studies mentioned above establish clearly the important effects which solvents can exert on the availability of amino acids in foods and indicate the importance of careful evaluation of possible nutritional effects of chemicals used in processing foods.

Effects of Smoking and Salting.   Dvorak and Vognarova (*13*) reported recently that the available lysine content of meat, as measured by Carpenter's DNFB procedure (*6*), was decreased markedly in products which had been smoked for 1 to 2 days.   The amount of available lysine decreased proportionately with the amount of smoke used.   In in vitro studies, a linear relationship was found between the amount of available lysine and the concentration of formaldehyde, which is one of the constituents of wood smoke.   The NPU of raw beef fillet was found to be 73, whereas that of formaldehyde-treated beef fillet was only 58.   Dvorak and Vognarova (*13*) concluded that the effects of formaldehyde were related to its ability to react with the free α-amino groups of lysine molecules in beef protein.   Similarly, sodium nitrite, used for curing meat to obtain a desirable color, destroyed lysine by reaction with the free α-amino group.   Since the amount of nitrite normally added to meat products is small, the reduction in available lysine content caused by nitrite addition is probably not of practical significance.

In contrast to the results obtained by Dvorak and Vognarova (*13*). Munro and Morrison (*56*) could detect no effect of salting and smoking on the biological value of cod protein, as indicated by PER and gross protein values, total lysine and methionine content, available lysine values, and plasma free lysine and methionine levels in human subjects given the fish products.   Undoubtedly, the effects of smoking on available lysine values are related to the amount of smoke to which the protein is exposed, as well as to other factors.

Table V.   Effects of Extracting Fish Protein for 16 Hours with Various Solvents on Methionine, Histidine, and Cystine Content

Solvent	Methionine, G./16 G. N		Histidine, G./16 G. N		Cystine, G./16 G. N	
	Acid	Enzyme	Acid	Enzyme	Acid	Enzyme
Nil	3.6	2.33	2.67	1.24	0.97	0.46
Hexane	3.1	1.76	2.30	0.88	0.92	0.42
Isopropyl alcohol	3.3	1.88	2.32	1.15	0.92	0.40
Ethylene dichloride	3.2	0.48	1.73	0.33	0.54	0.09
Ethanol	3.4	1.96	2.38	1.15	0.90	0.39

Differential Effects on Availability of Amino Acids. Under specific processing conditions, the availability of certain amino acids may be affected more than that of others. Heating casein with glucose, for example, markedly reduces its nutritional value (*24, 35*), and the nutritional damage is largely corrected by supplementing with lysine (*25, 42*). It has been postulated (*30*) that the reaction between proteins and sugars involves condensation of the carbonyl groups of the sugar with free amino groups of the protein to yield indigestible linkages. Considerable evidence exists that these linkages can be formed even under mild conditions (*28, 29*). Since lysine still contains a second reactive amino group even when its α-amino moiety is linked into the natural peptide chain, it is not surprising that this amino acid reacts readily with sugars.

Recently, Donoso *et al.* (*12*) heated pork protein with an equal weight of water, for 24 hours at 110°. The material contained tritium-labeled lysine, which was used to observe the fate of lysine in rats fed the heated protein. Chemical analysis showed losses of dry weight, nitrogen, sulfur, and all the essential amino acids. There was a 20% loss of lysine and a 25% loss of methionine plus cystine. The loss of cystine (44%) was particularly severe. The specific activity of the feces of rats fed the heated protein indicated reduced digestibility of lysine in the material. In contrast to the results with lysine, the observed reduced utilization of the sulfur and nitrogen of the heated protein was due to reduction in the biological value thereof. In other words, the unutilized portion of lysine was found in the feces, whereas the equivalent fractions of nitrogen and sulfur were found in the urine.

In more recent work, Narayana Rao *et al.* (*57*) utilized the casein-glucose system to determine whether specific types of heat treatment preferentially affect the availability of lysine or the sulfur amino acids. As shown in Table VI, they noted that autoclaving, or dry heating at 37° C. or 85° C., caused marked reductions in the amount of available lysine, as determined by the DNFB method, and smaller differences in available methionine levels. Narayana Rao *et al.* (*57*) concluded from their studies and those of previous workers that mild heating of materials rich in reducing sugars, such as milk, causes a greater fall in available lysine than in available methionine. In contrast, heating materials low in reducing sugars results in nutritional damage only if the conditions of heating are severe, and the fall in available methionine then is at least as great as that in available lysine. A simple explanation for these effects would be that in the presence of reducing sugars, even mild heating results in reactions with free amino groups, primarily those of lysine. When reducing sugars are absent, however, severe conditions are necessary to cause nutritional damage, which may result from internal ester or amide formation, or crosslinkage by hydrogen or S-S bonding. More resistant bonds

whose nature is not well understood also may be formed, as suggested
by Donoso *et al.* *(12)* and previous workers.

Table VI.   Available Lysine and Methionine in Casein-Glucose Mixtures

Test Material	Amino Acids, G./16 G. N		
	Total methionine	Available methionine	Available lysine
No. 1 (control)	4.1	3.1	5.4
No. 2 (85° C. for 40 min.)	4.2	2.8	4.2
No. 3 (37° C. for 10 days)	4.1	2.7	2.4
No. 4 (autoclaving at 15 p.s.i. for 30 min.)	4.4	2.4	2.1

Selection of Availability Procedure   It is pertinent, in view of
the preceding discussion, to ask which availability procedure to use in
evaluating protein foodstuffs.   Miller *et al.* *(47)* have pointed out that
available methionine values for animal protein concentrates correlated
closely with those for available lysine.   They suggested that either the
chemical estimation of available lysine or the microbiological procedure
with *Strep. zymogenes* for available methionine will not only assess the
particular amino acid involved but also give an indication of the over-all
value of an animal protein concentrate.

However, the type of food involved and the processing procedures
undergone by it will determine whether or not a particular test can predict
the over-all protein value.   For example, evidence cited above indicated
that the solvent used in processing FPC can exert specific effects on the
sulfur amino acids, and that in such products, measurement of available
lysine may provide a misleading estimate of the nutritive value of the
protein.   Similarly, in foods which contain appreciable amounts of reducing sugars, the nutritional damage caused by moderate amounts of
heat during processing appears to be related primarily to binding of lysine.
In such products, measurement of available lysine would appear to provide
a more valid estimate of nutritional damage than is provided by available
methionine values.   It is difficult to escape the conclusion that recom-
mendations regarding the most suitable availability test must apply only
to a given product processed in a specific manner.

Literature Cited

(1) Ascarelli, I. Gestetner, B., *J. Sci. Food Agr.* **13**, 401 (1962).
(2) Baliga, B. P., Bayliss, M. E., Lyman, C. M., *Arch Biochem. Biophys.* **84**, 1 (1959).
(3) Block, R. J., Mitchell, H. H., *Nutr. Abst. Revs.* **16**, 249 (1946–47).

(4) Bruno, D., Carpenter, K. J., *Biochem. J.* **67**, 13 (1957).
(5) Bunyan, J., Price, S. A., *J. Sci. Food Agr.* **11**, 25 (1960).
(6) Carpenter, K. J., *Biochem. J.* **77**, 604 (1960).
(7) Carpenter, K. J., Ellinger, G. M., *Ibid.*, **61**, xi-xii (1955).
(8) Carpenter, K. J., Jones, W. L., Mason, E. L., *Ibid.*, **73**, 11 (1959).
(9) Carpenter, K. J., Lea, C. H., Parr, L. J., *Brit. J. Nutr.* **17**, 151 (1963).
(10) Conkerton, E. J., Frampton, V. L., *Arch, Biochem. Biophys.* **81**, 130 (1959).
(11) Deshpande, P. D., Harper, A. E., Collins, M., Elvehjem, C. A., *Ibid.*, **67**, 341 (1957).
(12) Donoso, G., Lewis, O. A. M., Miller, D. S., Payne, P. R., *J. Sci. Food Agr.* **13**, 192 (1962).
(13) Dvorak, Z., Vognarova, I., *Ibid.*, **16**, 305 (1965).
(14) Evans, R. J., Butts, H. A., *J. Biol. Chem.* **178**, 543 (1949).
(15) Ford, J. E., *Brit. J. Nutr.* **16**, 409 (1962).
(16) Fraenkel-Conrat, H., Cooper, M., *J. Biol. Chem.* **154**, 239 (1944).
(17) Geiger, W. B., Kobayashi, F. F., Harris, M., *J. Res. Natl. Bur. Std.* **29**, 381 (1942).
(18) Gross, E., Witkop, B., *J. Biol. Chem.* **237**, 1856 (1962).
(19) Guggenheim, K., Halevy, S., Friedmann, N., *Arch. Biochem. Biophys.* **91**, 6 (1960).
(20) Guthneck, B. T., Bennett, B. A., Schweigert, B. S., *J. Nutr.* **49**, 289 (1953).
(21) Handwerck, V., Bujard, E., Mauron, J., *Biochem. J.* **76**, 54 (1960).
(22) Hankes, L. V., Riesen, W. H., Henderson, L. M., and Elvehjem, C. A., *J. Biol. Chem.* **176**, 467 (1948).
(23) Harper, A. E., de Muelenaere, H. J. H., *Proc. V. Intern. Congr. Biochem.* **8**, 82 (1963).
(24) Henry, K. M., Kon, S. K., *Biochem. Biophys. Acta* **5**, 455 (1950).
(25) Henry, K. M., Kon, S. K., *J. Dairy Res.* **15**, 341 (1947–48).
(26) Kuiken, K. A., *J. Nutr.* **46**, 13 (1952).
(27) Kuiken, K. A., Lyman, C. M., *Ibid.*, **36**, 359 (1948).
(28) Lea, C. H., Hannan, R. S., *Biochim. Biophys. Acta.* **4**, 518 (1950).
(29) *Ibid.*, **5**, 433 (1950).
(30) Liener, I. E., "Processed Plant Protein Foodstuffs" A. M. Altschul ed. p, 79, Academic Press, New York, 1958.
(31) Linkswiler, H., Fox, H. M., Fry, P. C., *J. Nutr.* **72**, 389 (1960).
(32) *Ibid.*, p 397.
(33) Linkswiler, H., Fox, H. M., Geschwender, D., Fry, P. C., *Ibid.*, **65**, 455 (1958).
(34) Linkswiler, H., Geschwender, D., Ellison, J., Fox, H. M., *Ibid.* **65**, 441 (1958).
(35) McInray, E. E., Murer, H. K., Thiessen, R., *Arch. Biochem.* **20**, 256 (1949).
(36) McKinney, L. L., Eldridge, A. C., Cowan, J. C., *J. Am. Chem. Soc.* **81**, 1423 (1959).
(37) McKinney, L. L., Weakley, F. B., Campbell, R. E., Eldridge, A. C., Cowan, J. C., Picken, J. C., Jr Jacobson, N. L., *J. Am. Oil Chemists Soc.* **34**, 461 (1957).
(38) McLaughlan, J. M., *Federation Proc.* **22**, 1122 (1963).
(39) McLaughlan, J. N., unpublished research.
(40) McLaughlan, J. M., Rogers, C. G , Chapman, D. G., Campbell, J A., *Can. J. Biochem. Physiol.* **37**, 1293 (1959).
(41) Mauron, J., Bujard, E., *Proc. Int. Congr. Nutr.* (*Edinburgh*), 167 (1963).
(42) Mauron, J., Mottu, F., *Arch. Biochem. Biophys.* **77**, 312 (1958).
(43) Mauron, J., Mottu, F., Bujard, E., Egli, R. H., *Ibid.*, **59**, 433 (1955).
(44) Miller, D. S., *J. Sci. Food Agr.* **1**, 337 (1956).
(45) Miller, E. L., Carpenter, K. J., *Ibid.*, **15**, 810 (1964).

(46) Miller, E. L., Carpenter, K. J., Morgan, C. B., Bayne, A. W., *Brit. J. Nutr.* **19,** 249 (1965).

(47) Miller, D. S., Donoso, G., *J. Sci. Food Agr.* **14,** 345 (1963).

(48) Miller, D. S., Naismith, D. J., *Nature* **182,** 1786 (1958).

(49) Miller, D. S., Payne, R. R., *Brit. J. Nutr.* **15,** 11 (1961).

(50) Moran, E. T., Jr., Jensen, L. S., McGinnis, J., *J. Nutr.* **79,** 239 (1963).

(51) Morrison, A. B., *Can. Federation Proc.* **8,** 61 (1965).

(52) Morrison, A. B., *Can. J. Biochem. Physiol.* **41,** 1589 (1963).

(53) Morrison, A. B., McLaughlan, J. M., *Can. J. Biochem. Physiol.* **39,** 511 (1961).

(54) Morrison, A. B., Munro, I. C., *Ibid.,* **43,** 33 (1965).

(55) Morrison, A. B., Sabry, Z. I., *Ibid.,* **41,** 649 (1963).

(56) Munro, I. C., Morrison, A. B., *J. Fish. Res. Bd. Canada* **22,** 544 (1963).

(57) Narayana Rao, M., Sreenivas, H., Swaminathan, M., Carpenter, K. J., Morgan, C. B., *J. Sci. Food Agr.* **14,** 544 (1963).

(58) Osborne, T. B., Mendel, L. B., *J. Biol. Chem.* **17,** 325 (1914).

(59) Patterson, W. I., Geiger, W. B., Mizell, L. R., Harris, M., *J. Res. Natl. Bur. Std.* **27,** 89 (1941).

(60) Raghavendar Rao, S., Carter, F. L., Frampton, V. L., *Anal. Chem.* **35,** 1927 (1963).

(61) Sanger, F., *Biochem. J.* **39,** 507 (1945).

(62) Schweigert, B. S., Guthneck, B., *J. Nutr.* **49,** 277 (1953).

(63) *Ibid.,* **54,** 333 (1954).

(64) Sheffner, A. L., Eckfeldt, G. A., Spector, H., *Ibid.,* **60,** 105 (1956).

(65) Smith, R. E., Scott, H. M., *Ibid.,* **86,** 37 (1965).

(66) *Ibid.,* p. 45.

(67) Watts, J. H., Allen, C. H., Booker, L. K., *J. Am. Dietet. Assoc.* **36,** 42 (1960).

(68) Watts, J. H., Booker, L. K., McAfee, J. W., Graham, D. C. W., Jones, F., Jr. *J. Nutr.* **67,** 497 (1959).

(69) Watts, J. H., Booker, L. K., McAfee, J. W., Williams, E. G., Wright, W. G., Jones, F., Jr., *Ibid.,* **67,** 483 (1959).

(70) Wheeler, P., Morgan, A. F., *Ibid.,* **64,** 137 (1958).

(71) Wooley, J. G., Sebrell, W. H., *J. Biol. Chem.* **157,** 141 (1945)

RECEIVED November 1, 1965.

13

Toxic Substances Associated with Seed Proteins

IRVIN E. LIENER

Department of Biochemistry, University of Minnesota, St. Paul, Minn.

The trypsin inhibitors and hemagglutinins of legumes are examples of proteins implicated in the poor nutritive value of unheated plant material. A number of amino acid derivatives are the active principles responsible for various forms of lathyrism which accompany the ingestion of peas belonging to genus Lathyrus. Among the glycosides, goiterogenic agents have been isolated from various cruciferous oil seeds, and cyanogenetic glycosides have been demonstrated in lima beans, linseed meal, and other legumes. Glycosides in soybeans include the saponins, which have hemolytic properties, and the isoflavones, with esterogenic activity. Among the miscellaneous toxic factors are gossypol (cottonseed), the causative agent of favism, the metal-binding constituent of soybean protein, and antivitamin factors in some legumes.

It is ironic that while Nature has generously provided man with a liberal supply of plant protein foods, she has at the same time seen fit to contaminate these foods with a variety of substances which may be considered "toxic" to the animal body. In our present discussion I do not wish to restrict myself to a definition of "toxic" that a toxicologist might use—a substance which when administered to an animal produces death at a certain level which is expressed in terms of an LD_{50}. Rather I would prefer, for want of a better term, the phrase "antinutritional" to describe any adverse physiological response which is produced by the ingestion of a particular plant protein, whether it be an acute lethal effect resulting in death, or a chronic effect resulting in poor growth or some glandular disorder.

It would manifestly be impossible to include a detailed coverage of all of the deleterious substances that are known to be present in plant materials. I concern myself here only with plants whose seeds have present or potential value as a source of protein for human feeding.   This will include such important oil-bearing seeds as the soybean, peanut, cottonseed, and a number of beans and peas which form an important part of the diet in India, Africa, Central and South America, and the Mediterranean countries. Although the subject of toxic substances in legumes has been reviewed (*31*), the present paper brings the subject matter up to date and emphasizes the chemical aspects of the problem.

From the point of the chemist, these toxic substances may be classified into three main categories as shown in Table I: proteins or protein derivatives, glycosides, and a miscellaneous group of substances of diverse but, in most cases, unknown chemical structure.

Table I.   Antinutritional Factors in Seed Proteins

I.   Proteins or amino acid derivatives
  1. Trypsin inhibitors
  2. Hemagglutinins
  3. Osteolathyrogens
  4. Neurolathyrogens

II.   Glycosides
  5. Goiterogens
  6. Cyanogens
  7. Saponins
  8. Isoflavone glycosides

III.   Miscellaneous
  9. Gossypol
  10. Causative principle of favism
  11. Metal-binding factor
  12. Antivitamin factors

Proteins and Protein Derivatives

Trypsin Inhibitors.   Perhaps the best known and certainly the most studied of all of the antinutritional factors is a trypsin inhibitor first isolated from the soybean by Kunitz in 1945 (*28*).   This is a protein having a molecular weight of about 20,000, and it forms an inactive complex with trypsin.   Since Osborne and Mendel in 1917 (*47*) had noted that raw soybeans supported growth poorly unless subjected to heat treatment, it was logical to assume that the trypsin inhibitor was the substance responsible for the poor nutritive value of the unheated bean. The hypothesis that its effect could be readily explained on the basis of its ability to inhibit intestinal proteolysis was an appealing one.   The fact that methionine also markedly improved the nutritive value of raw soybeans (Table II) was taken to indicate that the trypsin inhibitor somehow interfered with the availability or utilization of methionine from the raw legume.

Table II.   Effect of Heat and Methionine on Nutritive Value
of Soybeans (*34*)

Diet	Protein Efficiency
Raw soybean meal	1.33
Autoclaved soybean meal	2.62
Raw soybean meal + 0.6% methionine	2.42

It now appears that the explanation for the growth-inhibiting property of the trypsin inhibitor is not a simple one, and, although 20 years have elapsed since Kunitz first isolated his trypsin inhibitor, there is still a decided lack of agreement as to the mechanism whereby the trypsin inhibitor exerts its effect.   Furthermore, there are at least four trypsin inhibitors (*52*), and it is not certain whether all four produce the same physiological effects.   There is little doubt that pancreatic hypertrophy is one of the primary physiological effects of feeding raw soybean (*12*). Booth *et al.* (*7*) are of the opinion that pancreatic hypertrophy leads to an excessive loss of endogenous protein in the form of exocrine protein secreted by the pancreas.   Since this protein is rich in cystine, this represents a net loss of cystine from the body.   This increased need for cystine for protein biosynthesis during pancreatic hypertrophy is reflected by an increase in the conversion of methionine to cystine in the pancreas (*4*).   This would explain why the need for methionine is particularly acute in diets containing raw soybeans.

Trypsin inhibitors have also been found in a large number of other legumes including the peanut, navy bean, lima bean, and the various grams and pulses eaten in India, but the exact nutritional significance of these inhibitors is not clear.   In fact there appears to be no clear-cut correlation between the trypsin inhibitor content of legumes and the beneficial effect of heat on their nutritional value (*8*).

Hemagglutinins.   It was this lack of correlation that led our own laboratory to search for some other factor in legumes which might account for the poor growth-promoting quality of most legumes which are not heated.   We succeeded in isolating from raw soybeans a protein which had the rather peculiar property of being able to cause red blood cells to agglutinate (*35*).   Such substances have been known for some time to be present in many plants and are referred to as phytohemagglutinins (*32*).   Some of these are highly toxic, such as ricin from the castor bean (*62*).   Another fairly well known hemagglutinin is concanavalin A, which was first crystallized from the jack bean by Sumner (*61*).   Landsteiner had reported many years ago that even such common edible legumes as the navy bean, lentil, and garden pea also contained these hemagglutinins (*32*).

Until we got interested in the hemagglutinins over 10 years ago, the nutritional significance of these substances was largely overlooked.

In 1953 we showed that the purified soybean hemagglutinin was capable of significantly inhibiting the growth of rats (Table III).   It would appear, however, from the work of Birk and Gertler (*6*) that the growth impairment of rats and chicks fed raw soybean meal may be due largely to factors

Table III.   Growth-Inhibitory Effect of the Soybean Hemagglutinin (SBH) (*33*)

Protein Component of Diet	Wt. Gain in 2 Weeks, G.	% Growth Inhibition
25% heated soybean meal	60.0	0
25% raw soybean meal	28.0	43.2
25% heated soybean meal + 0.8% SBH	45.0	25.6

other than the soybean hemagglutinin.   These authors reported that the insoluble residue which remained after extraction of the raw meal with acid at pH 4.2 retained the capacity to inhibit growth, despite the fact that this fraction exhibited little hemagglutinating activity.

Table IV compares some of the physical properties of the soybean hemagglutinin (SBH) with ricin and concanavalin A.   SBH has been shown to be a mucoprotein containing about 5 to 6% carbohydrate, made up largely of mannose and glucosamine (*37*, *64*).   It also appears to be composed of two chains with alanine residues at each of the N-termini and serine and alanine at the C-termini (*64*).

Table IV.   Comparison of the Physical Properties of SBH with Ricin and Concanavalin A

Hemagglutinin	Source	Sedimentation Constant, $S_{20, w}$	Diffusion Constant, $D_{20, w}$	Mol. Weight	Isoelectric Point, pH	Ref.
SBH	Soybean	6.4	5.7	96,000	6.1	(*48*)
Ricin	Castor bean	6.4	6.0	98,000	5.5	(*62*)
Concanavalin A	Jack bean	6.0	5.6	96,000	5.5	(*61*)

When we turned our attention to the hemagglutinins from other legumes, the nutritional significance of these substances became even more apparent. We were particularly interested in legumes which enjoy popular consumption in underdeveloped countries.   For this purpose, we were able to obtain a black bean from Guatemala, Bengal and red gram from India, mung bean from the Philippines, and the domestic kidney bean. The effect of heat on the nutritive value of these beans is shown in Table V and the hemagglutinating and antitryptic activities are shown in Table VI.   Only the growth promoting values of the black bean and kidney bean were

Table V.   Effect of Heat on Nutritive Value of Some Legumes (22)

Source of Protein	Gain in Weight, G./Day	
	Raw[a]	Heated
Phaseolus vulgaris		
Black bean	−1.94 (4–5)	+1.61
Kidney bean	−1.04 (11–13)	+1.48
Cicer arietinum		
Bengal gram	+1.25	+1.16
Cajanus cajan		
Red gram	+1.33	+1.74
Phaseolus aureus		
Mung bean	+1.05	+1.07

[a] 100% mortality observed during period (in days) shown in parentheses.

Table VI.   Hemagglutinating and Antitryptic Activities of Crude Extracts of Raw Legumes (22)

Legume	Hemagglutinating Activity[a]	Antitryptic Activity[a]
	HU/Ml.	TIU/Ml.
Phaseolus vulgaris		
Black bean	2450	2050
Kidney bean	3560	1552
Cicer arietinum	0	220
Cajanus cajan	0	418
Phaseolus aureus	0	260

[a] HU = hemagglutinating units, TIU = trypsin inhibitor units as defined by Honavar et. al. (22).

improved by heat, and these beans were the only ones which displayed a significant level of hemagglutinating activity. For these reasons, the hemagglutinin was purified from each of these beans and fed at various levels to rats in a basal ration containing 10% casein   (Table VII).   A definite inhibition of growth was apparent at levels as low as 0.5% of the diet, the kidney bean hemagglutinin (KBH) being much more effective than the black bean hemagglutinin (BBH).   In fact, KBH at a level of 0.5% caused 100% mortality after about 2 weeks, whereas 1.2% BBH was necessary to produce a similar rate of mortality.   Data are also included which show that the toxicity of the hemagglutinins may be inactivated by heat.

As to the mechanism whereby the hemagglutinin exerts its effect, present evidence would suggest its site of action to be the lining of the intestinal tract.   Jaffé (25) noted a definite impairment in the absorption of protein and fat when rats were fed raw black beans or the hemagglutinin purified therefrom.   He was able to show that isolated intestinal loops taken from rats fed the raw bean or the purified hemagglutinin absorbed glucose at about half the rate of loops taken from control animals.   These results would indicate that the hemagglutinin might combine with the mucosal cells lining the intestinal wall, thus interfering with the absorption of essential nutrients.

Table VII.   Effect of Purified Hemagglutinin Fractions from the Black Bean and Kidney Bean on Growth of Rats (*26*)

Source of Hemagglutinin	Purified Hemagglutinin in Diet, %	Av. Gain in Weight, G./Day	Mortality[a], Days
Black bean	0	+2.51	
	0.5	+1.04	
	0.5[b]	+2.37	
	0.75	+0.20	
	1.2	−0.91	15–19
	2.3	−1.61	12–17
	4.6	−1.72	5–7
Kidney bean	0	+2.31	
	0.5	−0.60	13–16
	0.5[b]	+2.29	
	1.0	−0.87	11–13
	1.5	−1.22	4–7

[a] 100% mortality observed during period recorded. Blank space indicates no deaths observed.

[b] Solution of hemagglutinin boiled for 30 minutes and dried coagulum fed at level indicated. Hemagglutinating activity was completely destroyed by this treatment.

Amino Acid Derivatives

Lathyrism.   Lathyrism is a disease associated with the consumption of certain species of peas belonging to the genus *Lathyrus*.   A graphic description of this syndrome in India in the 1830's is provided by Sleeman (*2, 58*).   In 1829 and in 1831 the wheat crop failed in Sangor, and the inhabitants subsisted mainly on *L. sativus* which grew wild in the blighted fields.   By 1833 the younger part of the population of this area began to be deprived of the use of their limbs below the waist by paralytic strokes. None attacked recovered the use of their limbs.

In more recent times this disease has afflicted some segments of the population in India and the Mediterranean area, and is generally associated with the consumption of *L. sativus* (chickling vetch), *L. cicera* (flat-podded vetch), and *L. clymenum* (Spanish vetch).   The precise causative agent of human lathyrism has not been easy to elucidate because of the difficulty with which this disease can be produced in animals.   The aforementioned species of *Lathyrus* which have been implicated in human lathyrism are relatively nontoxic to most animals (*28*), although two other species of

Lathyrus—L. latifolius (perennial sweet pea) and *L. sylvestris* (flat pea)—produce neurological symptoms in rats which resemble those of human lathyrism *(30, 54)*. Three other peas, however—*L. odoratus* (sweet pea), *L. pusillus* (singletary pea), and *L. hirsutus* (Caley pea)—produce skeletal deformities in rats, symptoms which are different from human lathyrism *(29)*.

It is evident, therefore, that the concept of what actually constitutes lathyrism is not a simple one. Some clarity is achieved if one accepts the conclusion of Selye *(56)* that the consumption of *Lathyrus* can produce two distinctly different types of diseases, a "neurolathyrism" which involves damage to the central nervous system, and an "osteolathyrism" which affects bone and connective tissue. This permits the classification of lathyrogenic seeds as shown in Table VIII. The whole problem of

Table VIII.   Classification of Lathyrogenic Seeds According to Their Physiological Effects

(Neurolathyism)

In man	In rats
L. sativus (chickling vetch)	*L. latifolius* (perennial sweat pea)
L. cicera (flat-podded vetch)	*L. sylvestris* (flat pea)
L. clymenum (Spanish vetch)	*V. sativa* (common vetch)

(Osteolathyrism)

In rats only

L. odoratus (sweet pea)
L. pusillus (singletary pea)
L. hirsutus (Caley pea)

lathyrism has been considerably clarified in recent years by the isolation and characterization of what appear to be the causative principles of these two forms of lathyrism.

In 1954 two groups of workers, Dupuy and Lee *(16)* and McKay *et al.* *(39)*, isolated a compound from *L. odoratus* and *L. pusillus* which was capable of reproducing all of the symptoms associated with osteolathyrism. This proved to be $\beta-(N-\gamma-$glutamyl$)$-aminopropionitrile, although it was subsequently shown that β-aminopropionitrile (BAPN) was the active portion of the molecule (see Figure 1). This compound was notably absent from *L. sativus* and the other species of lathyrus known to cause human lathyrism.

In 1961, Ressler *et al.* *(53)* reported the isolation of α, γ-diaminobutyric acid (Figure 2) from *L. latifolius* and *L. sylvestris* which had previously been found to reproduce the neurotoxic symptoms similar to that noted in man. α,γ-Diaminobutyric acid produced the same symptoms as the

seeds themselves.   Strangely enough, however, this compound could not
be detected in species implicated in human lathyrism.

OSTEOLATHYROGENS

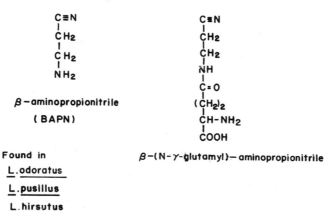

*Figure 1. Structure of compounds causing osteolathyrism
in rats*

Ressler's group has also isolated from *Vicia sativa* (common vetch)
β-cyano-L-alanine (Figure 2), which also produced neurotoxic symptoms
in rats—namely, tremors, convulsions, rigidity, and finally death. *V.
sativa* has been frequently reported to be a common contaminant of *L.
sativus* in human outbreaks of human lathyrism in India (*3*).   Ressler

NEUROLATHYROGENS

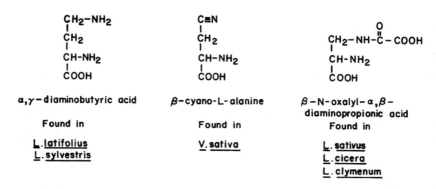

Figure 2.   Structure of compounds causing neurolathyrism in rats

has therefore suggested the possibility that the causative factor in human lathyrism may be the cyanoalanine provided by the common vetch as a contaminant of *L. sativus* rather than by *L. sativus* itself.

Two groups of workers in India (*1, 43*) have recently reported the isolation of a neurotoxic principle from *L. sativus* itself which was identified as β-*N*-oxalyl-α,β-diaminopropionic acid (Figure 2). Intraperitoneal injections of this compound produced neurotoxic symptoms in chicks manifested by an inability to stand, head retraction, paralysis of the legs, and convulsions. α,β-Diaminopropionic acid itself proved nontoxic, showing the essentiality of the oxalo group for toxicity. A final judgment as to whether this compound is the long-sought-for causative principle of human lathyrism must await further studies.

Glycosides

Goiterogenic Agents. Sometimes the adverse physiological effects of certain legumes do not manifest themselves in such obvious ways as growth inhibition, paralysis, or death. A case in point is the observation that unheated soybeans produce a marked enlargement of the thyroid gland of the rat and chick, an effect which can be counteracted by the administration of iodide or partially eliminated by heat (*49, 57*). Several workers (*23, 63*) have reported a number of cases of goiter in human infants fed soybean milk. Apparently the heat treatment employed for sterilizing these particular soybean preparations was not sufficient to destroy the goiterogenic agent. Iodine supplementation, however, alleviated this goiter condition in human infants (*63*). No goiterogenic agent has ever been isolated from soybeans, so it is not known what substance is actually responsible for the goiterogenicity of raw soybean.

On the other hand, the goiterogenic properties of peanuts have been attributed to a phenolic glycoside which is present in high concentrations in the red skin (60). It has been suggested that the phenolic metabolities formed from this glycoside are preferentially iodinated and thereby deprive the thyroid of available iodine.

It has been known for some time that some cruciferous oilseed proteins such as rapeseed, mustard seed, and crambe (Abyssinian kale) contain thioglycosides which, upon enzymatic hydrolysis, release goiterogenic isothiocyanates. As an example, the thioglycoside of the mustard seed, sinigrin, is hydrolyzed by the enzyme "myrosinase" to give allyl isothiocyanate (Figure 3). Other crucifers give related unsaturated isothiocyanates as well as cyclic oxazolidinethione derivatives which are also goiterogenic. Since the release of these goiterogenic substances is mediated by enzymes already present in the meal, the meal can be moistened to permit the enzymatic liberation of the isothiocyanates, which may then

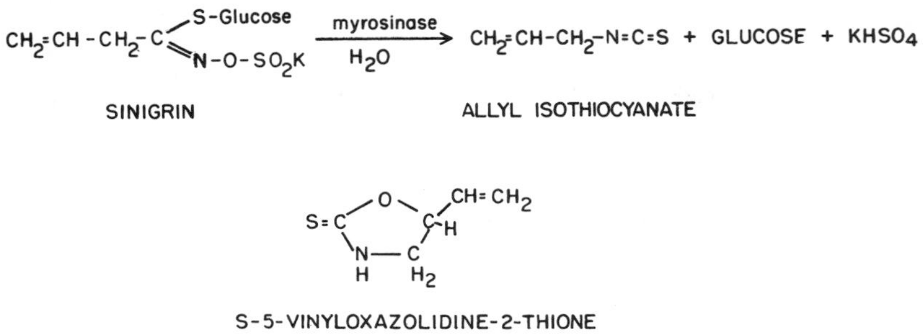

SINIGRIN   ALLYL ISOTHIOCYANATE

S-5-VINYLOXAZOLIDINE-2-THIONE

Figure 3. Structure of sinigrin and its enzymatic products according to Ettlinger and Lundeen (17).

Also shown, S-5-vinyl oxazolidine-2-thione, another goiterogenic product of certain thio glycosides present in some cruciferous plants

be removed by steam distillation (44). Unlike the goiterogenic effect of soybeans, dietary supplementation with iodide is not effective.

Cyanogenetic Agents. It has been known for a long time that a number of plants are potentially toxic because they contain glycosides from which HCN is released upon hydrolysis. Those most commonly eaten by man or animals are listed in Table IX in order of their HCN content. Acute cassava poisoning is not uncommon in the West Indies, South America, and West Africa, where the consumption of this plant is high. Many deaths of domestic animals have been attributed to the high HCN content of sorghum and linseed meal. As far as seed proteins for human consumption are concerned, the lima bean constitutes the most serious problem although lesser amounts of HCN are produced by other legumes. Serious outbreaks of poisoning attributed to the consumption

Table IX.   Cyanide Content of Certain Plants

Plant	HCN Yield, Mg./100 G.
Lima bean (*Phaseolus lunatus*)	
Samples incriminated in fatal human poisoning	210 –312
Normal levels	14.4–16.7
Sorghum	250
Cassava	113
Linseed meal	53
Black-eyed pea (*Vigna sinensis*)	2.1
Garden pea (*Pisum sativum*)	2.3
Kidney bean (*Phaseolus vulgaris*)	2.0
Bengal gram (*Cicer arietinum*)	0.8
Red gram (*Cajanus cajans*)	0.5

of lima beans have been reported from time to time in India, Puerto Rico, Mauritius, and even Europe (42).

The HCN is derived from cyanide-containing glycosides which upon hydrolysis yield sugar, HCN, and either acetone or benzaldehyde. As shown in Figure 4, phaseolunatin, the cyanogenetic glycoside of the lima bean, yields HCN, glucose, and acetone when hydrolyzed by the enzymes β-glucosidase and oxynitrilase (15, 50). These enzymes are contained in the plant, so that lima beans should be detoxicated by adequate cooking. Yet many cases of human intoxication have occurred even with cooked lima beans. It has been reported (19) that when lima beans, which had been cooked so as to destroy the enzymes responsible for cyanide formation, were fed to human subjects, cyanide could be detected in the urine. This has led to the supposition that perhaps enzymes secreted in the intestinal tract or by the microflora of the colon may be responsible for releasing HCN after ingestion of the beans.

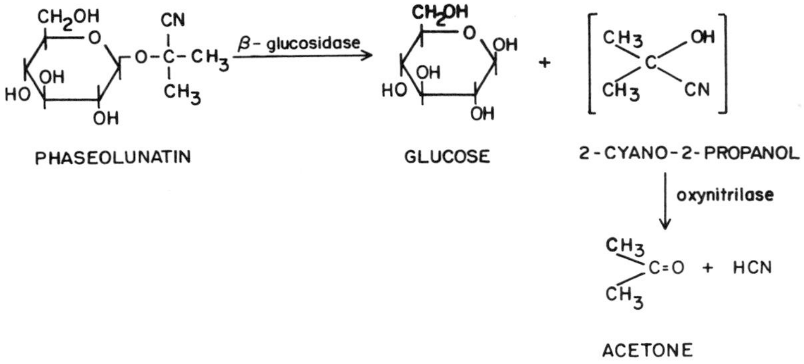

Figure 4.   Enzymatic products of phaseolunatin, the cyanogenetic glycoside of the lima bean

Saponins. Saponins are bitter-tasting, foam-producing glycosides in which the nonsugar residue (sapogenin) is a triterpenoid alcohol referred to as a soyasapogenol. Present evidence would indicate that at least five different saponins (65) exhibit varying degrees of hemolytic and foam-producing activity (20). The structures of the five soyasapogenols derived from these saponins are shown in Figure 5.

Because of their characteristic hemolytic activity and bitter taste, the soybean saponins have been thought to be one of the factors contributing to the poor nutritive value of unheated soybean protein (51). Birk et al. (5), however, have shown that the hemolytic activity of the soybean saponins is unaffected by the heat treatment necessary to produce optimum nutritive value of soybean meal. This would indicate that the hemolytic

food substances.   We are in a way fortunate that these toxic substances have been added by the good Lord and not by man; otherwise we might have the food faddist to contend with in our efforts to expand the use of plant proteins.   Only after the presence of these toxic factors has been recognized and studied can effective measures be taken so that the full nutritional potential of the seed proteins can be realized.   And therein lies a good measure of the hope that we will be able to combat the threat of protein malnutrition that faces the world of tomorrow.

Literature Cited

(1) Adiji, P. G., Podmanabar, G., Rao, S. L. N., Sarma, P. S., *J. Sci. Ind. Res (India)* **21,** 284 (1962).
(2) Altschul, A. M., "Proteins, Their Chemistry and Politics," p. 267, Basic Books, New York, 1965.
(3) Anderson, L. A. P., Howard, A., Simonsen, J. L., *Indian J. Med. Res.* **12,** 613 (1925).
(4) Barnes, R. H., Kwong, E., *J. Nutr.* **86,** 245 (1965).
(5) Birk, Y., Bondi, A., Gestetner, B., Ishaaya, I., *Nature* **197,** 1089 (1963).
(6) Birk, Y., Gertler, A., *J. Nutr.* **75,** 379 (1961).
(7) Booth, A. N., Robbins, A. J., Ribelin, W. E., De Eds, F., *Proc. Soc. Exptl. Biol. Med.* **104,** 681 (1960).
(8) Borchers, R., Ackerson, C. W., *J. Nutr.* **41,** 339 (1950).
(9) Carlson, C. W., Saxena, H. C., Jensen, L. C., McGinnis, J., *Ibid.,* **82,** 507 (1964).
(10) Carter, M. W., Matrone, G., Smart, W. G., Jr., *Ibid.,* **55,** 639 (1955).
(11) Carter, M. W., Smart, W. G., Jr., Matrone, G., *Proc. Soc. Expl. Biol. Med.* **84,** 506 (1953).
(12) Chernick, S. S., Lepkovsky, S., Chaikoff, I. L., *Am. J. Physiol.* **155,** 33 (1948).
(13) Daubert, B. F., in "Soybeans and Soybean Products," K. S. Markley, ed., p. 377, Interscience, New York, 1950.
(14) Dieckert, J. W., Norris, N. J., Mason, A. F., *Arch. Biochem. Bipohys.* **82,** 220 (1959).
(15) Dunstan, W. R., Henry, T. A., *Proc. Roy. Soc.* **72,** 285 (1903).
(16) Dupuy, H. P., Lee, J. G., *J. Am. Pharm. Assoc.* **43,** 61 (1954).
(17) Ettlinger, M. G., Lundeen, A. J., *J. Am. Chem. Soc.* **78,** 4172 (1956).
(18) Fitch, C. D., Harville, W. E., Dinning, J. S., Porter, F. S., *Proc. Soc. Exptl. Biol. Med.* **116,** 130 (1964).
(19) Gabel, W., Kruger, W., *Muench. Med. Wochschr.* **67,** 214 (1920).
(20) Gestetner, B., Ishaaya, I., Birk, A., Bondi, A., *Israel J. Chem.* **1,** 460 (1963).
(21) Hintz, H. F., Hogue, D. E., *J. Nutr.* **84,** 283 (1964).
(22) Honavar, P. M., Shih, C. -V., Liener, I. E., *Ibid.,* **77,** 109 (1962).
(23) Hydowitz, J. D., *New England J. Med.* **22,** 351 (1960).
(24) Ishaaya, I., Birk, Y., *J. Food Sci.* **30,** 118 (1965).
(25) Jaffé, W. G., *Arzneimittel-Forsch.* **12,** 102 (1961).
(26) Kratzer, F. H., *Poultry Sci.* **26,** 90 (1947).
(27) Kratzer, F. H., Williams, D. E., *J. Nutr.* **36,** 297 (1948).
(28) Kunitz, M., *J. Gen. Physiol.* **29,** 149 (1946).
(29) Lewis, H. B., Fajans, R. S., Esterer, M. B., Shen, C., Oliphant, M., *J. Nutr.* **36,** 537 (1948).
(30) Lewis, H. B., Schulert, A. R., *Proc. Soc. Expl. Biol. Med.* **71,** 440 (1949).

(31) Liener, I. E., *Am. J. Clin. Nutr.* **11**, 281, (1962.
(32) Liener, I. E., *Econ. Botany* **18**, 27 (1964).
(33) Liener, I. E., *J. Nutr.* **49**, 527 (1953).
(34) Liener, I. E., Deuel, H. J., Jr., Fevold, H. L., *J. Nutr.* **39**, 325 (1949).
(35) Liener, I. E., Pallansch, M. J., *J. Biol. Chem.* **197**, 29 (1952).
(36) Lin, J. Y., Ling, K. H., *J. Formosan Med. Assoc.* **61**, 484, 490, 579 (1962).
(37) Lis, H., Sharon, N., Katchalski, E., *Biochim. Biophys. Acta* **83**, 376 (1964).
(38) Luisada, A., *Medicine* **20**, 229 (1941).
(39) McKay, G. F., Lalich, J. J. Schilling. E. D., Strong, F. M., *Arch. Biochem. Biophys.* **52**, 313 (1954).
(40) McPhee, W. R., *Am. J. Clin. Pathol.* **26**, 1287 (1956).
(41) Magee, A. C., *J. Nutr.* **80**, 151 (1963).
(42) Montgomery, R. D., *West Indian Med. J.* **13**, 1 (1964).
(43) Murti, V. V. S., Seshadri, T. R., Venkitasubramanian, T. A., *Phyto-chemistry* **3**, 73 (1964).
(44) Mustakas, G. C., Kirk, L. D., Sohns V. E., Griffin, E. L., Jr., *J. Am. Oil Chemists Soc.* **42**, 33 (1965).
(45) Nilson, A., *Acta Physiol. Scand.* **56**, 230 (1962).
(46) Odell, B. L., Savage, J. E., *Proc. Soc. Exptl. Biol. Med.* **103**, 304 (1960).
(47) Osborne, T. B., Mendel, L. B., *J. Biol. Chem.* **32**, 369 (1917).
(48) Pallansch, M. J., Liener, I. E., *Arch. Biochem. Biophys.* **145**, 366 (1953).
(49) Patton, A. R., Wilgus, H. S., Jr., Harshfield, G. S., *Science* **89**, 162 (1939).
(50) Pigman, W., "The Carbohydrates. Chemistry, Biochemistry and Physiology," p. 551, 563, Academic Press, New York, 1957.
(51) Potter, G. C., Kummerow, F. A., *Science* **120**, 224 (1954).
(52) Rackis, J. J., Anderson, R. L., *Biochem. Biophys. Res. Commun.* **15**, 230 (1964).
(53) Ressler, C., Redstone, P. A., Erenberg, R. H., *Science* **134**, 188 (1961).
(54) Schulert, A. R., Lewis, H. B., *Proc. Soc. Exptl. Biol. Med.* **81**, 86 (1952).
(55) Schulze, E., *Z. Physiol. Chem.* **15**, 140 (1891).
(56) Selye, H., *Rev. Can. Biol.* **16**, 1 (1957).
(57) Sharpless, G. R., Pearsons, J., Proto, G. S., *J. Nutr.* **17**, 545 (1939).
(58) Sleeman, W. H., "Rambles and Recollections of an Indian Official," Hatchard, London, 1844.
(59) Smith, H. M., Smith, J. M., Spring, F. S., *Tetrahedron* **4**, 111 (1958).
(60) Srinivasan, V., Mougdal, N. R., Sarma, P. S., *J. Nutr.* **61**, 87, 97 (1957).
(61) Sumner, J. B., Gralen, N., Erickson-Quensel, I. –B., *Science* **87**, 395 (1936).
(62) Takahashi, T., Funatsu, G., Funatsu, M., *J. Biochem. (Japan)* **51**, 288 (1962); **52**, 50 (1962).
(63) Van Wyk, J. J., Arnold, M. B., Pepper, F., *Pediatrics* **24**, 752 (1959).
(64) Wada, S., Pallansch, M. J., Liener, I. E., *J. Biol. Chem.* **233**, 395 (1958).
(65) Willner, D., Gestetner, B., Lavie, D., Birk, Y., Bondi, A., *J. Chem. Soc.* **1964**, Suppl. 1, 5885.

RECEIVED October 12, 1965.

Mycotoxin Contamination of Foodstuffs

GERALD N. WOGAN

Department of Nutrition and Food Science, Massachusetts Institute of Technology, Cambridge, Mass.

Toxic metabolites (mycotoxins) of spoilage fungi growing on food commodities have caused acute and chronic toxicity syndromes in animals and man. "Alimentary toxic aleukia," a mycotoxicosis of man, results from ingestion of metabolites of fungi growing on cereal grains. Fungal spoilage of rice has resulted in luteoskyrin and a chlorine-containing peptide, toxic metabolites of Penicillium islandicum. The syndrome "facial eczema" of ruminants is caused by sporidesmin, a hepatotoxic metabolite of Pithomyces chartarum, which grows on rye grass pastures. The aflatoxins, metabolites of A. flavus, are potent hepatotoxins in many animal species and also hepatocarcinogens in the rat, duck, and rainbow trout. Mycotoxin contamination can present real or potential health hazards, and therefore impair maximum utilization of available protein sources and other foodstuffs.

Among the factors which must be established in the utilization of protein sources for human feeding is the absence of chemical substances which might have deleterious effects upon the health of the consumer. Such substances may derive from several sources, including the presence of normal genetically determined components of plants and animals used as foods. The toxic substances associated with seed proteins discussed elsewhere in this symposium are excellent examples of this type of toxic component. Also important among this group are such familiar compounds as gossypol, cycasin, tetrodotoxin, and the *Senecio* alkaloids. These substances have sometimes presented serious difficulties in the utilization of potentially significant protein sources. However, their occurrence is predictable and, in many instances, technological advances have made it possible to circumvent problems posed by their presence.

Mycotoxins are among a different group of substances important in this connection—namely, the so-called inadvert or unintentional contaminants which occasionally find their way into the food chain. This type of contamination poses more difficult problems in safety evaluation. The frequency and level of contamination are sporadic and the compounds as well as their toxic manifestations are frequently ill defined and diverse in nature.

The mycotoxins comprise a group of toxic secondary metabolites elaborated during the growth of certain contaminating fungi on foods or foodstuffs.

The majority of food raw materials are liable in some degree to growth of contaminating fungi at some stage during their harvest, storage, transportation, or processing. Since mold spores are ubiquitously distributed, the possibility for sporulation and subsequent growth of the fungal flora on a given product is determined principally by moisture content of the substrate, relative humidity, and temperature. During the entire post-harvest period, food crops are essentially in a state of storage, and mold damage is avoidable only by careful regulation of moisture content, temperature, and other environmental conditions. Commodities particularly prone to damage include grains, oilseeds, fruits, and vegetables. One recent estimate (26) reported the annual worldwide grain loss from all causes to be in the order of 55 million metric tons. Fungal spoilage contributed heavily to these losses. The annual postharvest loss of fruits and vegetables in the United States has been estimated (76) to be equivalent to the output of 13% of the producing acreage. In this instance also, mold damage constitutes a major factor in the loss.

Many types of crop damage result from mold growth, which diminishes or destroys the usefulness of the commodity as a food. For example, serious losses of tropical foods attributed to mold damage include the discoloration of rice and cocoa butter, loss of seed viability, mustiness of coffee beans, and lipolysis of plant oils (36).

While these deleterious effects have had serious economic consequences, fungal spoilage has, in several instances, created additional problems by contamination of the affected commodity with mycotoxins. Toxicity syndromes, recently given the generic name "mycotoxicoses" (28), resulting from the ingestion of such contaminated foodstuffs have been encountered in many forms. All of these have either posed direct hazards to human consumers or have caused significant losses in domestic animals fed contaminated feeds. The net result in either case has been a reduction in the utilizable food supply by directly limiting human consumption or by decreasing available animal protein.

It would not be possible, nor particularly germane to this discussion, to attempt a complete review of all of the recognized mycotoxins and mycotoxicoses. These have recently been reviewed in detail (28, 46, 84, 85). Several examples have therefore been selected to illustrate the range of variation in form and character encountered in this type of syndrome. Such factors as the causative fungi, chemical nature of the toxic compounds, commodities affected, and principal features of the toxicity in susceptible species will be considered.

Ergotism

From a historical viewpoint, no discussion of this subject would be complete without at least a brief allusion to ergotism, the earliest recognized form of mycotoxicosis. Arising from the growth of *Claviceps purpurea* on rye and other grains, epidemics of the chronic form of the toxicity were apparently frequent during the Middle Ages. The first association of ergot with the syndrome was in the mid-sixteenth century. It was not, however, until the 1930's that the group of six lysergic acid derivatives (*64*) responsible for the biological effects were isolated and identified. The last major incidence of ergotism in the United States was in 1825, but serious outbreaks have occurred as recently as 1926–27 in Russia and 1928 in England (*11*). Although the hazard to the human food supply has been essentially eliminated, contamination of some types of pasture grasses by the mold still causes frequent problems in veterinary practice (*30*).

Alimentary Toxic Aleukia

The most recently documented mycotoxicosis in humans is the syndrome known as "alimentary toxic aleukia" or ATA. The disease has been recorded sporadically in Russia, probably beginning in the nineteenth century, but occurred with special severity from 1942 to 1947. In the peak year, 1944, more than 10% of the population of one district was affected, and many fatalities occurred in nine of the 50 counties of this district (*41*). Symptoms of the disease, which have been described in detail (*28*), may be summarized as follows: initially, local inflammation appears in the mouth, pharynx, and esophageal mucosal tissues, apparently the result of direct contact with the toxic substances. Systemic effects appearing after 5 to 9 days include anemia and leukopenia, which grow progressively worse over a period of 3 to 4 weeks. These symptoms develop sequentially with continued intake of certain lots of grains or their products. If allowed to continue, the toxicity terminates in severe anemia and total exhaustion of the bone marrow, with panleukopenia and agranulocytosis. In many instances, death results from secondary infections.

This disease was found to be associated with the ingestion of grains that had overwintered in the field. Millet was an extensive vector of ATA because it is widely grown in the areas affected, but wheat and barley have also been implicated in a few outbreaks. The causes of the syndrome were identified as toxic compounds produced by fungi isolated from toxic grain samples (*38, 39*). It was originally thought that *Fusarium sporotrichioides* was the only fungus involved, but recent studies by Joffe (*40*) have also implicated *F. poae* and *Cladosporium epiphyllum*. Administration of cultures or culture extracts of these molds to various animals has revealed that the cow, sheep, and chicken are able to tolerate large amounts of toxic grain or extracts. On the other hand, it has been possible to reproduce the typical human symptoms in the cat, dog, monkey, and guinea pig (*28*).

Numerous investigations have been concerned with the chemical properties of the toxic compounds. Observations on contaminated grain samples revealed that the toxic substances are relatively stable to heat, withstanding a temperature of 118 C. for 18 hours or longer. Furthermore, grain samples stored for 6 years retained their toxicity. The toxic compounds are extractable with lipid solvents, and a standardized biological assay procedure was developed based on rabbit dermal toxicity of diethyl ether extracts of suspected material (*28*). Recently, toxins produced by species of *Fusarium* and *Cladosporium* have been isolated and structural formulas proposed for them (*40*).

FUSARIOGENIN

EPICLADOSPORIC ACID

FAGICLADOSPORIC ACID

The toxins produced by *C. epiphyllum* and *C. fagi* have been named epicladosporic acid and fagicladosporic acid, respectively. Similarly, the toxins produced by *F. sporotrichioides* and *F. poae* are distinguished as sporofusariogenin and poaefusariogenin.

Yellowed Rice Toxicity

Fungal damage of rice represents another significant example of the contamination of an important foodstuff by mycotoxins. This crop, in common with others, is prone to mold spoilage if storage conditions permit growth of contaminating fungi. The magnitude this problem can assume is illustrated by losses incurred in one major consumer country,

Japan. According to one author (*78*) more than 100,000 tons of rice imported during the period 1947 to 1954 were declared unfit for human consumption because of fungal damage. A systematic survey (*44*) of the mold flora of stored rice in Japan revealed the presence of some 200 genera and species with more than 50 penicillia represented.

Some lots of moldy rice were found to be highly toxic to domestic and experimental animals, and toxic mold metabolites were frequently identified as the causative agents. Although many of the rice fungi have been shown to produce toxic metabolites (*44*), three species of penicillia have been extensively studied. Ethanolic extracts of rice cultures of *Penicillium toxicarium*, Miyake, when administered orally to higher vertebrates induced ascending paralysis and respiratory and circulatory disturbances resembling the symptoms of beriberi (*53*). Cultures of *P. citrinum* induced severe damage in the renal tubules when fed to rats, an effect attributable to citrinin produced by the mold.

A third fungus, *Penicillium islandicum*, Sopp, first isolated in 1948 (*53*) produced severe liver cirrhosis when incorporated into rat diets. This finding was of considerable interest in view of the high incidence of liver cirrhosis and primary liver carcinoma among the Japanese and other Asiatic peoples (*46*), and as a consequence stimulated extensive investigation into the fungal metabolites responsible for the toxicity. Although consumption of moldy rice has not been directly associated with human disease, much useful information has resulted from these investigations.

Long-term studies (*53*) on mice fed either rice cultures of *P. islandicum* or fungal mats cultured on Czapek solution showed the presence of liver lesions ranging from acute atrophy to fully developed cirrhosis in correlation with the amount of mold culture ingested. Fully developed cirrhosis was found mostly in animals dying 220 days or later after feeding was begun. Parallel experiments in rats resulted in similar findings.

In a subsequent experiment (*45*) to determine whether this fungal culture was capable of hepatoma induction, moldy rice was fed to rats alone and in combination with a known hepatocarcinogen, *p*-dimethylaminoazobenzene (DAB). In animals fed only the mold culture, 5 out of 30 developed liver tumors; when fed in combination with 0.06% DAB, 14 out of 30 showed hepatomas, as compared with 6 out of 30 receiving DAB alone. These results reveal the carcinogenic properties of *P. islandicum* cultures as well as their promoting effect when fed in combination with DAB.

Attempts to identify the substances responsible for these effects have resulted in isolating two toxic compounds, luteoskyrin and a chlorine-containing peptide from mycelia of the fungus (*77*). The structures of these compounds are:

LUTEOSKYRIN

CHLORINE-CONTAINING PEPTIDE

Some of their biologic effects are summarized in Tables I and II. While these compounds are clearly associated with the hepatotoxic properties of the fungal cultures, further definitive experiments are required to establish whether they are the active carcinogenic agents.

Facial Eczema in Ruminants

Numerous instances of animal diseases of obscure etiology are encountered sporadically by veterinary practitioners. The outbreaks usually tend to be localized and the problems are frequently solved by empirical means, and the causative factors are not elucidated. However, on occasion the diseases reach epidemic proportions and consequently stimulate efforts to determine the etiologic agents involved. Several such syndromes which have resulted in serious losses of animals important to the food supply have been clearly attributed to contamination of the feed by mycotoxins.

Important among these is the disease known as "facial eczema," a photosensitization syndrome occurring in ruminants. While the major outbreaks have apparently been restricted mainly to New Zealand and Australia, syndromes of similar, but as yet unproved, etiologic character have been encountered in the southern United States (*31, 32, 43*). In

Table I. Toxicity of Luteoskyrin to Mice and Cell Cultures[a]

LD$_{50}$ in Mice

Intravenous	6.65 mg./kg.
Subcutaneous	147.0 mg./kg.
Oral	221.0 mg./kg.

Liver Injury

Acute lesion centrolobular necrosis and fatty change
Chronic lesion periportal fibrosis (slight) and hepatoma formation

Tissue Culture (Chang Liver Cells)

MED[b] (growth inhibition)	0.1 μg./ml.
LD[c] (cell destruction)	1.0 μg./ml.

[a] Adapted from Miyake and Saito (*53*).
[b] MED. Minimum effective dose.
[c] LD. Lethal dose.

Table II. Toxicity of Chlorine-Containing Peptide to Mice and Cell Cultures

LD$_{50}$ in Mice

Intravenous	338 μg./kg.
Subcutaneous	475 μg./kg.
Oral	6550 μg./kg.

Liver Injury

Acute lesion vacuolar degeneration, cell destruction periportal hemorrhage
Chronic lesion liver cirrhosis, monolobular

Tissue Culture (Chang Liver Cells)

MED[b] (growth inhibition)	$10^{0.5}$ μg./ml.
LD[c] (cell destruction)	$10^{1.5}$ μg./ml.

[a] Adapted from Miyake and Saito (*53*).
[b] MED. Minimum effective dose.
[c] LD. Lethal dose.

New Zealand, facial eczema in sheep has been a long-standing problem, to which special attention was drawn in 1936, when a severe epidemic took a heavy toll of animals (*27*). The disease manifests itself clinically as a marked exudative epidermitis of the face and other exposed skin. These symptoms are sequelae of severe liver damage resulting in accumulation of phylloerythrin, a metabolic product of chlorophyll, which results in photosensitization of exposed skin areas (*54*).

Continuing efforts to establish the causative agent resulted in association of the disease with growth of the mold *Pithomyces chartarum* on rye grass pastures used for grazing (60).   In 1959, Synge and White (54) were able to isolate from this fungus a metabolite which they named sporidesmin.   The structure of sporidesmin has recently been elucidated (29).

This substance, when fed to guinea pigs, produced liver lesions closely resembling those caused by feeding toxic rye grass.   Subsequent experiments (54) have shown that the natural syndrome can also be reproduced in sheep by administration of sporidesmin.   The principal biochemical, functional, and histological effects of oral administration of the compound to sheep are attributable to severe liver damage.   Doses of 3 mg per kg. of body weight are acutely toxic and most animals die within a few days. Lower levels produce subacute liver damage which eventually results in photosensitization in many treated animals.

The effects of sporidesmin toxicity on liver lipids in sheep have been extensively studied by Peters and Smith (61).   These investigators found that a single oral dose of 1 mg. per kg. of body weight caused a marked increase in liver triglycerides without affecting concentrations of other lipid fractions.   They concluded that the early hepatotoxic action of sporidesmin was an impairment of hepatic triglyceride-secreting mechanisms.   Studies of sporidesmin poisoning in rats (73) revealed this species to be resistant to the hepatotoxic effects and to respond in a qualitatively different manner.   Single doses of 6 mg. per kg. of body weight produced ascites and pleural effusion thought to be due to a direct effect of the toxin on capillary permeability.

It is difficult to estimate the magnitude of losses of domestic animals attributable to sporidesmin or similar mycotoxins.   However, diseases of animals involving photosensitization are known to occur in most major livestock-producing areas of the world, and at certain times in a given area, such as New Zealand, they may be of great economic importance.

Moldy Corn Poisoning

Other mycotoxicoses affecting livestock have been reported, although in most cases neither the syndromes nor the etiologic relationships have been as clearly defined as in facial eczema disease.   One of these, the so-called "moldy corn toxicosis," has been encountered sporadically in southeastern United States.   Outbreaks of the disease in swine were recognized as early as 1949, were particularly severe in 1952 and 1955, and have also been observed less frequently in cattle (*28*). In the severe outbreaks, mortality varied from 5 to 55% of herds consuming toxic grain. Animals dying of the acute toxicity showed signs of acute toxic hepatitis and profound hemorrhage.

Burnside *et al.* (*16*) isolated from toxic field corn two fungi which, when cultured on corn and fed to swine, produced a similar toxicity. One of these was an *Aspergillus flavus*, Link, and the other a strain of *Penicillium rubrum*, Stoll. Subsequent investigations on the toxicity of cultures of these organisms in swine revealed that the *P. rubrum* strain was the more potent.

The toxic substances responsible for these outbreaks have not been identified. It would seem possible that the toxicity of the *A. flavus* strain might be explained if this organism produced aflatoxins although there is no direct evidence leading to this conclusion. In further studies on the *P. rubrum* strain, Wilson and Wilson (*83*) were able to extract and concentrate substances lethal to mice, guinea pigs, rabbits, and dogs. We have also been investigating cultures of this mold and have recently succeeded in isolating a crystalline compound highly toxic to mice, rats, cats, dogs, and swine. Attempts are in progress to characterize the compound and the toxicity syndrome. Details of this work will be reported in full elsewhere.

Aflatoxicoses

The recent discovery of the aflatoxins and their potent biologic properties has focused increasing attention on the general problem of the mycotoxins and their potential significance as food contaminants. Detailed accounts of the development of knowledge of this mycotoxicosis have appeared (*2*, *46*, *84*) and only the major aspects of the problem are described here.

Toxicity syndromes of domestic animals ultimately attributed to aflatoxins were first recognized in England in 1960 and 1961. The first report of the syndrome in young turkeys (*14*) was followed within a short time by similar incidents in ducklings and chickens (*10*), as well as swine (*34*, *51*) and calves (*52*). The common factor in these episodes was a shipment of Brazilian peanut meal used in the animal rations. It was found that the active principle could be extracted from toxic meals (*3*, *67*) and such extracts reproduced the toxicity in susceptible species. It has since been suggested by examination of many types of agricultural commodities that peanut meals are probably more frequently contaminated than other crops (*36*), but the discovery of a highly contaminated cottonseed meal (*50*) illustrates the lack of a specific substrate-toxin production relationship.

Sargeant *et al.* (*66, 68*) discovered that the toxic compounds were produced by certain strains of *Aspergillus flavus* isolated from toxic meals. The generic name "aflatoxins" was subsequently applied to the group of toxic compounds produced by this fungus.

Isolation of the aflatoxins from toxic meals was greatly facilitated by the discovery that they were strongly fluorescent in ultraviolet light. This property has also provided a convenient means for monitoring isolation and purification procedures. The original investigations (*3, 67*) demonstrated that the compounds were extractable with methanol. A variety of extraction procedures have since been developed for use with various natural products or mold cultures on natural substrates, particularly in connection with chemical assays of agricultural commodities for aflatoxin contamination.

In producing and isolating quantities of aflatoxins from mold cultures on solid substrates, a convenient extraction and concentration procedure involves total extraction of the culture with chloroform and subsequent precipitation of the aflatoxins in petroleum ether (*6, 7*). The aflatoxins produced in cultures on liquid media are almost quantitatively removed by partitioning into chloroform (*1*).

Extracts produced by these procedures usually contain mixtures of fluorescent compounds, which are separable into their individual components by chromatography. Although several systems have been developed, the conditions most widely used involve separation on silica gel plates developed with 3 to 5% methanol in chloroform (*7, 24, 56*).

When such chromatograms of extracts containing aflatoxins are viewed under ultraviolet light, an array of fluorescent compounds is generally present. The known aflatoxins comprise four of the components. Two emit blue visible light, and were therefore named aflatoxins B_1 and B_2, and two fluoresce yellow-green (aflatoxins G_1 and G_2). On silica gel plates developed in 97 to 3: chloroform-methanol (*7*) aflatoxin B_1 migrates with an R_f in the order of 0.56; B_2, 0.53; G_1, 0.48; and G_2, 0.46, although absolute R_f values are poorly reproducible. The amounts and relative proportions of these four compounds present in culture extracts are variable, depending on such factors as mold strain, medium composition, and culture conditions. Typically, aflatoxin B_1 is present in largest relative amount, with G_1 at an intermediate concentration; B_2 and G_2 usually represent less than 2% of the total yield.

These four compounds were originally isolated by groups of investigators in England (*55, 68*) and Holland (*80*). The molecular formula of aflatoxin B_1 was established as $C_{17}H_{12}O_6$ and of aflatoxin G_1 as $C_{17}H_{12}O_7$, while aflatoxins B_2 and G_2 were found to be the dihydro derivatives of the parent compounds, $C_{17}H_{14}O_6$ and $C_{17}H_{14}O_7$ (*35*).

Structures based largely on interpretation of spectral data were proposed for aflatoxins B_1 and G_1 in 1963 (*6, 7*) and for B_2 (*21, 81*) and

G_2 shortly thereafter. The proposed structure of G_1 has been supported by x-ray crystallography (*22*).

These closely related compounds are highly substituted coumarins and the presence of the furocoumarin configuration places them among a large group of naturally occurring compounds. The bifuran structure, however, has previously been encountered in only one other compound of natural origin, sterigmatocystin, a metabolite of *Aspergillus versicolor* (*15*).

The spectral characteristics of the aflatoxins have been determined by several investigators (*6, 7, 23, 35, 80, 81*) and are summarized in Table III. The ultraviolet absorption spectra are very similar, each showing maxima at 223, 265, and 363 mμ. The molar extinction coefficients at the latter two peaks, however, demonstrate that B_1 and G_2 absorb more intensely than G_1 and B_2 at these two wavelengths. Because of the close similarities in structural configuration, the infrared absorption spectra of the four compounds are also very similar, as illustrated. The fluorescence emission maximum for B_1 and B_2 has been reported to be 425 mμ and that for G_1 and G_2 is 450 mμ (*35*). The intensity of light emission varies greatly among solutions of the four compounds.

The chemical properties and reactivity of the aflatoxins have received relatively little systematic study beyond work associated with structure

Table III.   Summary of Spectral Properties of Aflaxtoxins

Aflatoxin	*UV Absorption,*ϵ		*IR Absorption,* (*Cm.$^{-1}$*)			$\nu_{max}^{CHCl_3}$	*Fluorescence Emission* mμ
	265 mμ	363 mμ					
B_1	13,400	21,800	1760	1684	1632	1598	425
B_2	9,200	14,700	1760	1685	1625	1600	425
G_3	10,000	16,100	1760	1695	1630	1595	450
G_4	11,200	19,300	1760	1694	1627	1597	450

elucidation. However, it has been shown (*6, 7, 81*) that catalytic hydrogenation of aflatoxin B_1 to completion results in the uptake of 3 moles of hydrogen with the production of the tetrahydrodeoxy derivative. Interruption of the hydrogenation procedure after the uptake of 1 mole of hydrogen results in the production of aflatoxin B_2 in quantitative yield (*21, 81*).

Aflatoxin B_1 has also been reported to react additively with a hydroxyl group under the catalytic influence of a strong acid (*4*). Treatment with formic acid–thionyl chloride, acetic acid-ethionyl chloride, or trifluoroacetic acid results in addition products of greatly altered chromatographic properties but relatively unchanged fluorescence characteristics. The presence of the lactone ring makes the compound labile to alkaline hydrolysis, and partial recyclization after acidification of the hydrolysis product has been reported (*23*).

Although few systematic studies have been carried out on the stability of the aflatoxins, the general experience would seem to indicate that some degradation takes place under several types of conditions. The compounds appear partially to decompose, for example, upon standing in methanolic solution, and this process is greatly accelerated in the presence of light and/or heat. Substantial degradation also occurs on chromatograms exposed to air and ultraviolet or visible light. These processes may give rise to some of the nonaflatoxin fluorescent compounds typically seen in chromatograms of culture extracts. The nature of the decomposition products is still unknown, and the chemical reactions involved in their formation remain to be established.

The discovery of this group of compounds as contaminants of animal feeds and potential protein sources for human feeding has stimulated considerable research effort concerned with their effects in various biologic assay systems. The toxic properties of the aflatoxins manifest themselves differently, depending on the test system, dose and duration of exposure. Thus, they have been shown to be lethal to animals and animal cells in culture when administered acutely in sufficiently large doses and to cause histologic changes in animals when smaller doses were administered subacutely. Chronic exposure for extended periods has resulted in tumor induction in several animal species.

The aflatoxins are acutely toxic to most animal species. Aflatoxin B_1 has been most extensively studied, as regards its lethal potency, and its in vivo lethality to selected experimental animals is summarized in Table IV. Early experimental studies as well as field observations suggested that the duckling was the species most susceptible to acute poisoning. The LD_{50} of one-day-old ducklings is in the order of 0.5 mg. per kg. This value is considerably smaller than those for the rat and hamster, which are commonly used in toxicologic evaluations. However, studies in our laboratories indicate that the dog, rabbit, and guinea pig have LD_{50}

Table IV. Lethality of Aflatoxin B_1 to Several Animal Species

Animal	Age	Sex	Route	LD_{50}, Mg./Kg.	Ref.
Duckling	1 day	M	PO[a]	0.37	(20)
Rat	1 day	M-F	PO	1.0	(86)
	21 days	M	PO	5.5	(86)
	100 g.	M	PO	7.2	(18)
	150 g.	F	PO	17.9	(18)
Hamster	30 days	M	PO	10.2	
Guinea pig	Adult	M	IP[b]	Ca 1	
Rabbit	Weanling	M-F	IP	Ca 0.5	
Dog	Adult	M-F	IP	Ca 1	
	Adult	M-F	PO	Ca 0.5	
Pig	Weanling	M-F	PO	Ca 2	
Trout	100 g.	M-F	PO	Ca 0.5	(8)

[a] Oral.
[b] Intraperitoneal.

values in the same order of magnitude as the duckling (Table IV). This is also true for the rainbow trout (8).

The relative lethal potencies of the four aflatoxins in the day-old duckling have been examined by Carnaghan et al. (20). The oral 7-day LD_{50} reported for each compound were: aflatoxin B_1, 18.2 μg.; B_2, 84.8 μg.; G_1, 39.2 μg.; and G_2, 172.5 μg., all on a 50-gram body weight basis. These values illustrate clearly the relationships of structural configuration to acute lethality. Aflatoxin B_1 is most potent, followed by G_1, B_2, and G_2 in order of decreasing potency.

The toxic effects of aflatoxin B_1 have also been investigated in several in vitro cell culture systems and in embryonated eggs. These experimental systems are much more sensitive than in vivo systems in terms of the amounts of toxin required to produce effects. The early studies of Juhasz and Greczi (42) demonstrated that methanol extracts of peanut meals containing aflatoxins were toxic to calf kidney cells. No estimation of the aflatoxin concentrations was given. Legator and Withrow (49) have shown that very small concentrations (0.03 μg. per ml.) of aflatoxin B_1 significantly inhibit the mitotic process in human embryonic lung cells.

Platt et al. (63) observed that aflatoxin mixtures were toxic to chick embryos, and this observation has been amply confirmed and extended with aflatoxin B_1. The data of Verrett *et al.* (*82*) indicate the sensitivity of the chick embryo, in which the LD_{50} is 0.048 μg. per egg when administration is made via the yolk, and 0.025 μg. per egg when the compound is applied in the air cell. In both cases, the fertilized eggs were treated prior to incubation.

Although they have not yet been fully exploited, the great sensitivity of cell cultures and embryos to the toxic effects of aflatoxin makes them potentially important bioassay systems for detection of low-level contamination of foodstuffs. The relative lack of specificity of the embryo lethality response, however, requires that the test materials be available in highly purified form.

In all species except the sheep, animals which consume sublethal quantities of the compounds for several days or weeks develop a subacute toxicity syndrome which commonly includes moderate to severe liver damage as a prominent pathologic sign. The development of biliary hyperplasia represents the most consistently observed lesion. The extent and severity of this histopathologic change can be semiquantitatively evaluated by the pathologist and has been used as a criterion of aflatoxin activity, particularly in the young duckling (*86*). This response provided the basis for biological assays for aflatoxin contamination of foodstuffs (*5, 59*) and the response has been studied in some detail (*17, 58, 88*). When the toxin is administered repeatedly to the day-old duckling over a 5-day period, characteristic lesions are observed on the seventh day. Detailed examination (*86*) of the quantitative aspects of this response has revealed that the administration of aflatoxin B_1 to ducklings according to this dose schedule results in reproducible responses at a dose level of 0.5 μg. per day (approximately 2.5 μg. total dose). This level of sensitivity has made the assay useful in detecting contamination of foodstuffs.

Subacute toxic effects of the aflatoxins in monkeys have been reported by Tulpule *et al.* (*75*). In these experiments, young (1.5 to 2.0 kg.) Rhesus monkeys were fed either 1.0 mg. of aflatoxin per day or 0.5 mg. per day for 18 days, then 1.0 mg. per day thereafter. All animals developed anorexia and died in 14 to 28 days. The principal histopathologic findings included liver lesions similar to those seen in ducklings (portal inflammation and fatty change), suggestive of biliary cirrhosis. In these experiments, the animals received a total dose of 10 to 15 mg. per kg. of body weight of a preparation containing 60% aflatoxin B_1 and 40% G_1. This report comprises the only published information available to date concerning the effects of the compounds in primates.

The acute potency of the aflatoxins is clearly established by the effects described above. Equally significant effects result from prolonged administration of sublethal quantities of the compounds to animals. In early investigations of aflatoxin-contaminated peanut meals, investigators

at the Unilever Research Laboratories in England (*47*) fed diets containing
highly toxic peanut meals to rats.   After 6 months' feeding of 20% peanut
meal (aflatoxin content not stated) in a purified diet, 9 of 11 rats developed
multiple liver tumors, and two had developed lung metastases.   This
finding represented the first indication of the carcinogenic properties of
aflatoxin-contaminated, toxic peanut meals and has since been amply
confirmed (*12, 19, 48, 65, 69*).   Subsequent investigations have been
concerned with the demonstration that the aflatoxins were the responsible
carcinogenic agents and with the determination of dose, duration of exposure, and other conditions for tumor induction by these compounds.

Although precise dose-response conditions have not yet been established, some information is available regarding the dose-response
relationships between tumor incidence in rats and aflatoxin content of
contaminated peanut meals.   The results of studies on several such
meals (*57*) demonstrate good correlation between liver tumor incidence
and dietary aflatoxin content over the range of 0.06 to 1.8 p.p.m. of aflatoxin.   The highest level resulted in more than 90% tumor incidence
when fed over a period of 370 days.   The lowest level of aflatoxin detected
(0.005 p.p.m.) failed to induce liver tumors within a similar time period
(384 days).

Mice appear to be relatively resistant to acute poisoning by the
aflatoxins as evidenced by results of short-term feeding of heavily contaminated peanut meals.   Platonow (*62*) studied effects of diets containing
15, 30, or 80% of a peanut meal containing 4.5 p.p.m. each of aflatoxins
B_1 and G_1 and 0.6 p.p.m. each of aflatoxins B_2 and G_2.   These diets were
fed to groups of mice (20 to 25 grams) for at least 3 months.   During
this time, no effects were noted on feed intake or body weight, and no
mortality occurred.   Histopathologic examination revealed no significant
changes in liver or other tissues studied.

Recent experiments with purified aflatoxin preparations have indicated that continuous feeding is not required for hepatoma induction
in rats.   In the studies of Barnes and Butler (*12*), rats were fed 1.75
p.p.m. of aflatoxin (containing 80% aflatoxins with G_1 present in higher
quantities than B_1) in the diet for 89 days, then returned to an aflatoxin-
free diet.   All of three treated animals ultimately developed liver cancer
more than 300 days following withdrawal.

In somewhat similar experiments in our laboratories (*86*) we have
administered an unfractionated mixture of partially purified aflatoxins
(approximately 30% B_1, 20% G_1) to rats by stomach tube.   Each animal
was treated daily for 30 days, then held without treatment for a further
10 months.   Animals which received the highest dose (150 μg. per rat
per day) had well-developed liver tumors 5 months following withdrawal
of treatment.   Even those receiving the lowest dose studied (15 μg. per
rat per day) showed significant incidence of precancerous lesions, which

probably would have progressed to tumors over a longer period of time. These data would indicate that continuous exposure to the compounds is not required for liver tumor induction.

On the basis of these preliminary data, it has been possible to estimate the effective dose of aflatoxin B_1 for the induction of liver tumors in rats. Butler (18) has estimated this dose to be in the order of 10 μg. per day. When this value is compared with similar estimates for other hepato-carcinogens such as dimethylnitrosamine (750 μg. per day) and butter yellow (9000 μg. per day), the relative potency of the compound is readily apparent.

Recent studies by Ashley et al. (8, 9) and by Sinnhuber et al. (72) have suggested that the rainbow trout may be considerably more sensitive than the rat to the hepatocarcinogenic effects of the aflatoxins. These investigators have shown that rainbow trout develop liver tumors at significant incidence rates when fed purified diets containing only 0.5 to 2.0 μg. of aflatoxin B_1 per kilogram—i.e., 0.5 to 2.0 p.p.b. The apparent sensitivity of this species has led to the recognition (8) of the potential role of the aflatoxins as etiologic agents in the so-called "trout hepatoma syndrome" (33, 37).

In a different test system, Dickens and Jones (25) studied the effects of multiple subcutaneous injections of aflatoxins B_1 and G_1 in rats. A mixed preparation (about 38% B_1 and 56% G_1) of the compounds dissolved in peanut oil was administered to groups of rats twice weekly. One group received 50 μg. at each injection, and the treatment was continued for 50 weeks; a second group received 500 μg. at each injection for only 8 weeks, after which treatment was discontinued. In the former group, 6/6 animals developed sarcomas or fibrosarcomas at the injection site within a 60-week period. At the higher dose level, 5/5 animals developed tumors within a 30-week period. These observations indicate that the compounds are also carcinogenic for the subcutaneous tissues of the rat.

Biochemical alterations caused by aflatoxins have been studied in a number of biological systems. Smith (74) investigated the effects of aflatoxin B_1 on the rate of in vitro incorporation of leucine-C^{14} into proteins by rat and duckling liver slices. Significant reduction in the rate of incorporation in 80 mg. of rat liver slices was caused by adding 10 μg. of toxin, and almost complete suppression was effected by 200 μg. Duckling liver slices studied under similar conditions were more sensitive, showing significant reduction with 3.5 μg. of toxin. These observations suggested that the compound suppresses protein synthesis by some mechanism, and this activity has been investigated in other test systems.

We have studied (71) the in vivo incorporation of leucine into rat liver proteins at time intervals following single sublethal doses of aflatoxin B_1. A single oral dose of 4.76 mg. of toxin per kg. of body weight, immediately suppressed, then increased amino acid incorporation. Inhibition was clearly evident within 30 minutes following dosing, and was maximal at 6 hours, at which time the rate of incorporation was reduced to approximately 50% of the control value. This was followed by a 72-hour period during which the incorporation in the treated animals exceeded the control rate, being maximal 72 hours after toxin administration.

These results led to further investigation of effects on synthesis of specific proteins in which we have determined the influence of the toxin on liver tryptophan pyrrolase induction by hydrocortisone and by tryptophan in rats (87). The increase in activity of this enzyme in liver 6 hours following intraperitoneal injection of 150 mg. of hydrocortisone per kg. or 600 mg. of tryptophan per kg. was studied in weanling male rats. Animals receiving aflatoxin B_1 at a level of 1 mg. per kg. and hydrocortisone showed no increase in enzyme activity 6 and 12 hours following toxin administration, as compared to a fourfold increase in those receiving hydrocortisone only. Although this inhibitory effect was not apparent 5 days later, larger doses (3 or 5 mg. per kg.) of aflatoxin caused inhibition of enzyme induction which persisted for at least 10 days. Animals treated with 5 mg. of toxin per kg. showed no significant inhibition of enzyme induction by tryptophan. The inhibition of hydrocortisone induction, which involves *de novo* enzyme synthesis and the failure to inhibit tryptophan induction which depends upon enzyme stabilization without synthesis suggests that the toxin is an inhibitor of protein synthesis at some specific stage. The locus of this effect is currently under investigation.

Black and Altschul (13) have recently reported finding that gibberellic acid-induced increases in lipase and α-amylase activity of the germinating cottonseed are inhibited by aflatoxin. This effect is similar qualitatively to the inhibition of enzyme induction in rat liver described above although it is not yet clear whether the mechanism of inhibition is related in the two systems.

The aflatoxins also have interesting effects in tissues of plant origin. Schoental and White (70) have shown that aflatoxins in concentrations of 25 μg. per ml. inhibit the germination of the seeds of cress (*Lepidium sativum*, L.). Smaller concentrations apparently interfered with chlorophyll synthesis since there was complete absence of color when the germinating seeds were exposed to the compounds in concentrations of 10 μg. per ml.

The rapid development of knowledge concerning the aflatoxin problem has stimulated new research activities in the mycotoxin field, some of which have already begun to yield results. For example, workers in South Africa (79) have recently ioslated and chemically characterized a new compound, ochratoxin A.

This compound was isolated from cultures of *Aspergillus ochraceus*, an organism known to invade stored wheat, and has an LD_{50} in ducklings similar to that of aflatoxin B_1.   It is virtually certain that, as the search is intensified, additional toxic fungal metabolites will be discovered.

Conclusions

The background of information summarized here illustrates the range and diversity of problems which can arise from contamination of food stuffs by mycotoxins.   Utilization of world food resources with maximum efficiency and safety therefore will require the development of agricultural and processing methods which will prevent mycotoxin contamination or permit detection and removal of contaminants when present.   These factors will be of particular importance to the exploitation of new foods for human use.

Acknowledgment

The contributions of P.M. Newberne, R.C. Shank, and M.M. Abdel Kader to these studies are gratefully acknowledged.

Literature Cited

(1) Adye, J., Mateles, R. I., *Biochim. Biophys. Acta* **86**, 418 (1964).
(2) Allcroft, R., Carnaghan, R. B. A., *Chem. Ind.*, **1963**, 50.
(3) Allcroft, R., Carnaghan, R. B. A., Sargeant, K., O'Kelly, J. *Vet. Rec.* **73**, 428 (1961).
(4) Andrellos, P. J., Reid, G. B., *J. Assoc. Offic Agr. Chemists* **47**, 801 (1964).
(5) Armbrecht, B. H., Fitzhugh, O. B., *Toxicol. Appl. Pharmacol.* **6**, 421 (1964).
(6) Asao, T., Buchi, G., Abdel Kader, M. M., Chang, S. B., Wick, E. L., Wogan, G. N., *J. Am. Chem. Soc.* **85**, 1706 (1963).
(7) *Ibid.*, **87**, 882 (1965).
(8) Ashley, L. M., Halver, J. E., Gardner, W. K. Jr., Wogan, G. N., *Federation Proc.* **24**, 627 (1965).
(9) Ashley, L. M., Halver, J. E., Wogan, G. N., *Ibid.*, **23**, 105 (1964).
(10) Asplin, F. D., Carnaghan, R. B. A., *Vet. Rec.* **73**, 1215 (1961).
(11) Barger, G., "Ergot and Ergotism," Gurney and Jackson, London, 1931.
(12) Barnes, J. M., Butler, W. H., *Nature* **202**, 1016 (1964).
(13) Black, H. S., Altschul, A. M., *Biochem. Biophys. Res. Commun.* **19**, 661 (1965).
(14) Blount, W. P., *J. Brit. Turkey Fed.* **9**, 52, 55–8, 61, 77 (1961).
(15) Bullock, E., Roberts, J. C., Underwood, J. G., *J. Chem. Soc.* **1962**, 4179–83.

(16) Burnside, J. E., Sippel, W. L., Forgacs, J., Carll, W. T., Atwood, M. B., Doll, E. R., *Am. J. Vet. Res.* **18**, 817 (1957).
(17) Butler, W. H., *J. Pathol. Bacteriol.*, **88**, 189 (1964).
(18) Butler, W. H., in "Mycotoxins in Foodstuffs," G. N. Wogan, ed., p. 175, M. I. T. Press, Cambridge, 1965.
(19) Butler, W. H., Barnes, J. M., *Brit. J. Cancer* **17**, 699 (1964).
(20) Carnaghan, R. B. A., Hartley, R. D., O'Kelly, J., *Nature* **200**, 1101 (1963).
(21) Chang, S. B., Abdel Kader, M. M., Wick, E. L., Wogan, G. N., *Science* **142**, 1191 (1963).
(22) Cheung, K. K., Sim, G. A., *Nature* **201**, 1185 (1964).
(23) DeIongh, H., Beerthuis, R. K., Vles, R. O., Barrett, C. B., Ord, W. O., *Biochim. Biophys. Acta* **65**, 548 (1962).
(24) DeIongh, H., Vles, R. O., De Vogel, P., in "Mycotoxins in Foodstuffs," G. N. Wogan, ed., p. 235, M. I. T. Press, Cambridge, 1965.
(25) Dickens, F., Jones, H. E. H., *Brit. J. Cancer* **17**, 691 (1964).
(26) Dobrosky, T. M., *Grain Storage Newsletter* **1** [1] (1959).
(27) Dodd, D. C., in "Mycotoxins in Foodstuffs," G. N. Wogan, ed., p. 105, M. I. T. Press, Cambridge, 1965.
(28) Forgacs, J., Carll, W. T., *Advan. Vet. Sci.* **7**, 274 (1962).
(29) Friedrichsons, J., Mathieson, A. McL., *Tetrahedron Letters* **26**, 1265 (1962).
(30) Garner, R. J., "Veterinary Toxicology," p. 303, Williams & Wilkins, Baltimore, 1961.
(31) Gibbons, W. J., *Vet. Med.* **52**, 297 (1958).
(32) Glenn, B. L., Monlux, A. W., Panciera, R. J., *Pathol. Vet.* **1**, 469 (1964).
(33) Halver, J. E., in "Mycotoxins in Foodstuffs," G. N. Wogan, ed., p. 209, M. I. T. Press, Cambridge, 1965.
(34) Harding, J. D. J., Done, J. T., Lewis, G., Allcroft, R., *Res. Vet. Sci.* **4**, 217 (1963).
(35) Hartley, R. D., Nesbitt, B. F., O'Kelly, J., *Nature* **198**, 1056 (1963).
(36) Hiscocks, E. S., in "Mycotoxins in Foodstuffs," G. N. Wogan, ed., p. 15, M. I. T. Press, Cambridge, 1965.
(37) Hueper, W. C., Payne, W. W., *Natl. Cancer Inst. J.* **27**, 1123 (1961).
(38) Joffe, A. Z., *Bull. Res. Council Israel* **8D**, 81 (1960).
(39) *Ibid.*, **9D**, 101 (1960).
(40) Joffe, A. Z., in "Mycotoxins in Foodstuffs," G. N. Wogan, ed., p. 77, M. I. T. Press, Cambridge, 1965.
(41) Joffe, A. Z., *Plant Soil* **18**, 31 (1963).
(42) Juhasz, S., Greczi, E., *Nature* **203**, 961 (1964).
(43) Kidder, R. W., Beardsley, D. W., Erwin, T. C., *Florida Agr. Exptl. Sta. Bull.* **620** (1961).
(44) Kinosita, R., Shikata, T., in "Mycotoxins in Foodstuffs," G. N. Wogan, ed., p. 111, M. I. T. Press, Cambridge, 1965.
(45) Kobayashi, Y., Uraguchi, K., Sakai, F., Tatsuno, T., Tsukioka, M., Noguchi, Y., Tsunoda, H., Miyake, M., Saito, M., Enomoto, M., Shikata, T., Ishiko, T., *Proc. Japan Acad.* **35**, 501 (1959).
(46) Kraybill, H. D., Shimkin, M. B., *Advan. Cancer Res.* **8**, 191 (1964).
(47) Lancaster, M. C., Jenkins, F. P., Philp, J. McL., *Nature* **192**, 1095 (1961).
(48) LeBreton, E., Frayssinet, C., Boy, J., *Compt. Rend.* **255**, 784 (1962).
(49) Legator, M. S., Withrow, A., *J. Assoc. Office Agr. Chemists* **47**, 1007 (1964).
(50) Loosmore, R. M., Allcroft, R., Tutton, E. A., Carnaghan, R. B. A., *Vet. Rec.* **76**, 64 (1964).

(51) Loosmore, R. M., Harding, J. D. J., *Ibid.*, **73**, 1362 (1961).
(52) Loosmore, R. M., Markson, L. M., *Ibid.*, **73**, 813 (1961).
(53) Miyake, M., Saito, M., in "Mycotoxins in Foodstuffs," G. N. Wogan, ed., p. 133, M. I. T. Press, Cambridge, 1965.
(54) Mortimer, P. H., Taylor, A., Done, J., *Res. Vet. Sci.* **3**, 147 (1962).
(55) Nesbitt, B. F., O'Kelly, J., Sargeant, K., Sheridan, A., *Nature* **195**, 1062 (1962).
(56) Nesheim, S., *J. Assoc. Office Agr. Chemists* **47**, 1010 (1964).
(57) Newberne, P. M., in "Mycotoxins in Foodstuffs," G. N. Wogan, ed., p. 187, M. I. T. Press, Cambridge, 1965.
(58) Newberne, P. M., Carlton, W. W., Wogan, G. N., *Pathol. Vet.* **1**, 105 (1964).
(59) Newberne, P. M., Wogan, G. N., Carlton, W. W., Abdel Kader, M. M., *Toxicol. Appl. Pharmacol.* **6**, 542 (1964).
(60) Percival, J. C., *New Zealand J. Agr. Res.* **2**, 1041 (1959).
(61) Peters, J. A., Smith, L. M., *Biochem. J.* **92**, 379 (1964).
(62) Platonow, N., *Vet. Rec.* **76**, 589 (1964).
(63) Platt, B. S., Stewart, R. J. C., Gupta, S. R., *Nutr. Soc. Proc.* **21**, xxx (1962).
(64) Rothlin, E., Bircher, R., *Prog. Allergy* **3**, 434 (1952).
(65) Salmon, W. D., Newberne, P. M., *Cancer Res.* **23**, 571 (1963).
(66) Sargeant, K., Carnaghan, R. B. A., Allcroft, R., *Chem. Ind. (London)* **1963,** 53.
(67) Sargeant, K., O'Kelly, J., Carnaghan, R. B. A., Allcroft, R., *Vet. Rec.* **73**, 1219 (1961).
(68) Sargeant, K., Sheridan, A., O'Kelly, J., Carnaghan, R. B. A., *Nature* **192**, 1096 (1961).
(69) Schoental, R., *Brit. J. Cancer* **15**, 812 (1961).
(70) Schoental, R., White, A. F., *Nature* **205**, 57 (1965)
(71) Shank, R. C., Wogan, G. N., *Federation Proc.* **23**, 200 (1964).
(72) Sinnhuber, R. O., Wales, J. H., Engebrecht, R. H., Amend, D. F., Kray, W. D., Ayres, J. L., Ashton, W. E., *Ibid.*, **24**, 627 (1965).
(73) Slater, T. F., Strauli, U. D., Sawyer, B., *Res. Vet. Sci.* **5**, 450 (1964).
(74) Smith, R. H., *Biochem. J.* **88**, 50P (1963).
(75) Tulpule, P. G., Madhavan, T. V., Gopalan, C., *Lancet* **1**, 962 (1964).
(76) U. S. Department of Agriculture, Washington ,D. C., **ARS-20–1** (1954).
(77) Uraguchi, K., Tatsuno, T., Sakai, F., Tsukioka, M., Sakai, Y., Yonemitsu, O., Ito, H., Miyake, M., Saito, M., Enomoto, M., Shikata, T., Ishiko, T., *Japan J. Exptl. Med.* **31**, 19 (1961).
(78) Uraguchi, K., Tatsuno, T., Tsukioka, M., Sakai, Y., Sakai, F., Kobayashi, Y., Saito, M., Enomoto M., Miyake, M., *Ibid.*, **31**, 1 (1961).
(79) Van der Merwe K. J., Steyn, P. S., Fourie, L., Scott, De B., Theron, J. J., *Nature* **205**, 1112 (1965).
(80) Van Der Zijden, A. S. M., Koelensmid, W. A. A., Boldingh, J., Barrett, C. B., Ord, W. O., Philp, J., *Nature* **195**, 1060 (1962).
(81) Van Dorp, D. A., Van Der Zijden, A. S. M., Beerthuis, R. K., Sparreboom, S., Ord, W. O., De Jong, K., Keuning, R., *Rec. Trav. Chim. Pays-Bas* **82**, 587 (1963).
(82) Verrett, M. J., Marliac, J. P., McLaughlin, J., Jr., *J. Assoc. Office Agr. Chemists* **47**, 1003 (1964).
(83) Wilson, B. J., Wilson, C. H., *J. Bacteriol.* **84**, 283 (1962).
(84) Wogan, G. N., *Bacteriol. Rev.* in press.
(85) Wogan, G. N., Editor, "Mycotoxins in Foodstuffs," M. I. T. Press, Cambridge, 1965.

(86) Wogan, G. N., in "Mycotoxins in Foodstuffs," G. N. Wogan, ed., p. 163, M. I. T. Press, Cambridge, 1965.
(87) Wogan, G. N., Friedman, M. A., *Federation Proc.* **24,** 627 (1965).
(88) Wogan, G. N., Newberne, P. M., *Ibid.,* **23,** 200 (1964).

RECEIVED October 12, 1965. Contribution 750, Department of Nutrition and Food Science. Work supported by contract PH 43–62–468 with the National Cancer Institute, National Institutes of Health.

15

Some Approaches to the Elimination of Aflatoxin From Protein Concentrates

LEO A. GOLDBLATT

Southern Regional Research Laboratory, New Orleans, La.

Three approaches to eliminating aflatoxin from protein concentrates are: prevention, removal, and inactivation. The best approach is prevention. Mechanical damage should be avoided during harvesting and handling; and moisture, temperature, and infestation with insects should be controlled during storage. Mechanically removing the contaminated kernels or seeds may be effective. Alternatively, removing aflatoxin with selective solvents presents good potential. Polar solvents can be used to remove aflatoxin from oilseeds during processing to oil and meal or from the finished protein concentrates. Aflatoxin must be inactivated without destroying nutritive value or leaving toxic residues. Exposure to moist heat and treatment with gaseous reagents such as ammonia, or with reagents added during processing, may offer practical means of detoxification.

Aflatoxin is the product of a mold. Molds and mold damage have long been of interest to those concerned with agricultural products because of economic losses due to obvious decay and more insidious adverse changes in the odor, taste, appearance, and nutritive value, and because, mold causes seeds to lose their viability, making them unsuitable for planting. Much research has been done to find ways to minimize such losses. Most of this research has been directed toward practical methods of preventing or minimizing mold growth by determining at which stages mold develops during the growth, harvesting, and subsequent handling of a commodity and which conditions at these stages favor or inhibit the growth of molds. In consequence, although precise information may be lacking, we know how to reduce molds sharply. When the aflatoxin problem was recognized, the importance of this knowledge increased since much of the information already developed was relevant to minimizing the occurrence of this specific fungal metabolite in agricultural products.

Prevention

All molds do not produce aflatoxin, and even growth of aflatoxin-producing molds is not necessarily accompanied by production of aflatoxin. In general, however, a product for human consumption should not be prepared from damaged seeds or from seeds of bad cultural history.   Prevention, then, comprises the first approach.   Much of my discussion of prevention is drawn from a report recently issued by the Agricultural Research Service, United States Department of Agriculture (*24*).

Modern farming know-how and equipment make it possible to keep mold levels to a minimum.   Although procedures recommended for preventing mold damage vary with the crop, its stage of maturity, and environmental conditions, certain broad principles apply to most oilseed and grain crops.   Mold prevention begins on the farm with properly planting and growing the crop.   There is much evidence that sound, healthy seed is more resistant to mold growth and production of aflatoxin than damaged seed.   Using sound, fungus-free, viable seed, fertilizing properly, and controlling insects and diseases not only increase vigor of the young plants but also reduce the likelihood that mold will become established in the plant at maturity.

Although we do not know enough about how specific cultural practices during crop growth affect the later development of mold in a crop, we know that harvesting and handling phases are critical.   In harvesting, equipment should be adjusted and operated to avoid mechanical damage. Machinery now used may have to be slowed down or even redesigned. Harvesting promptly at maturity is generally to be recommended.   Permitting the crop to stand in the field after ripening is an invitation to invasion by insects and mold.   Oilseed and grain crops should be cleaned thoroughly to remove foreign matter and damaged seed, and storage areas should be weather-tight, clean, and free of insects.   Kernels attacked by insects are especially susceptible to invasion by molds.

Moisture control is crucial in mold prevention.   Moisture content is higher in immature crops.   Warm temperatures also encourage mold, especially in combination with high relative humidity.   Consequently it is important to dry the commodity to a safe moisture level as soon after harvesting as practicable and maintain it at that level.   For this, proper aeration is required.   Without adequate aeration, significant differences in temperature between different locations in stored material may build up, causing the moisture to concentrate to damaging levels in the colder spots and resulting in serious mold growth, even when the average moisture content would appear to be at a safe level. Mold produces moisture as it grows, so once fungal growth has started in one excessively wet kernel the moisture content of adjacent kernels increases and further fungal proliferation may proceed, resulting in a pocket of highly contaminated material. Accordingly, adequate sampling and testing are a must.

Peanuts. Damaged peanuts are particularly susceptible to mold. Damage prevention begins with effective pod-insect and disease control during the growing period and continues through harvest.

Peanuts are more like green vegetables than most oil and cereal crops in the care they require in harvest, handling, and storage to prevent mold damage. When dug, peanuts usually have an average moisture content between 35 and 55%, with individual seeds on the same plant ranging from below 30 to as much as 70% moisture. For safe storage, the moisture must be reduced to about 8%. Combines pick up some earth and foreign matter, which should be removed promptly. Machinery should be operated so that the peanuts are not damaged—for example, by operation at excessive speed.

Cottonseed. In the past, concern over *Aspergillus flavus* in growing cotton centered on the fact that the organism yellows and downgrades the lint. Mold in cottonseed was also known to increase the free fatty acids in the oil and thus reduce its value. We know that some strains of *A. flavus* can produce aflatoxin in cottonseed. Overfertilization and overirrigation promote rank growth and boll rot, which is caused by some molds, in the lower portion of the plant. Bottom defoliation when these lower bolls are mature prevents boll rot. Cotton should be harvested as soon after opening as is economically feasible, but not when the cotton is damp. Mechanical cotton pickers and gins should be operated to prevent or minimize seed cracking. Moisture should be reduced as promptly as possible. If moisture in the seed cotton is high or large amounts of green leaves or other trash are present, the cotton may deteriorate and mold begin to grow within 24 hours. Cottonseed with about 10% moisture content has been stored without significant damage.

Soybeans. With soybeans, as with other oilseeds and small grains, avoiding seed damage and reducing the moisture content to safe levels promptly after harvest are important to prevent mold. Combines should be operated at a speed that does not crack the seed. Since the moisture content of the field may change during the day, it may be necessary to adjust the combine periodically to reduce splits and other damage.

Removal

The potential for molds and possibility of toxicity of mold metabolites accent a long-standing concern for quality. Advances in basic knowledge and in techniques for growing, harvesting, and handling crops will make it easier to produce and market commodities free of mold damage.   However, damage may occur despite the most strenuous efforts directed at prevention.   Hence, two other approaches must be considered—removal and inactivation.

Let us examine first the potential for removal.   Two approaches may be considered: physical removal or culling of contaminated from sound seed or kernels, and removal of the aflatoxin.

Removal of Contaminated Kernels or Seed.   The fortuitous circumstance that the vast majority of the aflatoxin in contaminated materials may reside in a relatively small number of seeds affords an exceptional opportunity for effectively yet economically reducing the aflatoxin content of selected materials by mechanically removing contaminated seeds. In the case of peanuts, even in rare lots having relatively large amounts of aflatoxin—and we have diligently sought such lots for investigation—only a very small percentage of the kernels contain aflatoxin.   For example, we have found a number of peanuts with more than 100,000 parts per billion of aflatoxin and a few with more than a million p.p.b.   If just one peanut with a million p.p.b. of aflatoxin is admixed with 10,000 kernels that contain none, the whole lot will assay at the relatively high level of 100 p.p.b. of aflatoxin.   Although low incidence of contaminated kernels makes sampling very difficult, it affords an excellent opportunity for economical culling.

The peanut industry has recognized that culling on the basis of physical characteristics, such as size (including immatures), obvious damage, and discoloration, appears feasible and has taken steps to improve mechanical separation.   Electronic sorters seem to be very effective.   In a series of experimental runs, it was demonstrated conclusively that suspect material can be removed from raw peanuts by electronic and manual picking procedures, although further improvement resulted when the picking procedures were repeated following roasting and blanching (*13*, *17*). Segregation after splitting peanut kernels may be necessary to eliminate aflatoxin resulting from mold invasion of the interior not manifest on the surface.   Also, peanut kernels invaded by mold between the two cotyledons appear to be distinctly harder to split than sound kernels.   The mold or mycellium seems almost to cement the two cotyledons together. Careful control of the splitting operation and removal of the whole kernels may offer a practical way to cull kernels with hidden mold damage.

In the case of cottonseed, segregation on the basis of density may be possible.   A projection device to separate infested from noninfested grain kernels had been described by Katz, Farrell, and Milner (*12*).   Several years ago various projection devices such as the ARS differentiator and the cottonseed cleaning belt unit were developed at the Southern Utilization Research and Development Division and operated on a pilot-plant scale to separate trash from cottonseed. These devices graded cotton-seed according to density and other characteristics. The bulk of the foreign matter and the very light immature and decayed seed collect relatively close to the projector, and the seeds that project further are of higher quality—i.e., higher in oil and nitrogen content and lower in free fatty acid in the oil (9).

A high correlation has been reported (6) between fat acidity and incidence of aflatoxin, at least in the case of peanuts:

Relation of Aflatoxin to Fat Acidity in Peanuts

Fat Acidity	% Samples Containing Aflatoxin
< 0.3	8
0.31–1.0	30
> 1.0	70

Accordingly, since high free fatty acid in fresh cottonseed oil is associated with mold damage, such a device may afford a means of mechanically removing all or major portions of aflatoxin-contaminated cottonseed. When this hypothesis was tested experimentally, a marked separation was obtained; some portions contained relatively large amounts of aflatoxin, whereas other portions contained relatively little or none. Classification of cottonseed on an air table is an effective way of selecting cottonseed to give maximum emergence after planting, the denser seed giving the higher emergence (11). Impermeable seed coat cottonseed, so-called "hard seed," has been reported to develop much less fat acidity than "soft" cottonseed stored under the same conditions (4). Thus, the possibility exists of controlling mold invasion, and hence production of aflatoxin in cottonseed, by genetic means. The Crops Research Division, U. S. Department of Agriculture, in cooperation with several state agricultural experiment stations, has undertaken long-range research to investigate genetic resistance and the way it is inherited, and to breed varieties of peanuts with pods and seeds relatively more resistant to molds that produce toxins.

Removal of Aflatoxin from Contaminated Kernels or Seed. The feasibility of removing aflatoxin by a simple washing or "laundering" operation—for example, washing whole peanut kernels with water or dilute alkali—has been the object of much discussion. The aflatoxin contents of different parts of peanut kernels containing large amounts of aflatoxin can be determined (5). In Figure 1 is illustrated one cotyledon of such a peanut kernel. The other cotyledon of this kernel, not illustrated, contained more than a million parts per billion of aflatoxin. Thin layers were carefully sliced from the curved surface of the half kernel shown in Figure 1. Other selected portions were completely excised with a razor blade and various portions were analyzed separately (5). The

Treatment with ammonia or ammonium hydroxide has been reported to detoxify tung meal (*23*) and castor meal (*8*).   Recently Masri reported (*16*) that treating a toxic peanut meal (about 1000 p.p.b. aflatoxin B$_1$) with ammonia eliminated the toxicity. Cooperative work at the Southern Regional Research Laboratory has confirmed and extended this significant finding. Accordingly, it appears that alkali treatment of oilseeds during processing or of the finished protein concentrate offers a promising approach to the elimination of aflatoxin.

Acknowledgment

The contributions and cooperation of L. P. Codifer, Jr., A. F. Cucullu, F. G. Dollear, P. H. Eaves, A. O. Franz, H. K. Gardner, Jr., G. R. Hennessey, L. S. Lee, G. E. Mann, R. Y. Mayne, W. A. Pons, Jr., J. A. Robertson, D. B. Skau, and H. L. E. Vix of the Southern Utilization Research and Development Division, and of F. DeEds and M. S. Masri, of the Western Utilization Research and Development Division, are gratefully acknowledged.

Literature Cited

(1) Allcroft, R., Carnaghan, R. B. A., Sargeant, K., O'Kelly, J., *Vet. Rec.* **73**, 428 (1961).
(2) Austwick, P. K. C., Ayerst, G., *Chem. Ind. (London)* **1963**, 55.
(3) Blount, W. P., *J. Brit. Turkey Fed.* **9** (2) 52, 55–8, 61, 77, esp. 58 (1961).
(4) Christiansen, M. R., Moore, R. P., Rhyne, C. L., *Agron. J.* **52**, 81 (1960).
(5) Cucullu, A. F., Lee, L. S., Mayne, R. Y., Goldblatt, L. A., (Abs.) *J. Am. Oil Chemists' Soc.* **42** (3), 151A (1965); **43**, 89 (1966).
(6) Dupont de Dinechin, B., "Observations on Agricultural Conditions Liable to Influence Aflatoxin Development on Groundnuts in Senegal," UNICEF Meeting on Groundnut Toxicity Problems at Tropical Products Institute, London, Oct. 28–29, 1963.
(7) Fischbach, H., Campbell, A. D., *J. Assoc. Offic. Agr. Chemists* **48**, 28 (1965).
(8) Gardner, H. K., Jr., D'Aquin, E. L., Koltun, S. P., McCourtney, E. J., Vix, H. L. E., Gastrock, E. A., *J. Am. Oil Chemists' Soc.* **37**, 142 (1960).
(9) Holzenthal, L. L., D'Aquin, E. L., Molaison, H. J., Gentry, W. T., Jr., Vix, H. L. E., *Oil Mill Gaz.* **6**, No. 6, 19 (1956).
(10) Interdepartmental Working Party on Groundnut Toxicity, London, Research Report, p. 18, 1962.
(11) Justus, N., Loe, R. H., Dick, J. B., Christiansen, M. N., "Effect of Gravity Separation on Cottonseed," Misssippi State University Expt. Station, Information Sheet **880** (March 1965).
(12) Katz, R., Farrell, E. P., Milner, M., *Cereal Chem.* **31**, 316–25 (1954).
(13) Kensler, C. J., "Present Status and Future Outlook," Symposium on Food Toxins of Fungal Origin, Institute of Food Technologists, Kansas City, Mo. May 16–20, 1965.
(14) King, W. H., Kuck, J. C., Frampton, V. L., *J. Am. Oil Chemists' Soc.*, **38**, 19 (1961).

(15) Kraybill, H. F., Shimkin, M. B., *Advan. Cancer Res.* **8**, 191–246, esp. 211 (1964).

(16) Masri, M. S., "Biochemical Evaluation of Aflatoxin" (Abs.), Western Experiment Station Collaborators Conference on Importance of Mold Metabolites in Agricultural Products, 1965, program and abstracts of papers, Western Utilization Research and Development Division, U. S. Department of Agriculture, Albany, Calif., pp. 9–10, 1965.

(17) National Peanut Council, Washington, D. C., Voluntary Code of Good Practices for Purchasing, Handling, Storage, and Processing of Peanuts, 1965.

(18) Pomeranz, Y., *Cereal Sci. Today* **9** (4), 93–4, 96, 150 (1964).

(19) Pons, W. A., Jr., Goldblatt, L. A., *J. Am. Oil Chemists' Soc.* **42**, 471 (1965).

(20) Raymond, W. D., Mycotoxin Problems in the United Kingdom," Symposium on Food Toxins of Fungal Origin, Institute of Food Technologists, Kansas City, Mo., May 16–20, 1965; *WHO/FAO/UNICEF—Protein Advisory Group News Bull.* **5**, 79 Group, (April 1965).

(21) Robertson, J. A., Jr., Lee, L. S., Cucullu, A. F., Goldblatt, L. A., *J. Am. Oli Chemists' Soc.* **42, 467** (1965).

(22) Sreenivasamurthy, V., Jayaraman, A., Parpia, H. A. B., "Aflatoxin in Indian Peanuts. Analysis and Extraction," in "Mycotoxins in Foodstuffs," G. N. Wogan, ed., pp. 251–60, Massachusetts Institute of Technology Press, 1965.

(23) Ulrey, D. G., U. S. Patent **2,641,542** (June 9, 1953).

(24) U. S. Agricultural Research Service, "Preventing Mold-Caused Toxins in Farm Commodities," U. S. Agr. Res. Serv. ARS-22-92 (March 1965).

RECEIVED October 12, 1965.

Discussion

Bernard L. Oser: Dr. Goldblatt has pointed out that of the several alternatives—prevention, removal, or inactivation of aflatoxin—the first was the consummation most devoutly to be wished. Even if removal or inactivation were feasible, these procedures might have little possibility of application in the United States, where the attitude of the Food and Drug Administration (FDA) is opposed to treating or reconditioning an adulterated food to make it conform with the sanitary requirements for wholesome foods.

Furthermore, in the case of aflatoxin, we are dealing with a substance whose carcinogenicity has been well established in several species of animals. Whether the prohibition under the Delaney clause is applicable in this instance or can be successfully avoided on the ground that the toxic mold is not "added" is a moot question. For example, would FDA permit the reconditioning of botulinum-infected food? Aflatoxin is in the same order of magnitude as a toxic agent.

If removal or inactivation processes are not 100% effective, the problem of "zero tolerance" would still remain, in which connection the recent report of the Pesticide Residue Committee of the National Academy of Sciences/National Research Council is relevant.

It is important to bear in mind the impact of our Government's standards of purity and quality of food on the attitude of other countries, even in so-called underdeveloped areas of the world. Why should a country import a food product which according to U.S. standards is considered adulterated? The positions taken by the FDA with respect to whole fish flour as a food for man or the supplementation of wheat flour with lysine to improve its protein quality are cases in point. The view that these are not permitted or not needed, certainly tends to discourage technological research in their respective fields.

16

Better Protein Quality in Maize

EDWIN T. MERTZ, OLIVER E. NELSON, LYNN S. BATES, and OLIVIA A. VERON

Departments of Biochemistry and Botany and Plant Pathology, Purdue University, Lafayette, Ind.

Maize endosperm homozygous for the opaque-2 mutant gene has a different protein and amino acid composition than normal maize endosperm. Both lysine and tryptophan are increased. The increased lysine content in the endosperm is due to increased lysine in the acid-soluble fraction and in the zein fraction, and reduction in the ratio of zein to glutelin. Feeding tests with young albino rats show that opaque-2 maize proteins are superior to the proteins of any cultivated cereal grain and have a protein efficiency ratio equal to that of heat-treated soybean meal. The opaque-2 gene exerts its effect in a high protein background. A second mutant gene, floury-2, also increases the lysine and, in addition, the methionine content of normal maize endosperm.

For optimum performance, corn is never fed as the sole source of protein in animal rations because of its relatively low protein content and poor balance of essential amino acids. Howe, Jansen, and Gilfillan (*12*) discuss the limiting amino acids in corn and other cereals as determined by feeding tests in animals. An excellent demonstration of its palatability and source of many nutrients was made 12 years ago, when we devised a special diet to determine the amino acid requirements of swine (*1*). The ration in Table I was fed to 5- to 6-week-old crossbred barrows averaging 24.3 pounds. They gained an average of 1 pound a day for 35 days, with a protein efficiency of 3.1 pounds of gain per pound of crude protein. This efficiency is greater than the values of 2.1 to 2.6 obtained with high quality natural proteins (*1*). In this diet (Table I), corn containing 8.2% crude protein (N × 6.25) was supplemented with a mixture of the ten amino acids found in earlier studies to be essential for the weanling pig.

These data show that corn is a good source of nitrogen, carbohydrate, and lipids, and needs only to be supplemented with minerals, vitamins, and certain amino acids to become a complete feed.   A level of 18% protein is usually recommended for the 25-pound weanling pig on a diet of natural feedstuffs.   The diet in Table I contains only 13.2% crude protein, yet is more effective than the natural diet with a higher protein content.

Improving Quality of Corn Proteins by Breeding

The amino acid pattern of whole corn can be changed by breeding for larger germ size in the kernel (*7, 8*).   The protein content of the endosperm can be increased by selective breeding and nitrogen fertilization (*10, 11*).   Unfortunately, the zein content usually increases with increases in nitrogen.   Recently, Telle *et al.* in Mexico City (*30*) determined the lysine content of 182 varieties of corn and found mean values ranging from 260 to 364 mg. per 100 grams of whole kernel.   The average value of two standard Indiana hybrids harvested in 1964 was 300 mg. per 100 grams of whole kernel (*23, 24*).   Telle *et al.* believe that lysine content is a racial characteristic and plan to select specimens for breeding work leading to more nutritious corn hybrids.

Table I.   Experimental Corn–Amino Acid Diet[a]

Component	% of Ration
Corn	88.00
Ten amino acids	6.44
Diammonium citrate	0.57
Minerals	4.30
Liver extract	0.50
Cerelose	0.19
	100.00

[a] Corn contained 8.2% crude protein, 14.1% moisture. Vitamin supplement fed daily.

Extraction and Fractionation of Corn Proteins

The classical Osborne method (*3, 27, 28*) and its modifications (*5, 25*) utilize a dilute salt solution to remove albumins and globulins, an aqueous ethyl alcohol solution to extract zein, and a dilute alkali solution to dissolve the glutelins in maize endosperm.   The methods are time-consuming and in our hands have never resulted in a recovery of more than 85% of the total nitrogen.

In 1957, we developed a copper reagent (Table II) that extracted 89 to 98% of the nitrogen from the defatted endosperm of 11 varieties and 89 to 100% of the nitrogen from the defatted germ of six varieties (*2, 20, 21*). The copper extract was adjusted to pH 3 to precipitate the zein and glutelin.

These fractions may not be identical with the classical zein and glutelin fractions described by Osborne. Mertz and Bressani (20) discuss possible differences.

The supernate contains acid-soluble proteins and was labeled "acid-soluble fraction." The precipitate was dissolved in 66% ethanol at pH 11.5. At this pH the glutelins as well as zein are soluble. The glutelins were then precipitated from solution by dropping the pH to 6.0, leaving the zein in the supernate. This permitted recovery of the three fractions described in Table II.

When the endosperms of several varieties of corn (*Zea mays*) were extracted and fractionated, the distribution of nitrogen among the acid-soluble, zein, and glutelin fractions closely resembled that obtained with saline, ethanol, and alkali extractions in the classical Osborne method (2, 21). The acid-soluble fraction varied from 16 to 26, the zein from 41 to 60, and the glutelin from 17 to 31% of the endosperm nitrogen (Table I).

Table II.   Protein Fractions from Copper Extract[a]

Fraction	Properties	Total Nitrogen Endosperm	Germ, %
Residue	Insoluble in reagent	2–11	0–11
Acid-soluble	Not precipitated from extract at pH 3	16–26	30–40
Zein	Precipitated at pH 3; soluble ethanol, pH 6	41–60	5–10
Glutelin	Precipitated at pH 3; insoluble ethanol, pH 6	17–31	49–54

[a] Copper reagent; 0.4% $CuSO_4 \cdot 5H_2O$, 0.05% Na_2SO_3, 0.2% NaOH.

Chemical Nature of Corn Proteins

Most of the work on corn proteins has been confined to the zein and glutelin components of the endosperm. Zein from endosperm is soluble in neutral (aqueous) ethanol and is therefore classed as a prolamine. Purified zein is a heterogeneous protein with molecules having molecular weights in the range of 20,000 to 50,000 (14). The molecules are long, with an axial ratio of about 20 to 1 (9).

Glutelin is soluble in alkali and in alkaline ethanol (21) but insoluble in neutral (aqueous) ethanol. Purified glutelin is a heterogeneous protein with molecules ranging in weight from 20,000 to more than 1,000,000 (15). Like zein, the smaller molecules have an axial ratio of about 20 to 1 (15).

Since lysine is the most limiting essential amino acid in corn, it is of interest to compare the lysine content of various fractions obtained by the copper method (*2*). The acid-soluble and "glutelin" fractions of germ contain 6.4 and 5.8% of lysine in the proteins, respectively, and these two fractions together represent 90 to 95% of the nitrogen (*2*). The acid-soluble and glutelin fractions of the endosperm contain 2.9 and 2.2% of lysine in the proteins, respectively. Thus, the acid-soluble and glutelin fractions of the endosperm contain less lysine than the corresponding fractions of the germ. These data represent values from composite samples but nevertheless should indicate comparative values among the fractions. As expected, the zein of endosperm contained the lowest level of lysine found in any fraction (0.08%).

Mutant Gene Changing Protein Composition of Endosperm

With the development of the copper extraction-fractionation method for separating maize proteins (*2, 15, 20, 21*), we searched for maize with a lower zein and a higher lysine content. The importance of examining the separated endosperms was recognized (*16*). In 1963, a survey of mutants suspected of having blocks in zein production showed that a strain homozygous for the recessive mutant gene, *opaque-2* (o_2), had in the endosperm a lysine content (4% of the protein) twice that found in typical hybrid corn (*18*). (Unless indicated otherwise, all amino acid analyses were made with a Spinco automatic amino acid analyzer.)

Copper fractionation (*21*) of protein from *opaque-2* endosperm revealed 15.7% zein and 42.3% glutelin based on total protein (*17*). Endosperms from normal North American and Guatemalan maize lines (*2*) contained 41 to 52% zein and 17 to 28% glutelin on the same basis. Thus, there is a reversal in the ratio of zein to glutelin in the *opaque-2* endosperm when compared with normal maize lines. Two additional strains containing the *opaque-2* gene in different genetic backgrounds from each other, and from the *opaque-2* first tested, also had lysine levels twice that found in normal endosperms.

To make a critical test of the hypothesis that the *opaque-2* mutant is responsible for the increased lysine content, the normal and *opaque-2* kernels from a single backcross ear ($+/o_2 \times o_2/o_2$) were separated (*18*). The amino acid composition of the defatted acid-hydrolyzed endosperms is shown in Table III. Both types of endosperms contain 8.69% crude protein (N $\times$ 6.25) on a fat and moisture-free basis. Thus, the amino acid contents are directly comparable.

The *opaque-2* endosperm (Table III) contains 69% more lysine than the normal endosperm. The former contains less glutamic acid, alanine, leucine, and tyrosine, and more lysine, histidine, arginine, aspartic acid, and glycine, than the latter. These changes have been confirmed in

Table III. Amino Acids in Normal and Opaque Endosperms from Same Ear of Corn

(Grams per 100 g. protein)

Amino Acid	Endosperm	
	Opaque	Normal
Lysine	3.39	2.00
Histidine	3.35	2.82
Amide ammonia	3.41	3.28
Arginine	5.10	3.76
Aspartic acid	8.45	6.17
Glutamic acid	19.13	21.30
Threonine	3.91	3.48
Serine	4.99	5.17
Proline	9.36	9.67
Glycine	4.02	3.24
Alanine	6.99	8.13
Valine	4.98	4.68
Cystine	2.35	1.79
Methionine	2.00	2.83
Isoleucine	3.91	3.82
Leucine	11.63	14.29
Tyrosine	4.71	5.26
Phenylalanine	4.96	5.29

several different genetic backgrounds homozygous for the *opaque-2* gene (see Tables VI and VII).

Copper fractionation (*21*) of duplicate 0.5-gram portions of ground, defatted *opaque-2* endosperm, and of a single 0.5-gram portion of normal endosperm from the same ear of corn used in Table III gave the following distributions based on soluble nitrogen: *Opaque-2:* 35% acid-soluble, 26% alcohol-soluble (zein), and 39% alkali-soluble (glutelin); normal: 34% acid-soluble, 37% alcohol-soluble (zein), and 29% alkali-soluble (glutelin). This confirms the reduction in the zein-glutelin ratio observed previously (*17*).

Data on the amino acid content of the above separated soluble copper fractions show that along with the reduction in the zein to glutelin ratio important changes occur in the amino acid patterns of the acid-soluble and alcohol-soluble (zein) fractions (*19*). Table IV shows that all three basic amino acids are increased markedly in the acid-soluble fraction of *opaque-2* endosperm. Using the *opaque-2* values as numerators and the normal values as denominators, the ratios are: lysine: 3.2, histidine: 3.4, and arginine: 2.3. The *opaque-2* acid-soluble fraction also contains a much higher level of aspartic acid, and a lower level of leucine.

Table IV also shows that the major change in the alcohol-soluble (zein) fraction is a marked increase in lysine. The level is 3.3 times that found in the normal endosperms from the same ear of corn. However, the "normal" endosperms carry the *opaque-2* gene as a recessive, which may cause a slight elevation of the lysine level. The lysine level in the *opaque-2* zein (Table IV) is more than ten times the amount (0.08 gram) found in a composite of zein fractions from U.S. and Guatemalan endosperms. The higher level of lysine found in *opaque-2* zein isolated by copper fractionation may be a consequence of the method of fractionation. Mossé (personal communication), and Bates, Concon, and Jimenez (personal communication) found no difference in the lysine contents of zeins extracted from *opaque-2* and normal maize endosperm with alcohol by the Osborne method.

Table IV shows that only minor differences in amino acid composition exist between the alkali-soluble (glutelin) fractions of *opaque-2* and normal endosperms.

The embryos of the kernels used in Tables III and IV were defatted, acid-hydrolyzed, and analyzed in the same manner as the endosperms (*19*). Table V shows that only minor differences exist between the embryos of *opaque-2* and normal kernels. Both contain a relatively high level of lysine (about 6%). The effect of the *opaque-2* gene is therefore primarily (or perhaps exclusively) confined to the endosperm.

Table IV. Amino Acids in Protein Fractions

(Grams per 100 g. protein)

Amino Acid	In Acid-Soluble Fractions		In Alcohol-soluble Fractions		In Alkali-Soluble Fractions	
	Opaque	Normal	Opaque	Normal	Opaque	Normal
Lysine	5.9	1.8	1.0	0.3	3.7	3.6
Histidine	6.5	1.2	2.1	1.6	3.8	4.2
Ammonia	2.8	3.1	4.5	2.5	1.9	2.2
Arginine	10.0	2.8	3.1	2.5	5.8	5.3
Aspartic acid	7.4	4.8	5.8	6.0	6.8	6.9
Glutamic acid	15.9	15.7	23.5	26.0	12.9	14.6
Threonine	2.3	2.4	3.4	3.4	3.3	3.4
Serine	3.7	3.9	5.6	6.5	3.7	3.7
Proline	9.9	10.9	10.5	10.5	8.7	10.1
Glycine	3.1	2.6	2.6	2.1	3.3	3.8
Alanine	4.8	5.4	8.8	10.2	4.5	4.7
Valine	2.4	2.4	4.2	4.5	5.4	5.6
Cystine	—	—	—	—	—	—
Methionine	0.8	1.4	1.6	2.5	1.4	1.1
Isoleucine	2.2	3.0	4.2	4.2	3.4	3.4
Leucine	7.4	10.1	18.8	20.3	8.1	8.6
Tyrosine	2.8	3.4	4.8	5.4	2.9	3.1
Phenylalanine	3.2	3.2	7.1	7.1	3.8	3.8

On the basis of these findings, the increased content of lysine in the *opaque-2* endosperm can be attributed to three factors: increased lysine in the acid-soluble fraction, increased lysine in the zein fraction, and reduction in the ratio of zein to glutelin.

Table V.   Amino Acids in Maize Embryos

(Grams per 100 g. protein)

Amino Acid	Opaque	Normal
Lysine	5.9	6.1
Histidine	2.9	2.9
Ammonia	2.1	2.2
Arginine	9.2	9.1
Aspartic acid	9.2	8.2
Glutamic acid	13.9	13.1
Threonine	3.7	3.9
Serine	5.0	5.5
Proline	5.3	4.8
Glycine	5.5	5.4
Alanine	5.8	6.0
Valine	4.4	5.3
Cystine	0.9	1.0
Methionine	1.5	1.7
Isoleucine	2.5	3.1
Leucine	5.6	6.5
Tyrosine	2.2	2.9
Phenylalanine	3.6	4.1

A Second Mutant Gene Affecting Amino Acid Composition of Maize Endosperm Proteins

In the 1963 survey of mutant varieties, a strain homozygous for the recessive mutant gene, *floury-2* (fl$_2$), had a lysine content (3.2% of the endosperm protein) intermediate between that of normal maize and *opaque-2* maize. Further examination of this mutant was postponed until the preliminary examination of *opaque-2* selections could be completed. A comparison was then made of the amino acid patterns of the endosperms of five different mutants of similar phenotype, *opaque-1* (o$_1$), *opaque-2* (o$_2$), *floury-1* (fl$_1$), *floury-2* (fl$_2$), and soft starch (h). The data (*26*) in Table VI compare the amino acid levels in a normal (nonmutant) inbred and the five mutants investigated. The normal inbred was W64A. The *opaque-2* (o$_2$) stock analyzed here was a mutant that occurred spontaneously in the W64A stock and presumably differs from W64 only at the *opaque-2* locus. Apart from *opaque-2*, only *floury-2* has a major effect on amino acid levels. For *floury-2*, two analyses of the same line are given. One sample was grown in 1958 and analyzed in 1964, the other grown in 1964 and analyzed in 1965. It is apparent that the level of lysine in

Table VI. Amino Acid Levels for Endosperm Mutants

(Grams per 100 g. protein)

Amino Acid	W64A +	W64Ao₂	o₁	fl₁	fl₂ᵃ	fl₂ᵇ	h
Lysine	1.6	3.7	1.7	1.8	3.2	3.7	1.8
Tryptophan	0.3	0.7ᶜ	—	—	—	—	—
Histidine	2.9	3.2	2.3	3.2	2.0	2.6	2.7
Ammonia	4.3	3.3	3.7	3.1	2.4	4.2	4.3
Arginine	3.4	5.2	3.3	3.7	4.6	4.6	3.8
Aspartic acid	7.0	10.8	6.1	4.9	7.4	11.8	7.0
Threonine	3.5	3.7	3.3	3.1	3.0	3.9	3.6
Serine	5.6	4.8	4.9	4.7	4.2	5.8	5.7
Glutamic acid	26.0	19.8	21.5	20.2	17.5	22.2	23.7
Proline	8.6	8.6	9.4	11.9	7.6	10.8	10.4
Glycine	3.0	4.7	2.9	2.8	3.0	4.0	3.4
Alanine	10.1	7.2	8.2	7.7	7.3	9.3	9.4
Cystine	1.8	0.9	2.2	—	2.0	1.7	1.5
Valine	5.4	5.3	4.7	4.4	4.8	6.1	5.0
Methionine	2.0	1.8	2.2	2.5	3.0	3.7	2.8
Isoleucine	4.5	3.9	4.2	3.8	3.8	4.6	4.3
Leucine	18.8	11.6	15.4	15.1	12.7	15.0	16.8
Tyrosine	5.3	3.9	5.0	4.9	4.3	5.1	5.6
Phenylalanine	6.5	4.9	5.7	5.3	4.8	5.9	6.2
% protein	11.1	7.5	10.4	10.8	13.6	12.6	10.8

ᵃ 1958 crop.
ᵇ 1964 crop.
ᶜ Analyzed by the Spies-Chambers method (*29*), by J. M. Concon.

floury-2 is approximately twice that of *normal*, *opaque-1*, *floury-1*, or *soft starch*, and nearly as high as *opaque-2*. The protein content of this *floury-2* line is higher than the *opaque-2* line with which it is compared. Further, *floury-2* has a higher methionine level (3 to 3.7 grams per 100 grams of protein) than any line (normal or mutant) tested heretofore.

The enhanced lysine level in *opaque-2* stocks results in part from the production of zein with a greater percentage of lysine (as discussed above). Preliminary investigations indicate that the lysine level of *floury-2* zein (0.3 gram per 100 grams of zein) is only one third that found in *opaque-2* zein. In addition, starch gel electrophoresis of *floury-2* zein gives a pattern like that of normal zein and different from that of *opaque-2* (*13*). Apparently the biochemical basis of elevated lysine level in *floury-2* is different from that in *opaque-2*, raising the definite possibility that in the double mutant stocks now being derived in our breeding program, there may be higher lysine levels than in either mutant alone.

Growth of Rats Fed on Opaque-2 Maize

Based on chemical composition, the protein of *opaque-2* endosperms should be of greater food value than that of normal endosperms. Suffi-

Table VII.   Amino Acids in Opaque-2 and Normal Defatted Corn[a]

(Grams per 100 g. protein)

Amino Acid	Opaque-2	Normal Corn
Lysine	4.7	2.8
Histidine	3.0	3.0
Ammonia	2.7	3.4
Arginine	6.5	4.8
Aspartic acid	10.6	6.7
Glutamic acid	17.9	20.8
Threonine	3.9	3.6
Serine	4.9	4.8
Proline	8.1	10.0
Glycine	4.8	3.8
Alanine	6.9	7.9
Valine	5.5	5.0
Cystine	1.4	1.2
Methionine	1.9	2.0
Isoleucine	3.8	4.0
Leucine	9.8	13.9
Tyrosine	3.6	4.0
Phenylalanine	4.8	5.2

Values for trytophan not available.

cient amounts of *opaque-2* maize were harvested in the fall of 1964 to permit two feeding tests with rats (*23, 24*).   Table VII shows the amino acid composition of the *opaque-2* and normal maize used in the second feeding test (*23*).   The *opaque-2* maize was from a backcross progeny and the whole seed contained 1.69% nitrogen.   The plants were self-pollinated in order to exclude pollen from normal plants.   The normal or nonopaque maize was a standard hybrid, Indiana 453, grown in a yield trial in which pollination was not controlled.   The whole seed contained 1.68% nitrogen. For each 16 grams of nitrogen, the ground, defatted whole kernel of *opaque-2* maize contained 4.7 grams of lysine and the standard hybrid, 2.8 grams of lysine (Table VII).   The lysine values, which are higher than those obtained on the endosperm only (see Tables III and VI), reflect the presence of the embryo, which contains approximately 6 grams of lysine for each 16 grams of nitrogen (see Table V).   With the exception of histidine, the differences in amino acid composition of the whole kernel (Table VII) are similar to those observed in mutant and normal endosperms from the same ear of maize (Table III).

In the second feeding trial (*23*), groups of six weanling rats (Wistar strain), each weighing 40 to 57 grams were kept in individual wire-mesh cages, and given unrestricted access to one of the following diets: diet A, 90% *opaque-2* maize, 5% corn oil, 4% Hawk-Oser salt mixture No. 3, and 1% of Vitamin Fortification Mixture (General Biochemicals); diet B, the same as diet A except that Indiana hybrid 453 replaced *opaque-2* maize; diet C, 10% casein, domestic, 75% starch, 10% corn oil, 4% Hawk-Oser salt mixture No. 3, and 1% Vitamin Fortification Mixture; diet D, the same as diet C but containing 20% of high quality heat-treated soybean meal, no casein, and 65% corn starch.

The results of feeding the rats on these diets are shown in Table VIII. In spite of special feed cups, scattering was a problem in all groups, with the greatest incidence in the group fed on hybrid maize (diet B).   Protein efficiency ratios (PER) were calculated for all animals, but the average PER values include only animals which did not scatter food, or scattered only slightly.   Howe, Jansen, and Gilfillan (*12*) surveyed the PER values of nine unsupplemented, ground, whole cereal grains fed to rats on diets containing 7.8 to 10% protein, and found oats to have the highest value (1.8) when compared with casein (2.5).   Barley, rice, maize, bulgar, rye, wheat, sorghum, and millet were below oats in PER.   The feeding tests summarized in Table VIII suggest that in young rats *opaque-2* maize proteins have a food value equal to that of heat-treated soybean meal and superior to any cultivated cereal grain.

Diets A and B were labeled with 1% metallic oxide, and the digestibility of the proteins was measured as described by Mertz, Rennert, and Cole (*22*).   The digestibility of the maize proteins was approximately 85% in both diets (*23*); this indicates that better digestibility of proteins does not appear to be a factor contributing to the growth-promoting properties of *opaque-2* maize.

In the first feeding test with the same number of rats (*24*), the average gain in weight for 28 days was 86 grams for rats fed a different strain of *opaque-2* maize and 23 grams for rats fed Indiana hybrid 257, a 3 7-fold difference.   In the second feeding test (*23*), a 3.6-fold difference was observed (Table VIII).   Figure 1 shows average weekly gains of the animals on diets A and B (Table VIII).   Similar curves were obtained in the first feeding test (24).

The greater efficiency of *opaque-2* maize endosperm proteins in rats provides a basis for assuming that they would also be superior to ordinary maize proteins in the diet of man and domestic animals.   To date, the limited quantities of *opaque-2* maize have restricted feeding tests to the white rat, but we expect to have several thousand pounds of this mutant available in the fall of 1965.   Feeding experiments with weanling pigs and chicks, as well as with children and adults, have been planned for the 1965–66 school year.   Sufficient amounts of the *floury-2* mutant should also be available in the fall of 1965 to permit feeding tests with rats.

**Table VIII. Gains in Weight, Protein Consumption, and
Protein Efficiency Ratios (28 Days)**

Animal No.	Gain, G.	Protein Eaten, G.	PER[a]	Animal No.	Gain, G.	Protein Eaten, G.	PER[a]
Diet Containing Casein				*Diet Containing Indiana Hybrid 453*			
C-1	70	20.3	3.4	B-13	32	38.6[b]	0.8[b]
C-2	54	17.2	3.1	B-14	33	19.8	1.7
C-3	72	31.6[b]	2.3[b]	B-15	23	21.5[b]	1.1[b]
C-4	73	21.0	3.5	B-16	23	14.3	1.6
C-5	43	17.4[c]	2.5[c]	B-17	23	19.7[b]	1.2[b]
C-6	85	26.7	3.2	B-18	30	19.5	1.5
Av.	66		3.1	Av.	27		1.6
Diet Containing Opaque-2 Maize				*Diet Containing Soybean Meal*			
A-7	86	30.0	2.9	D-19	67	35.6[b]	1.9[b]
A-8	102	38.0[b]	2.7[b]	D-20	95	34.0	2.8
A-9	134	41.6	3.2	D-21	95	36.0	2.6
A-10	81	30.7	2.6	D-22	101	37.2[c]	2.7[c]
A-11	96	37.0	2.6	D-23	78	28.7	2.7
A-12	85	38.2[b]	2.2[b]	D-24	105	37.3	2.8
Av.	97		2.8		90		2.7

[a] Protein efficiency ratio (grams gained divided by grams protein eaten). Percentage of protein (N × 6.25) in diets: diet C, 8.1; diets A and B, 9.5; diet D, 10.0.
[b] Value not included in average because of food scattering.
[c] Rat scattered food slightly, but value included in average.

Incorporation of Opaque-2 Gene into High Protein Maize Lines

In preliminary studies (*23*), we found that the *opaque-2* gene exerts its effect in a high protein background, and selection is feasible for lines that are high in both lysine and protein. The ratio of zein to glutelin in the endosperm of high protein maize is reduced when the maize is homozygous for the *opaque-2* gene. In one example, the level of zein in the endosperm was reduced from 75 to 45% (*19*). Opaque kernels in high protein background (*23*) gave endosperms containing 19.2% protein, 2.7% of which was lysine. Nonopaque kernels on the same ear yielded endosperms with 19.2% protein, 1.3% of which was lysine. It is reasonable to assume that *opaque-2* maize containing 20% protein and 3 grams of lysine per 100 grams of protein can be produced. One hundred and fifty grams of this maize should provide the minimum daily lysine requirement of most 70 kg. adults (*4*). Whether it would also provide the daily requirement for tryptophan and total nitrogen is not known at present. The data in Table VI show that *opaque-2* endosperm contains twice as

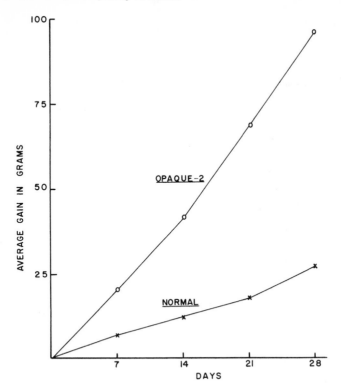

*Figure 1. Average weekly gains of rats fed on opaque-2
maize and Indiana hybrid 453*

much tryptophan as normal endosperm.   No analyses of tryptophan have
been made on high protein *opaque-2* endosperms, and therefore no pre-
dictions can be made as to whether tryptophan would be limiting.

Improvement of Protein Quality of Other Cereals by Mutant Genes

Closely related cereal species could be expected to have loci similar
to the *opaque-2* locus in maize.   Therefore, this breeding discovery in
maize should be relevant to other cereal species.   The *waxy* (*wx*) mutant
first found in maize was later found in sorghum, rice, and barley.   Male
sterility and restoration first found and applied in hybrid corn production
also have been demonstrated in wheat, sorghum, millet, and rice.   Primi-
tive races of the cereals may possibly be valuable sources of genetic material.
We hope that the discovery of the nutritional value of the *opaque-2* gene,
a mutant gene known for 30 years (*6*) and used only as a genetic marker,
will stimulate research workers to look for mutants in other cultivated
cereal grains.

Literature Cited

(1) Beeson, W. M., Jackson, H. D., Mertz, E. T., *J. Animal Sci.* **12**, 870 (1953).
(2) Bressani, R., Mertz, E. T., *Cereal Chem.* **35**, 227 (1958).
(3) Chittenden, R. H., Osborne, T. B., *Am. Chem. J.* **13**, 453, 529 (1891).
(4) Clark, H. E., Yang, S. P., Walton, W., Mertz, E. T., *J. Nutr.* **71**, 229 (1960).
(5) Csonka, F. A. *J. Agr. Res.* **59**, 765 (1939).
(6) Emerson, R. A., Beadle, G. W., Fraser, A. C., Cornell Univ. Agr. Expt. Sta., Mem. **180** (1935).
(7) Frey, K. J., *Cereal Chem.* **28**, 123 (1951).
(8) Frey, K. J., Brimhall, B., Sprague, G. F., *Agron. J.* **41**, 399 (1949).
(9) Greenberg, D. M., ed., "Amino Acids and Proteins," Chas. C. Thomas, Springfield, Ill., 1951.
(10) Hamilton, T. S., Hamilton, B. C., Johnson, B. C., Mitchell, H. H., *Cereal Chem.* **28**, 163 (1951).
(11) Hansen, D. W., Brimhall, B., Sprague, G. F., *Ibid.*, **23**, 329 (1946).
(12) Howe, E. E., Jansen, G. R., Gilfillan, E. W., *Am. J. Clin. Nutr.* **16**, 315 (1965).
(13) Jimenez, T. J. R., unpublished data.
(14) Krull, L. H., Wall, J. S., Dimler, R. J., *Anal. Biochem.* **6**, 375 (1963).
(15) Lloyd, N. E., Mertz, E. T., *Cereal Chem.* **35**, 156 (1958).
(16) Mertz, E. T., *Cereal Sci. Today* **5**, 32 (1960).
(17) Mertz, E. T., Proceedings of 18th Annual Hybrid Corn Industry-Research Conference, Dec. 12 and 13, 1963, Pub. **18**, Washington, D. C., American Seed Trade Association, pp. 7–12 (1963).
(18) Mertz, E. T., Bates, L. S., Nelson, O. E., *Science* **145**, 279 (1964).
(19) Mertz, E. T., Bates, L. S., Veron, O. A., Knox, J. N., Nelson, O. E., unpublished data.
(20) Mertz, E. T., Bressani, R., *Cereal Chem.* **34**, 63 (1957).
(21) Mertz, E. T., Lloyd, N. E., Bressani, R., *Ibid.*, **35**, 146 (1958).
(22) Mertz, E. T., Rennert, S. S., Cole, E. W., *J. Nutr.* **56**, 437 (1955).
(23) Mertz, E. T., Veron, O. A., Bates, L. S., Nelson, O. E., *Science* **148**, 1741 (1965).
(24) Mertz, E. T., Veron, O. A., Nelson, O. E., *Federation Proc.* **24**, 629 (1965).
(25) Nagy, D., Weidlein, W., Hixon, R. M. *Cereal Chem.* **18**, 514 (1941).
(26) Nelson, O. E., Mertz, E. T., Bates, L. S., *Science*, in press.
(27) Osborne, T. B., *J. Am. Chem. Soc.* **19**, 525 (1897).
(28) Osborne, T. B., Mendel, L. B., *J. Biol. Chem.* **18**, 1 (1914).
(29) Spies, J. R., Chambers, D. C., *Anal. Chem.* **21**, 1249 (1949).
(30) Telle, F., Alvarez-Tostado, M. A., Alvarado, G., *Cereal Chem.* **42**, 368 (1965).

RECEIVED October 12, 1965.

Discussion

M. L. Anson: The discovery of a variety of corn with much more lysine and tryptophan than usual corn is, as everybody must realize, of historic importance not only because of the prospect of getting corn of greatly enhanced protein-nutritional value but because of the stimulus it will surely give to the research for better varieties, protein-wise, of other protein crops.

It seems self-evident that there ought to be undertaken as soon as possible an immense crash program to analyze the total protein contents and the amino acid compositions of all available varieties of all the major grains, oilseeds, and pulses. This should be accompanied by research on easier, quicker methods for the estimation of the critical amino acids, preferably without hydrolysis of the proteins. It is important that non-commercial as well as commercial varieties be studied. The opaque corn and the original cotton with gland-free seed are noncommercial varieties.

Whatever the cost of the immense crash program, it would be small compared with the possible, if not very likely, rewards. Grains with improved protein contents and compositions offer great and unique advantages for animal and human nutrition in general and for the fight on protein malnutrition in particular. The time available for the fight on human malnutrition is so short that the possibility of buying time is worth any effort, any cost, any risk.

E. E. Howe: Related to the world food supply, I believe this is the most important development since the intrauterine device. It is generally agreed that population control is the most important problem. If some means cannot be found for greatly decreasing the rate of population increase, nothing we do concerning food supply will have any appreciable long-term effect.

The second most important problem is to satisfy the energy requirements of the people of the developing countries. Raymond Ewell of the University of Buffalo is very pessimistic about our being able to do this. He predicts a famine of unprecedented magnitude in the 1970's. Others are more optimistic. However, if famine is prevented, it will be accomplished largely by increasing the production of cereal grains by using improved agricultural technology, such as increased use of fertilizer and higher yielding hybrid strains. Most of the people of the underdeveloped countries will have to subsist almost entirely on cereal grains. What then will be their protein intake? Simple calculations show that if the energy requirements of man in any stage of his development are supplied entirely by cereals, his protein intake will be adequate in quantity, even with rice which has the lowest protein content, but not in quality, since kwashiorkor, a protein-deficiency disease, occurs in some children who subsist entirely on cereals.

A great deal has been made of the fact that recent experiments show that adult men can be maintained in nitrogen balance on a diet consisting almost entirely of cereal grains. Why this finding should receive such emphasis is perplexing since in the underdeveloped countries many men live out their lives on a predominantly cereal diet. Whether they would be better off with a higher quality protein is not known. Whether the better health enjoyed in a country such as ours can be attributed partially to our intake of high quality protein or entirely to better sanitation, freedom from parasites, etc., is open to question. Certainly, until it is shown that high quality protein is not beneficial to adults, it would seem reasonable for them to consume it if it can be made economically available.

This, however, is not the problem. The problem is in the nutrition of the children. Children who receive enough of their mothers' milk to supply caloric requirements do not develop kwashiorkor. A certain percentage of those subsisting on cereals do develop this disease, even though the total protein intake is as great or greater than that obtained from mothers' milk. It follows, therefore, that if a child received an adequate caloric supply from cereals, he would, if the protein of the cereal were comparable with milk protein, almost certainly be free from protein malnutrition. Mertz's work has shown that a corn can be grown, whose protein is comparable to casein. Moreover, steps have already been taken to introduce the high quality protein gene into high yielding hybrid varieties.

It is certainly much better to induce nature to add the necessary components to cereal proteins to improve their protein quality than to add man-made amino acids. While for technical reasons it is more difficult to obtain high quality protein-containing cereals other than corn, unquestionably it can be done. It is strongly urged that all available plant breeders be mobilized to attack this problem, the solution of which would go far to preventing protein deficiency in the vast cereal-eating areas of the world. I hope this important development by Mertz and his associates will be given the emphasis it deserves.

Safflower, A Potential Source of Protein for Human Food

G. O. KOHLER

Western Regional Research Laboratory, Western Utilization Research and Development Division, U. S. Department of Agriculture, Albany, Calif.

Safflower has been grown for centuries in the Nile Valley and in parts of Asia. It is a newly established U.S. crop and is expected to become a major one. In dry climates where adequate soil moisture is available it yields over a ton of seed per acre, rich in high quality oil and protein. Chick experiments indicate that the meal is relatively free of physiologically deleterious components and, properly supplemented, produces high growth rates. The relatively high content of sulfur amino acids and low content of lysine suggest combinations with soybean protein. Preliminary work has yielded low fiber, palatable foods. More research is needed to develop the potential of safflower as a source of human food.

The critical nature of the problem of feeding an expanding world population, large segments of which are already undernourished, has been documented thoroughly (*2, 28, 29*). Since both calorie and protein deficits present primary problems, it is logical to look to the oilseeds as major direct food sources of the future because oilseeds are rich in both calories (as oil) and protein.

During the past decade a "new" oilseed crop, safflower (*Carthamus tinctorius* L.), has been developing at a healthy rate in the United States. Initially grown as a source of industrial oil, broader markets are developing for the oil as a food oil. Research on the protein-rich meal indicates that safflower has promise as a major source of protein for direct food use as well as a source of calories. A useful bibliography on safflower is available (*17*). Reviews of production, processing, and utilization of safflower have been published (*11, 13*) and a symposium on safflower was presented at the 1965 meeting of the American Oil Chemists' Society (*1*).

Although it is a new commercial crop in the United States, safflower is actually one of the oldest of the cultivated plants. It has been grown since ancient times in the Nile Valley, the Middle East, and the Orient, primarily as a source of the dyestuff, carthamin—for example, some of the linen wrapping cloths of the mummies of Egypt were dyed with safflower flower extracts (*9, 33*). Commercial types of safflower are thistle-like annual plants which grow from 1½ to 4 feet in height and produce light yellow to deep orange flower heads (Figure 1), each of which contains 15 to 50 white seeds resembling sunflower seeds in shape but somewhat smaller.

Figure 1. Safflower flowers. Left. Seed head with flower. Right. Cut in half to show developing seeds. Courtesy of P. F. Knowles, University of California, Davis, Calif.

The plant is adapted to dry climates such as are found in the Central Valleys of California and extensive plain areas from Arizona and New Mexico to southwestern Canada. Yields in unirrigated areas average 350 to 1500 pounds of seed per acre. On irrigated land, yields are in the range of 1800 to 3000 pounds per acre. Experimental and commercial yields as high as 2½ tons per acre have been recorded, showing that the productive capacity of the crop is extremely high (*13*).

Although safflower was introduced to this hemisphere by early Spanish immigrants (*12*), no serious effort was made to develop it as an oilseed crop until the introduction of new seeds and beginning of research by the U.S. Department of Agriculture in 1925. Outstanding in the early research effort was the pioneering work done at the University of Nebraska under its chemurgic project in the 1930's and early 1940's.

Although several abortive attempts were made to develop commercial supplies prior to 1948, successful development of the crop started when production was begun in California where there was a good environment for the crop and strong support from a few oilseed processors. The subsequent growth in annual production, shown in Figure 2, was based on development of improved disease-resistant, high oil varieties, on improved agronomic practices, on development of industrial uses for the oil through technological research (24), and on increasing export markets for the seed, largely in Japan. The large spurt in 1963 reflects the entry of safflower oil into the food market. Riding the crest of public interest in the blood cholesterol–depressing effects of polyunsaturated oils, new producers and processors swelled production of safflower oil as the polyunsaturated oil par excellence (80% linoleic acid). The resultant overproduction and temporary imbalance between production and marketing were serious but are now history and, regardless of the medical significance of blood cholesterol–lowering effects, resumption of the steady growth pattern is expected, with safflower oil selling at prices competitive with corn or cottonseed oil.

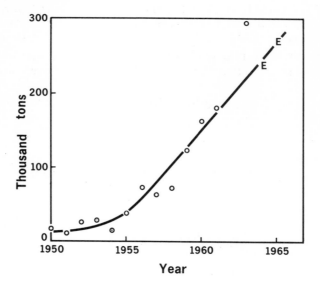

Figure 2. U. S. production of safflower seed

At present the United States produces about one half of the world supply of safflower seed, which was roughly estimated at 640,000 tons in 1964. The second and third largest producers of safflower seed are

India and Mexico, which produce about 750,000 and 60,000 tons, respectively. Successful experimental crops in Australia and Venezuela may lead to expanded production in these and other countries (*30*).

Early varieties of safflower seed contained 49 to 52% hull (*20*). Typical seeds of present commercial varieties are made up of 55 to 65% kernel and 35 to 45% hull (*15*). The whole seeds contain about 35 to 40% of oil and about 13 to 17% of protein. Almost all of the oil and protein are located in the kernel, so that a completely dehulled or decorticated kernel contains about 60% of oil. The completely decorticated, oil-extracted kernel contains about 60 to 70% of protein. Figure 3 shows the products theoretically obtainable from 1 ton of seed. Safflower has wide genetic variability, and plant breeders are well along in the development of thin-hulled gray, brown-striped, and white varieties which contain only half as much hull as present commercial types. These new types of seed contain proportionately higher levels of oil and protein and can be expected to replace the present types (*18*, *27*). Types of safflower seeds have also been found, the oils of which are strikingly different from the safflower oil of commerce, e.g., oils containing up to 75% oleic acid (*14*). These new types give promise of expanded broader uses of safflower oils with the accompanying increased supply of protein.

Table I compares the essential amino acids of safflower kernel protein (*24*) with those of 50% protein soybean meal and with the FAO-recommended provisional amino acid reference pattern (*7*). The data on safflower and soybean meal were obtained by the method of Moore and Stern (*21*), using correction factors established for safflower protein for

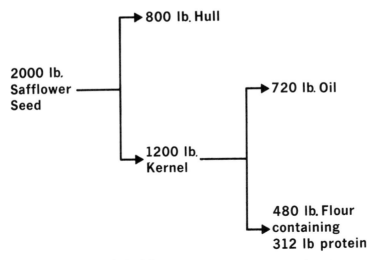

Figure 3. Theoretical yields of products from one ton of safflower seed

Table I.   Safflower Seed and Soybean Proteins Compared with FAO Provisional Reference Amino Acid Pattern

	Provisional Pattern G./16g. N		Safflower			Soybean		
	Orig.	*Adjusted*	*G./16 g. N*	*% of Pattern*		*G./16 g. N*	*% of Pattern*	
				Orig.	*Adjusted*		*Orig.*	*Adjusted*
Isoleucine	4.2		4.0	95	95	4.8		
Leucine	4.8		6.2			7.3		
Lysine	4.2		3.1	74[a]	74[a]	5.8		
Phenylalanine	2.8		4.4			4.8		
Tyrosine	2.8		3.1			3.0		
Total sulfur AA	4.2	3.4	3.3	79	97	2.9	68	85
Methionine	2.2	1.7	1.7	78		1.4	64[a]	83[a]
Threonine	2.8	3.3	3.3			3.8		
Tryptophan	1.4	1.1	1.6			1.7		
Valine	4.2	2.8	5.7			5.0		

[a] Chemical score is per cent of pattern for first limiting amino acid.

the labile amino acids (threonine, serine, and tyrosine) and for the difficultly released amino acids (isoleucine and valine). By applying the fluorodinitrobenzene method (*26*) it was found that the apparent availability of the lysine in safflower flour was 100%. The first limiting amino acid of safflower is lysine. However, methionine is limiting to about the same degree, based on the 1957 FAO reference pattern. More recent results on human requirements (*10, 23*) suggest that several of the figures for individual amino acids in the original pattern are too high and, in one case, too low. The numbers under "provisional pattern" adjusted in Table I refer to adjusted FAO pattern figures for four of the amino acids in question. Using the adjusted FAO reference value for methionine, safflower is limited only by lysine, and isoleucine and methionine are borderline. Soybean protein shows a lower chemical score than safflower based on the 1957 pattern. Reducing the methionine in the adjusted pattern raises the score of soybean meal since methionine is the first limiting amino acid.

Another comparison of safflower, and soybean, with egg protein as a reference protein, is shown in Table II. This is calculated as suggested in the 1965 FAO/WHO report (*10*). Safflower protein is comparable to soybean protein in ratio of essential to total amino acids (*E/T* value) and in score. When lysine is added to the safflower, its "egg reference" score goes up to about 85, and methionine and isoleucine become about equally limiting. Based on the adjusted 1957 reference pattern, a combination of ⅓ safflower and ⅔ rice protein would have a chemical score of 81, higher than either one alone but still limited by both lysine and me-

Table II.   Comparison of Safflower and Soybean Proteins
(Egg protein as reference pattern)

	Egg	Safflower	Soybean
Ratio g. essential amino acids per g. N (E/T)	3.22	2.17	2.58
Chemical score based on egg protein	100	71	70
Limiting amino acid	—	Lysine	Methionine

thionine.   By combining safflower protein with soybean on a 3 to 2 basis, a score of 93 is obtained.   Thus safflower and soybean proteins show excellent mutual supplementation.   Similarly, milk, fish, pulses, and other protein sources rich in lysine will adequately supplement safflower (3).

A comparison of safflower and soybean protein from the standpoint of amino acids not included in the provisional pattern is shown in Table III.   Safflower contains adequate amounts of histidine to meet the needs of children.   It is a rich source of glycine and arginine, which are essentials for the chick.

Since safflower shows great genetic variability in fatty acid composition, seed shape and color, hull thickness, etc., we wondered if amino acid composition might also be controlled by breeding.   In a very preliminary study (24) of some 20 widely different seed types, we found that none of the essential amino acids varied more than about 7% from the mean. More research is needed along these lines, including tests of individual plants from widely divergent sources.

Literature reports on biological evaluation of safflower protein are very sparse.   According to Baliga et al.   (3, 16) the biological values

Table III.   Amino Acids Not in FAO Provisional Reference Amino Acid Pattern

	Amino Acid, G./16 G. N	
	Safflower	Soybean
Histidine	2.4	2.5
Arginine	9.3	6.9
Glycine	5.8	4.0
Aspartic acid	9.8	10.6
Glutamic acid	19.4	17.6
Serine	4.4	5.1
Proline	4.1	5.2
Alanine	5.8	4.1
Total (% of protein)	61.0	56.0

(BV) of safflower protein of two samples of safflower meal were 84.9 and 86.0%. The coefficient of true digestibility was 92.4 for a 35.7% protein sample and 76.5 for a 21.8% protein sample. The only protein efficiency ratio (PER) value found in the literature was 1.3 for hydraulic pressed safflower cake (*22*).

Our results, adjusted to the casein standard (*4*), on two samples of commercial partially decorticated meal were 1.40 and 1.26, respectively. PER values of a sample of pilot plant produced meal from brown-striped thin-hulled seed and a sample of laboratory-produced unheated safflower flour were 1.24 and 1.35, respectively. Supplementation of the laboratory-produced 58% protein safflower flour with methionine alone (Table IV) raised the PER only slightly. Adding lysine as well raised the PER to 2.09. In other experiments adding lysine without methionine had little effect on PER. Thus the PER assays verify the chemical score estimates based on rat requirements and show that lysine and methionine are almost equally limiting amino acids for the rat.

Table IV.   Effect on PER of Supplementation of Safflower Flour with Methionine or Methionine Plus Lysine

	Cystine plus Methionine, G./16 G. N.	Lysine, G./16 G. N	PER
Safflower flour (58% protein)	3.34	3.09	1.39
Same plus methionine	4.20	3.07	1.59
Same plus methionine and lysine	4.20	5.00	2.09

Since the amino acid balance appeared excellent when methionine and lysine were added, we set up chick experiments to determine whether methionine-supplemented safflower meal could provide the basis for a bioassay of available lysine. Quadruplicate equalized groups of seven 5-day-old broiler type chicks were fed rations devised to be complete in all known required nutrients except lysine. Partially decorticated safflower meal (44% protein), supplemented with methionine, was used as the primary source of protein with corn or glucose as the primary energy source. Graded levels of L-lysine were added. The results given in Figure 4 show that the types of dose response curves obtained were satisfactory for assay purposes.

The results show two other important points. First, even when safflower protein is fed at levels high enough to supply over 93% of the chicks' protein intake—e.g., glucose safflower ration—there is no evidence of any inhibitors such as are found in unheated soybeans and in raw cottonseed meal. Second, at optimum levels of lysine addition, safflower consistently produces faster growth than optimally treated soybean meal. Further data substantiating this observation are shown in Table V. In

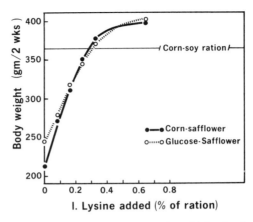

Figure 4. Dose-response curves for chicks for lysine supplementation of safflower meal–based rations

all cases safflower meal produced better rates of gain than did soybean meal. Fisher *et al.* (*6*) showed a similar growth effect of safflower during the course of net protein value (NPV) assays with chicks. In this study the safflower-fed chicks grew better than soybean-fed chicks, even though the NPV for safflower supplemented with methionine and lysine was only 46.2 as compared with 68.8 for methionine-supplemented, decorticated soybean meal (*6*). It does not seem likely that the effect is due to amino acid imbalance in soybean protein since attempts to increase growth by amino acid supplements to the soybean ration have been unsuccessful. More research will be needed to determine whether this difference between safflower and soybean meals is due to the presence of inhibitors in the soybean meal, the presence of an unidentified growth factor in the safflower meal, or some ration imbalance in the soybean protein not immediately apparent.

The high fiber content of safflower meal makes it unacceptable as a protein source for human foods. It is generally considered that high protein products, at least for children, should contain less than 5% fiber. Hull has not been separated commercially from kernel to produce such products from safflower. For the past several years one company has been selling a partially decorticated safflower meal containing 42% protein for use in poultry and swine rations. This product contains about 15% fiber and is thus undesirable for a human food.

We have been able to prepare products with 57 to 60% protein and about 3% fiber from thin-hulled seeds by an experimental laboratory process based on air separation, roller milling, and screening operations (*8*).

Although a great deal more laboratory and development research will be required to develop a commercially feasible process, the difficulties do not appear insurmountable. The products obtained by this experimental process were very light colored but had a bitter taste. Preliminary experiments showed that practically all of the bitter principle could be extracted with acetone or alcohol with less than 5% loss of nitrogen. The washed product, which contained about 70% protein, had a rather characteristic mild flavor which was not deemed undesirable by an informal taste panel. Further preliminary tests showed that meat-like patties containing this 70% protein safflower flour were acceptable to the panel. When the product was added to a bread at a 5% level based on the flour, loaf volume was reduced only slightly and a detectable but not unpleasant flavor was noticeable. More extensive tests are in progress.

Other promising routes to human products lie in preparation of protein isolates (*32*) and in preparation of textured products (*5*) from safflower. Here again, considerably more research will be needed to bring preliminary results to commercial usage.

Table V.   Growth of Chicks Fed Safflower[a] as Compared with Soybean Meal[b]

Protein in Ration, %	Duration of Experiment, Weeks	% Increase[c]
22	2	6.4
	2+	6.8
	2+	6.3
	2+	12.2
	2+	10.0
	3	3.7
	3+	4.0
	4	17.8
	4	6.0
20	2	3.3
18	2	17.6
	2+	18.6

[a] With added methionine and lysine.
[b] With added methionine.
[c] $\dfrac{\text{Weight gain on safflower meal} - \text{weight gain on soybean meal}}{\text{weight gain on soybean meal}} \times 100.$

Conclusions

Safflower is a rapidly expanding commercial oilseed crop which may well become a major world crop. It is adapted to semiarid lands of the types found in many protein-deficient areas of the world. It is already a high yielding plant, but its genetic variability gives promise of still further improvements through breeding.   It produces high yields of edible oil as well as protein.   The protein is highly nutritious if properly supplemented with lysine.   Its relatively high content of sulfur amino acids and low lysine content suggest its use in combinations with soybean protein.   Preliminary work has shown that conversion to palatable food products is possible, although much research and development work are needed.

Acknowledgments

Acknowledgments are made to A. R. Gramps and K. V. Smith for assistance in processing; M. Heid and Elizabeth Erman for formulating and preparing the meatlike products and bread, respectively; D. D. Kuzmicky for assisting in carrying out chick assays; Rhoda Palter for carrying out amino acid analyses; A. N. Booth and Dorothy J. Robbins for running rat PER assays; and John Kneeland, Pacific Vegetable Oil Corp., Richmond, Calif., for generously supplying substantial quantities of commercially produced partially decorticated safflower meal.

Literature Cited

(1) American Oil Chemists' Soc., *J. Am. Oil Chemists' Soc.*, **42**, 457A (1965).
(2) American Society of Agronomy, Madison, Wis., "World Population and Food Supplies, 1980," Publ. **6**, (1965).
(3) Baliga, B. R., Rajagopalan, R., Shivaromiah, K., *Indian J. Med. Sci.*, **8**, 704–8 (1954).
(4) Derse, P. H., *J. Am. Oil Chemists' Soc.*, **45**, 418 (1962).
(5) Elmquist, L. F., U. S. Patent **3,175,909** (March 30, 1965).
(6) Fisher, H., Summers, J. D., Wessels, J. P. H., Shapiro, R., *J. Sci. Food Agr.*, **13**, 658 (1962).
(7) Food and Agriculture Organization, United Nations, "Protein Requirements," Report of FAO Committee, Rome, Italy, October 1955, FAO Nutritional Studies **16** (1957).
(8) Goodban, A. E., Kohler, G. O., unpublished results, 1965.
(9) Goodman, D. H., *J. Allergy* **35**, 38 (1964).
(10) Joint FAO/WAO Expert Group, "Protein Requirements," FAO Nutrition meeting report Series **37**, and WHO Tech. Report Series **301** (1965).
(11) Kneeland, J. A., "Processed Plant Protein Feedstuffs," A. Altschul, ed., Academic Press, New York, 1958.
(12) Knowles, P. F., *Crops and Soils*, **12**(4), 17 (1960).
(13) Knowles, P. F., *Econ. Botany* **9**, 273 (1955).
(14) Knowles, P. F., *Econ. Botany* **19**, 53 (1965).
(15) Kohler, G. O., Guggolz, J., Herring, V., unpublished data, 1965.
(16) Kuppaswanu, S., Srinivasan, M., Subrahmanyan, V., "Proteins in Foods," Indian Council of Medical Research, New Delhi, India, 1958.
(17) Larson, N. G., "Safflower 1900–1960, A List of Selected References," Library List **73**, Natl. Agr. Lib., Washington, D. C., 1962.

Analytical Procedures.   Moisture contents were determined by drying to constant weight in an oven at 110°C. (1 to 2.5 hours). All results are expressed as per cent of dry weight.

Nitrogen was determined by a manual modification of the micro-Kjeldahl procedure of Ferrari (4) with selenium catalyst.

Protein in extracts was determined by the biuret procedure of Weichselbaum (11).

Amino acids were determined by the method of Moore and Stein (8) with a Technicon automatic amino acid analyzer (Technicon Corp., Chauncey, N. Y.).

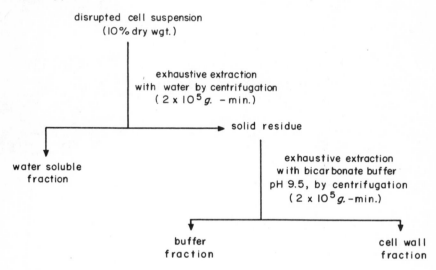

Figure 1. Isolation of soluble protein fractions

Results and Discussion

The physical effect of homogenization on the cells can be seen in Figure 2. There are relatively few intact cells remaining in suspension, and those which appear intact may be partially ruptured. A second pass of the cells through the homogenizer creates a very fine particle dispersion, which is difficult to sediment at the speeds ordinarily used for centrifugation.

The amino acid content of various cell fractions from *B. megaterium* is summarized in Table III. In the precipitate from the water-soluble fraction, the concentration of amino acids was almost twice that in the whole cells. In addition, this fraction is readily reconstituted into solution with water. The nature of the non-amino acid constituents of this fraction is not known. The discrepancy between per cent protein by biuret and amino acid content of the buffer fraction is not readily understood. There

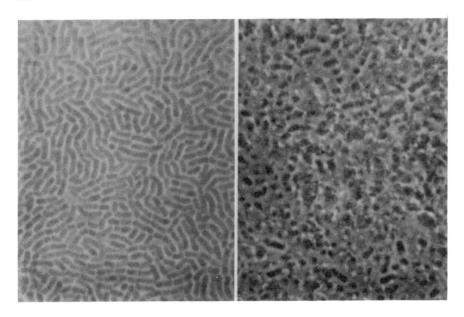

Figure 2. Disruption of B. megaterium cells (× 1000)

Left. Cell suspension of B. megaterium (ca. 10% dry weight)

Right. Suspension at same concentration after homogenization

at 8000 to 10,000 p.s.i.

is no significant interference in this method from compounds such as nucleic acid, glucosamine, or N-acetylglucosamine.

The cell wall fraction constituted a large proportion of the cell (57% by weight) and contained a high percentage of the total cell amino acids (Table III). No further protein could be extracted from this fraction with

Table III.   Amino Acid Content of Cell Fractions of *B. megaterium*

	% N	% Protein by Biuret	% Amino Acids	% of Total Cell Amino Acids
Whole cells	6.3	—	38	—
Water-soluble fractions				
TCA precipitate		68	68	15
HCl precipitate		77	—	—
Buffer-soluble fraction				
TCA precipitate		100	52	37
HCl precipitate		99	—	—
Cell wall fraction	5.3	—	33	48

salt solutions over a wide pH range. Preparation of purified cell walls generally entails digestion with a number of different enzymes. The cell wall preparation from *B. megaterium* reported by Salton (9) represented 20 to 25% of the weight of the cell, and contained 5.3% nitrogen. In this case, assuming an even distribution of amino acids throughout this fraction, it would appear that a minimum of approximately 25% of the amino acids in the cell would be unavailable.

Table IV. Amino Acid Composition of Whole Cells and Water-Soluble Fraction of *B. megaterium*
(G./16 g. nitrogen)

Amino acid	Whole Cells	Water-Soluble Fraction	Cow's Milk (9)
Arginine	6.7	5.4	3.7
Histidine	2.3	2.3	2.7
Lysine	6.3	8.6	7.9
Leucine	11.0	9.3	10.0
Isoleucine	4.4	6.3	6.5
Methionine	3.1	2.6	2.5
Cystine	a	1.0	0.9
Phenylalanine	5.4	4.9	4.9
Tyrosine	5.0	3.8	5.1
Threonine	4.8	4.3	4.7
Valine	6.5	6.6	7.0
Aspartic acid	9.1	9.2	
Glutamic acid	18.9	13.7	
Serine	3.4	3.9	
Proline	b	3.1	
Glycine	4.0	3.8	
Alanine	10.1	5.7	

a Not measurable.
b Not determined.

The amino acid compositions of *B. megaterium* whole cells and of the water-soluble fraction of these cells are compared in Table IV with that of whole cow's milk protein. The results on whole cells are not in good agreement with those of Garibaldi *et al.* (6), who were able to account for only 50 to 60% of total nitrogen by microbiological assay. The possible presence of large amounts of D-amino acids in the cells might account for part of this difference. Anderson and coworkers (2) reported 11.8% lysine and 3.4% methionine in *B. megaterium* using microbiological assay, indicating that differences among various workers may be due to the particular strain of the organism studied.

The results in Table IV do not show large differences in essential amino acid content between the whole cells and the water-soluble fraction of *B. megaterium* and cow's milk protein, with the possible exception of a low value for lysine in whole cells. As previously discussed, the values for whole cells may be misleading because of the probable unavailability of some of the amino acids. The final nutritional evaluation of whole cells, disrupted cells, and protein fractions derived from the cell will have to await comparative feeding studies in animals. The present availability of a method for disrupting large quantities of cells will make this study possible.

Literature Cited

(1) Anderson, R. F., Jackson, R. W., *Appl. Microbiol.* **6,** 369 (1958).
(2) Anderson, R. F., Rhodes, R. A., Nelson, G. E. N., Shekelton, M. C., Barreto, A., Jr., Arnold, M., *J. Bacteriol.* **76,** 131 (1958).
(3) Bunker, H. J., "Microbial Food," in "Biochemistry of Industrial Microorganisms," C. Rainbow and A. H. Rose, eds., Academic Press, New York, 1963.
(4) Ferrari, A., *Ann. N. Y. Acad. Sci.* **87,** 792 (1960).
(5) Fuld, G. J., Dunn, C. G., *Appl. Microbiol.* **6,** 15, (1958).
(6) Garibaldi, J. A., Ijichi, K., Snelli, M. S., Lewis, J. C., *Ind. Eng. Chem.* **45,** 838 (1953).
(7) Ikawa, M., Snell, E. E., *Biochim. Biophys. Acta* **19,** 576 (1956).
(8) Moore, S., Stein, W. A., "Chromatographic Determination of Amino Acids by the Use of Automatic Recording Equipment," in "Methods in Enzymology," S. P. Colowick and N. O. Kaplan, eds., Academic Press, New York, 1963.
(9) National Academy of Sciences–National Research Council, Pub. **1100** (1963).
(10) Salton, M. R. J., "The Bacterial Cell Wall," pp. 42ff, Elsevier, New York, 1964.
(11) Weichselbaum, T. E., *Am. J. Clin. Pathol.* **10,** 40 (1946).

RECEIVED October 12, 1965. Contribution 746, Department of Nutrition and Food Science, Massachusetts Institute of Technology, Cambridge, Mass.

Fungi and World Protein Supply

WILLIAM D. GRAY

Department of Botany, Southern Illinois University, Carbondale, Ill.

In view of the magnitude of the problem of producing additional protein for a rapidly increasing population, it is suggested that certain of the fungi imperfecti can make large contributions to the world protein pool by converting carbohydrate and inorganic nitrogen to protein. On the bases of results of experiments conducted with cane molasses, sugar beets, potatoes, sweet potatoes, manioc, corn, and rice, projections were made which indicate that sufficient protein for a world population of 4.5 billion can be produced by conversion of the carbohydrates of these seven crop plants to fungal protein.

Although the rapid rate of human population increase has created many serious problems, the major immediate problem which man has created for himself through the increase of his species is a nutritional one and specifically is that of producing ever-increasing amounts of nutritionally adequate protein in high enough concentration to meet the requirements of an expanding population. At the present rate of increase, world population now becomes larger by approximately 55 million people annually. From this, and the fact that each individual should be supplied with about 52 pounds of protein annually, we can easily illustrate the magnitude of the problem confronting us. If present population trends continue, the world is faced with the staggering problem of producing 2.8 billion more pounds of protein each year than it produced the previous year. Such an expansion of protein production cannot continue indefinitely, but perhaps it could be achieved for a period long enough to institute an effective crash educational program designed to establish the concept that population-regulation measures must be established on a world-wide basis. How long such a program would require before this concept is generally accepted cannot be estimated at this time. However, it is safe to predict that many years will be required since countries with a high percentage of illiteracy or those which adhere strictly to Marxian concepts cannot be expected to accept such views quickly.

Although the United States is now in a favorable position with respect to protein, in the long-term view its problem may be greater than that of countries in which the eating habits are different from those of this country. Since our protein of choice is animal protein, far greater amounts of vegetable protein must be produced in this country than in countries which have the same rate of population increase but in which the protein consumed directly by the human population is primarily vegetable rather than animal. Assuming that eating habits remain unchanged, to meet the requirements of our additional U.S. citizens we must increase meat production by the equivalent of an additional million head of beef animals each year, which demands the production of far greater amounts of vegetable protein to be used for conversion to animal protein.

Two other aspects of the protein problem must be considered. In addition to total quantity of protein, attention must be paid to concentration of protein in materials used for food, and quality of protein must also be considered. In the work presented here, only quantity and concentration are considered, although the importance of protein quality is fully recognized.

Barring a major breakthrough in the area of protein chemistry, it is highly improbable that any single program or process will provide a complete answer to the protein problem. However, if significant contributions to the world protein pool can be made by several different methods, the spread of protein deficiency may be halted until world-wide population regulation is a reality.

Fungi as Protein Synthesizers

Since many fungi are rapidly growing organisms and can synthesize their amino acids and hence their protein directly from carbohydrate and inorganic nitrogen compounds, a program was initiated in the Mycology Laboratories of the Ohio State University in 1960 to explore certain fungi as potential synthesizers of protein since, unlike animal protein, such protein would not be formed inefficiently and at the expense of previously synthesized vegetable protein. In September of 1964 this project was transferred to Southern Illinois University, where it still continues.

The idea of using microorganisms is not new (3), and man has undoubtedly eaten fungi for many centuries. However, fungi have rarely been viewed as a staple item of the diet, and for that reason and in view of the present population problem it seems necessary to call attention again to the potential resident in this type of organism. Although much lay opinion and other folklore mitigate strongly against acceptance of the concept of placing fungi in widespread usage as a food source, there are no valid reasons why many could not be eaten. There are a number of poisonous fungi, but so are there poisonous species in every major group of living organisms; however, such species represent a small minority. What seems to be a natural antipathy for considering fungi as food is reflected in the mushroom industry in the United States—in spite of the fact that there are several hundred species of edible fleshy fungi, only one species is produced commercially.

In selecting fungi for use in the present project, only members of the fungi imperfecti were considered, because members of this group are numerous, ubiquitous, and rapid-growing. The initial work has been described (*6, 7*) and need not be repeated here except to list the criteria which were used to form the basis for selection of fungi to be used.

The fungus must be capable of utilizing inorganic nitrogen as a sole source of nitrogen.

It must be able to grow well in submerged culture.

It must grow rapidly; 4 days were arbitrarily set as the maximum acceptable period for growth.

It must efficiently convert substrate carbon to tissue carbon and at the same time convert inorganic nitrogen to organic nitrogen.

Initial screening experiments involved culturing many imperfect fungi on a standard medium, which permitted growth (although it was not necessarily optimum) but did permit comparison of yields and judgments as to how well the above criteria were met. A surprising number of fungi were found suitable, although, as might be expected, some performed better than others. Results of some of the screenings, reported by Gray, Och, and AbouElSeoud (*8*), illustrate that of the first 175 fungi tested, over 50% had economic coefficient values of 3.00 or less, and 7.4% had values of 2.01 or less; in other words, they were capable of producing 1 unit weight of dried fungus mycelium from 2.01 or less unit weights of glucose.

$$\text{Economic coefficient} = \frac{\text{grams dry weight of sugar utilized}}{\text{grams dry weight of fungus produced}}$$

Percentages of crude protein of the 18 fungi which yielded best in the above series ranged from 13.4 to 30.8; in other experiments crude protein percentages as high as 38% have been obtained. Subsequent work has shown that both economic coefficient values and protein percentages can be improved by proper alteration of environmental conditions.

Once the feasibility of the process was established by demonstration that 1 unit weight of crude fungus protein could be synthesized during the utilization of 5 to 8 unit weights of glucose, the work was expanded to include the use of crude carbohydrate-containing waste products and plant materials. Thus far white potatoes, sweet potatoes, sugar beets, manioc, cassava flour, rice, corn, citrus molasses, beet molasses, blackstrap molasses, beet shreds, wood pulp, and wood flour have been considered. With the exception of the last three, all of the above crude raw materials can be used satisfactorily as a source of carbohydrate for the synthesis of fungus protein, and the last three can probably be used successfully if further investigated.

With few exceptions these fungi produce spherical mycelial pellets in submerged liquid culture. These pellets vary in size with species, amount of aeration and agitation, and size of inoculum and are usually white or nearly white in glucose medium but may have the color of the substrate when cultured on such materials as ground sweet potato. Freshly harvested mycelial pellets are odorless or have a faint mushroom odor but when dried are virtually odorless and tasteless. They may be dried and ground to a flour, made into flakes, or pressed into tablets.

Imperfect fungi have been found which can synthesize 1 unit weight of crude protein from 6 unit weights of sugar. Since protein values were based upon Kjeldahl nitrogen $\times$ 6.25, they are subject to the same criticism as all such values so derived. Furthermore, the cell walls of the imperfect fungi are chitinous, and the amount of chitin varies not only with species (2) but with age (1). Therefore our crude protein values are probably high, and hence the following projections which are concerned with the synthesis of fungal protein from crude raw materials are conservatively based upon the assumption that 1 unit weight of protein will be formed in the course of 8 unit weights of carbohydrate being utilized.

Manioc

Grown throughout the tropical and subtropical world, manioc is a staple item of diet in many such areas. The long fleshy roots contain 32% carbohydrate but only 0.7% protein; hence protein deficiency is widespread in manioc-eating areas. Assuming that manioc protein is complete (which it is not), an individual would have to eat about 24 pounds of fresh roots daily to obtain his required 65 grams of protein. As carbohydrate sources in fungus growth medium we have used minced, fresh, whole roots as well as the crudely ground native cassava flour which is available in such areas as coastal West Africa; while both materials are suitable sources, fresh roots were found to be the better substrate. Since yields from fresh roots are generally higher, the following calculations are based on this raw material.

World production of manioc during the 1962/63 season was 75.5 $\times$ 10^6 metric tons (4), which contained 54.144 $\times$ 10^9 pounds of carbohydrate. Assuming that the proper fungus (Cladosporium, No. 83, which has grown so well experimentally on manioc) will synthesize 1 pound of protein from 8 pounds of carbohydrate, it would be possible to produce 6.768 $\times$ 10^9 pounds of protein: a 5.7-fold increase in protein over and above that initially present (1.18 $\times$ 10^9 pounds) in the manioc. Thus, over six times as much

19. GRAY *Fungi* 265

protein can be produced from the same yield from the same crop on the same acreage. Since under the usual conditions of tropical agriculture manioc yields are not nearly so high as they might be, a conservative estimate would be that yields could be tripled with no great difficulty. A tripling of yield, followed by a fungal conversion process, could result in the production of an additional 22.676×10^9 pounds of protein over that currently produced on the same land by manioc cultivation alone. Assuming that this protein is complete (which it probably is not, but could be supplemented), it would supply the total annual protein requirements for an additional 434 million people.

Rice

This cereal grain is nutritionally far more adequate as a food source than manioc, since it contains about 70% carbohydrate, but more importantly 7.5% protein. In the 1962/63 season world production of paddy rice was 247.4×10^6 metric tons, which contained 387.923×10^9 pounds of carbohydrate and 41.563×10^9 pounds of protein. Using I–108 (*Dactylium dendroides*) or I–193 (*Trichoderma* sp.) it would be possible to produce an additional 48.49×10^9 pounds of protein. Thus it would be possible to produce a total quantity of protein (rice plus fungus) sufficient (on purely quantitative grounds) to meet the annual requirements of 1.743×10^9 people. Since yields of rice per unit area of land in Japan greatly exceed those of India, world yields of rice can be greatly increased by improving rice cultivation in India.

Sugar Cane and Sugar Beets

Man's major source of sucrose has traditionally been sugar cane grown in tropical and subtropical areas, but as the demand grows, more and more is being produced in temperate regions from sugar beet. In the 1962/63 season cane was harvested from over 18×10^6 acres and beet from over 16×10^6 acres; so on this basis it would appear that there is nearly equal production of the two crops. If we assume yields of cane of 40 tons (containing 12% sugar) and of beets of 18 tons (containing 16% sugar) per acre, we find that the total cane crop contained 172.8×10^9 pounds of sugar, compared with 92.16×10^9 pounds in the beet crop. However, most cane is an 18-month crop, and if cane sugar production is calculated on an annual basis it was 115.2×10^9 pounds as compared with 92.16×10^9 pounds of beet sugar. Thus from the total sugar produced in one year by cane and beets, 25.92×10^9 pounds of protein could be produced by a fungus conversion process using I–75 (*Cladosporium* sp.). To this may be added the 4.32×10^9 pounds present in the beets (cane protein is not included because of its low concentration), making a total of 30.24×10^9 pounds of protein—sufficient, on quantitative grounds, to meet the annual requirements of 581 million people.

Other Crops

Experimental work has also been conducted with minced white potatoes, minced sweet potatoes, and ground corn. Projections based upon results obtained with these materials are presented in Table I along with those discussed above. On the basis of results obtained so far it is a safe prediction that any cereal grain or any high carbohydrate fleshy plant part could be used in a project such as that described, although use of each material would entail a search for the most suitable fungus and optimum conditions. From the calculations summarized in Table I, it is obvious that during the 1962/63 season sufficient protein was produced in six crop plants (cane is omitted because of its low protein content) to provide 52.2 pounds of protein for each of 1.87 billion people. However, if the carbohydrate of these six crop plants plus the carbohydrate of cane had been used as a carbon source for the culture of imperfect fungi, sufficient additional protein could have been produced to provide 52.2 pounds of protein for each of an additional 2.697 billion people. In other words, from these seven crop plants, sufficient protein could have been produced to meet the annual needs (in so far as quantity is concerned) of 4,567,000,000 people—a figure approximately 50% greater than the world population in early July of 1962. Thus, with respect to total

Table I.   World Protein Production Potential (1962/63) Based on Using Fungi as

Crop	World Production (4) 1962/63, Million Tons	Carbohydrate, %	Total Carbohydrate, Billion Lb.	Protein, %
Manioc	84.600	32	54.144	0.7
Sugar beet	288.000	16	92.160	0.75
Sugar cane	480.000	12	115.200	—
Paddy rice	277.088	70	387.923	7.5
Corn	243.600	60	292.320	7.0
Yams and sweet potatoes	130.704	28	73.194	1.8
Potatoes	294.324	19	112.434	2.0
Totals	1798.316	—	1127.375	—

quantity of protein the potential exists for producing far more than is now required for the current world population.

Concentration and Quality of Fungus Protein

From the standpoint of protein concentration no special problems would be encountered with fungus mycelium since the majority of fungi we have examined, even on standard medium which is not optimum, have crude protein contents of 20% or higher. Furthermore, protein content can usually be increased by proper manipulation of environmental conditions.

With regard to fungus protein quality we are still in a great unknown area. In short-term mice-feeding experiments with I–9 (*Heterocephalum aurantiacum*) as the sole source of food, adult mice maintained their weight and weanling mice showed as great a weight gain as controls on commercial mice food. Such feeding trials will have to be repeated, lengthened, and expanded to include many other species. Unfortunately, most of the nutritional studies using mold mycelia have been conducted with species of *Aspergillus* and *Penicillium*. Thus, Skinner (*9*) used *P. flavo-glaucum*, Takata (*11*) used *A. oryzae*, Skinner *et al.* (*10*) used *A. fischeri, A. oryzae,* and *P. chrysogenum*, and Woolley and his associates (*13*) used *A. sydowi* and all found the proteins of these fungi to be inadequate. Foster (*5*), presumably on the basis of the above reports, states that mold proteins

**Conversion of Carbohydrate of Seven Crop Plants to Protein,
Agents of Biosynthesis**

Total Crop Protein Billion Lb.	Protein Available By Fungus Conversion Billion Lb.	Total Protein, Billion Lb.	Factorial Increase in Protein	No. of People Who Can Be Supplied with 52.2 Lb./Yr., Millions
1.184	6.768	7.952	6.71 ×	152
4.320	11.520	15.840	3.66 ×	305
—	14.400	14.400	—	276
41.563	48.490	90.053	2.19 ×	1725
34.094	36.540	70.634	2.07 ×	1350
4.705	9.149	13.854	2.94 ×	265
11.772	14.057	25.829	2.19 ×	494
97.638	140.924	238.562	—	4567

are inadequate to satisfy the protein requirements of animals wholly—an exceptionally broad statement in view of the fact that less than a fraction of 1% of the fungi have ever been tested. On the other hand, Vinson et al. (12) found that mycelia of *Fusarium lini* (if supplemented with thiamin) and *F. graminearum* (if supplemented with multiple B vitamins) were satisfactory sources of protein for normal growth, reproduction, and lactation in mice.

In view of the vast numbers of species and strains of imperfect fungi that exist, it would seem that this is a very fruitful area to explore. There is a very real possibility that some strains will be poisonous, and, like the proteins of green plants, some will be more nutritionally adequate than others. It is not suggested that by themselves the fungi will solve all of the world's protein problems; however, it is time to dispel some of the myths of mycology and have a much closer look at a group of living organisms which appear to have a very real potential in the area of protein synthesis.

Literature Cited

(1) Behr, G., *Arch. Microbiol.* **1**, 418–44 (1930).
(2) Blumenthal, H. J., Roseman, S., *J. Bacteriol.* **74**, 222–4 (1957).
(3) Bunker, H. J., in "Global Impacts of Applied Microbiology," Wiley, New York, 1964.
(4) Food and Agriculture Organization, United Nations, Rome, "FAO Production Yearbook," Vol. 17, 1963.
(5) Foster, J. W., "Chemical Activities of Fungi," Academic Press, New York, 1949.
(6) Gray, W. D., *Develop. Ind. Microbiol.* **3**, 63–71 (1962).
(7) Gray, W. D., Tech. Documentary Rept. AMRL-TDR-62-116, pp. 265–381 (1962).
(8) Gray, W. D., Och, F. F., AbouElSeoud, M., *Develop. Ind. Microbiol.* **5**, 384–9 (1964).
(9) Skinner, C. S., *J. Bacteriol.* **28**, 95–106 (1924).
(10) Skinner, J. T., Peterson, W. H., Steenbock, H. *Biochem. Z.* **267**, 169–78 (1933).
(11) Takata, R., *J. Soc. Chem. Ind. Japan* **32**, 243–4 (1929).
(12) Vinson, L. J., Cerecedo, L. R., Mill, R. P., Nord, F. F., *Science* **101**, 388–9 (1945).
(13) Woolley, D. W., Berger, J., Peterson, W. H., Steenbock, H., *J. Nutr.* **16**, 465–76 (1938).

RECEIVED October 12, 1965.

Microbial Synthesis of Food From Coal-Derived Material

MELVIN P. SILVERMAN,[1] JOAN N. GORDON and IRVING WENDER

Pittsburgh Coal Research Center, Bureau of Mines, U. S. Department of the Interior, Pittsburgh, Pa.

Cell yields of four strains of the yeast Candida grown on u-hexadecane ranged from 433 to 719 mg. dry weight per gram of hydrocarbon added; growth on 1-octadecene decreased about one half. A normal paraffin fraction from petroleum gave yields of 244 to 430 mg.; three Fischer-Tropsch fractions and one low-temperature coal tar fraction gave yields within this range. Bacteria, but not yeasts, grew on three coal-acid mixtures and a synthetic mixture of polynuclear aromatic hydrocarbons with yields below 100 mg. In general, high growth yields of yeasts were favored by substrates that were high boiling, contained a high ratio of normal paraffins to olefins, and were low in phenols. The crude protein content of Candida grown on a Fischer-Tropsch fraction was 41.1%.

The problem of the world's population explosion is compounded by an over-all global food shortage. New or unusual sources of food, especially high-quality protein, are needed as dietary supplements for both humans and animals. The Permanent Section on Food Microbiology and Hygiene, International Association of Microbiological Societies, called for an increased contribution of microbiology to world food supplies in a unanimous resolution outlining several research areas, including hydrocarbon microbiology, which might lead to increased world food production (14).

Some recent reports have dealt with the microbial conversion of petroleum hydrocarbons to protein, vitamins, or amino acids. High yields of yeast cells rich in protein and vitamins have been obtained at the expense of the n-alkanes (preferably C_{10} or higher) in crude petroleum

---

[1] Present address: Ames Research Center, Exobiology Division, National Aeronautics & Space Administration, Moffett Field, Calif.

fractions (*2–6*), feedstocks (*13, 16*), or the pure hydrocarbons themselves (*1, 4, 9, 12*).Microbial synthesis of amino acids from petroleum products has also been reported (*16, 19*). Early papers discussed the use of kogasin, a synthetic fuel derived from coal, for microbial substrates (*8, 10, 11*).

The rate of microbial synthesis of protein far exceeds the rate at which animals synthesize protein. A cow weighing 500 kg. when fed by grazing can synthesize 0.5 kg. of protein per day (*18*), whereas 500 kg. of microorganisms growing on paraffinic hydrocarbons could synthesize 1250 kg. of protein per day (*3*). According to one estimate, 3 million tons of protein per year (equal to the world's present protein deficit) could be produced by microorganisms at the expense of only 1% of the world's annual production of 700 million tons of crude paraffinic petroleum (*3*).

Since coal is one of the world's cheapest and most abundant sources of fixed carbon, we investigated the question whether coal, like petroleum, could be converted by microorganisms into high-protein food. This report gives the results of a comparative evaluation of coal-derived materials, pure hydrocarbons, and petroleum-derived material as raw materials for microbial production of food. The use of coal-derived liquid fractions was emphasized because of the intriguing possibility of extending the utility of fuel and chemical products obtained from coal conversion processes.

Experimental

Materials. Three fractions of Bureau of Mines Fischer-Tropsch synthetic liquid fuel (iron catalyst) were used: fraction FTL (boiling range 0 to 204°C), fraction FTD (boiling range 204 to 316°), and fraction FTW (boiling point > 316°). The analysis of Fischer-Tropsch fraction SASOL (from the South African Coal, Oil, and Gas Corp.) is given in Table I.

Two fractions of hexane-soluble material from Rockdale lignite low-temperature tar were obtained from the Texas Power and Light Co.: hexane-soluble foreruns (HSF) and a hexane-soluble distillate (HSD). The HSF fraction constituted 7%, and the HSD fraction 46% of the primary tar. The compositions of fractions HSF and HSD are given in Table II. Phenolic compounds were removed by chromatographing fractions HSF and HSD on alumina with petroleum ether as the eluent to obtain phenol-free fractions HSFφ and HSDφ. About 20 weight-% of starting material was removed by this procedure.

A paraffin-rich fraction (CTP) and a linear paraffin-olefin fraction (CTPO), both derived from the neutral oil of low-temperature tar, were supplied by the Bureau of Mines' Morgantown Coal Research Center. Their analyses of fractions CTP and CTPO are given in Table III. The normal paraffin fraction (PET) was derived from petroleum by an industrial firm. Our mass spectrometric analysis of this fraction is given in Table IV.

Three mixtures of coal acids were tested asg rowth substrates: DOW, a 56% aqueous solution from the Dow Chemical Co.; HOW, a water-soluble mixture of aromatic acids from alkaline oxidation of coal by the Carnegie Institute of Technology; and ANTH, the acid-soluble residue

Table I.   Analysis of Fischer-Tropsch (SASOL) Fraction

Hydrocarbon		FIA Analysis	
Carbon No.	%	Compounds	%
C_{11}	2	Aromatics	Nil
C_{12}	11	Olefins[a]	33
C_{13}	17	Paraffins[a]	64
C_4	16	Oxygenates	3
C_{15}	15		
C_{16}	13		
C_{17}	11		
C_8	9		
C_{19}	4		
C_{20}	2		

[a] Normal Hydrocarbons ca. 90%

from 1000-hour nitric acid oxidation of anthracite by the Bureau of Mines' Anthracite Research Center (7).

Substrate CTA, a synthetic mixture of polynuclear aromatic hydro-carbons found in relatively large amounts in high-temperature coal tar, consisted of 1-methylnaphthalene, 59.2; 2-methylnaphthalene, 16.3; naphthalene, 11.9; and phenanthrene, 12.5 wt.-%.

Microorganisms and Culture Media. Cultures were obtained from soil by standard enrichment culture techniques or from the culture collections of the University of Pittsburgh, Syracuse University, and the University of Iowa.

Basal medium N was prepared by adding NH_4NO_3 (5.0 grams), K_2HPO_4 (2.5 grams), and $MgSO_4 \cdot 7H_2O$ (1.0 gram) to 1 liter of tap water. The pH was adjusted to 7.0 and any insoluble salts were removed by filtration. The clear medium was sterilized by autoclaving. Medium NX was prepared by adding sufficient filter-sterilized yeast extract to medium N to make a final concentration of 0.01%.

Measurements of Growth Yields. Yeast inocula were prepared from cultures grown overnight in 50 ml. of Mycophil broth (Baltimore Biological Laboratory, Baltimore, Md.). The resultant growth was collected by centrifugation, washed twice in sterile medium N, and resuspended in 20 ml. of the same solution. One milliliter of washed yeast-cell suspension was the standard inoculum for all experiments.

For studies on growth yield of yeasts, these standard inocula were added to 50 ml. of medium NX in 300-ml. Erlenmeyer flasks in triplicate. A quantity of substrate equivalent to 0.3 ml. was weighed into each flask. Controls consisted of triplicate inoculated flasks without added substrate. Cultures were incubated at 30°C. on a rotary shaker (225 r.p.m.) for 6 days. The resultant growth was collected on 2-inch diameter Alpha-8 Metricel filters of 0.20 μ pore size (Alpha Metricel, a regenerated cellulose (rayon) membrane, is a product of the Gelman Instrument Co., Ann Arbor, Mich.). The growths were washed with 10-ml. volumes of acetone and

Table II.   Approximate Composition of Rockdale Lignite Low-Temperature Tar Fractions

(Volume-%)

Type of Constituent	HSF	HSD
Caustic-solubles	6–8	10–15
Acid-solubles	2–4	1–3
Neutral oil	88–92	80–90
Paraffins	13–15	15–20
Olefins	40–55	40–50
Alpha-olefins	17–20	17–20
Aromatics	30–47	35–45

n-hexane, dried overnight in air, and then weighed. All reported data are corrected for growth of controls.

Bacterial inocula consisted of 1 ml. of cultures grown for 3 days in 50 ml. of medium N or NX supplemented with 1 weight-% of coal acid (DOW or HOW) or 0.5 ml. of CTA. Procedures for determining bacterial growth yields were similar to those for yeast cultures, except that 1 weight-% of coal acid (DOW or HOW) or 0.5 ml. of CTA was weighed into 50 ml. of medium N or NX. Incubation times were 4 days for CTA cultures and 6 days for coal-acid cultures.

Results

More than 200 cultures of bacteria, yeasts, and fungi were screened for viability on coal-derived materials. Only bacteria (no yeasts or fungi) grew on the coal acids and CTA. Conversely, yeasts and fungi produced the

Table III.   Analyses of Paraffin-Rich (CTP) and Paraffin-Olefin (CTPO) Fractions from Rockdale Lignite Low-Temperature Tar

(Weight-%)

Carbon No.	CTP		CTPO	
	n-Paraffin	n-Olefin	n-Paraffin	n-Olefin
C_8	0.2	—	—	—
C_9	3.2	—	0.1	0.2
C_{10}	11.7	0.7	1.3	1.6
C_{11}	18.2	1.5	3.6	5.3
C_{12}	22.4	3.3	5.8	7.6
C_{13}	20.7	2.8	7.8	9.5
C_{14}	10.8	3.7	7.5	10.9
C_{15}	0.8	—	6.7	9.4
C_{16}	—	—	4.6	5.6
C_{17}	—	—	2.3	2.9
C_{18}	—	—	4.2	3.1
	88.0	12.0	43.9	56.1

most vigorous growth on Fischer-Tropsch, low-temperature tar, and petroleum-derived fractions. Of these, the yeasts *Candida lipolytica* strains 409, 409A, 409B, and *Candida tropicalis* strain 410 were selected as the most promising cultures with respect to total cell yield and ability to grow in reasonably high concentrations of substrate.

These studies also indicated that growth yields on Fischer-Tropsch fraction FTL, low-temperature tar fractions HSF and HSFϕ, and the coal acid ANTH were negligible. No further studies were made with these materials.

Table IV.   Analysis of *n*-Paraffin Fraction (PET) from Petroleum

Carbon No.	Volume-%
C_9	0.5
C_{10}	7.2
C_{11}	37.9
C_{12}	29.1
C_{13}	23.4
C_{14}	1.9

Growth Yields of Yeasts on Pure Compounds and Coal-Derived Material. Absolute growth yields, in milligrams of dry weight of yield per gram of added substrate, and relative growth yields are given in Table V. The highest yields for all cultures (433 to 719 mg. dry weight) were obtained with *n*-hexadecane as substrate; *C. lipolytica* 409 and 409A gave the best yields with *n*-hexadecane. Growth yields of 300 mg. or higher were obtained when 1-octadecene (*C. lipolytica* 409 and *C. tropicalis* 410) and Fischer-Tropsch fraction FTW (*C. lipolytica* 409B) served as growth substrates. Other substrates yielding more than 200 mg. dry weight were paraffin-rich low-temperature coal tar fraction CTP (all cultures), and Fischer-Tropsch fractions FTD (*C. lipolytica* 409B) and FTW (*C. lipolytica* 409).

All cultures yielded less than 100 mg. dry weight on low-temperature tar fraction HSDφ. On all substrates tested, with the exception of low-temperature tar fraction HSDφ, *C. lipolytica* 409B consistently gave yields greater than 50% relative to yields on *n*-hexadecane and appears to be the most versatile culture. *C. tropicalis* 410 is noteworthy for its ability to utilize the terminal olefin 1-octadecene (76% relative to *n*-hexadecane).

Growth Yields of Yeasts on Petroleum-Derived and Coal-Derived Material. The results of a second experiment, comparing the absolute and relative growth yields of yeast cultures on coal-derived material with the yields on a normal paraffin fraction derived from petroleum (PET), are given in Table VI. The three *C. lipolytica* cultures yielded over 300 mg. dry

Table V. Growth Yields of Yeasts on Pure Compounds, Low-Temperature Tar, and Fischer-Tropsch Fractions

Substrate	*C. lipolytica*			*C. tropicalis*
	409	*409A*	*409B*	*410*
Low-temperature tar	Growth Yield[a]			
HSDφ[b]	83 (0.12)	43 (0.07)	0 (0)	62 (0.14)
CTP	272 (0.38)	276 (0.44)	294 (0.68)	208 (0.46)
Fischer-Tropsch				
FTD	134 (0.19)	115 (0.18)	280 (0.65)	—
FTW	287 (0.40)	127 (0.20)	344 (0.79)	200 (0.44)
Pure compounds				
1-Octadecene	357 (0.50)	295 (0.47)	244 (0.56)	344 (0.76)
n-Hexadecane	719 (1.00)	628 (1.00)	433 (1.00)	453 (1.00)

[a] Average of triplicate cultures. Data in milligrams of dry weight of yield per gram substrate added, corrected for growth in controls. Values in parentheses are growth yields relative to that on *n*-hexadecane.

[b] Phenols removed by two passages through alumina column.

weight on petroleum fraction PET. Yields greater than 300 mg. dry weight were also obtained on Fischer-Tropsch fraction FTW with *C. lipolytica* 409 and 409B. All cultures gave yields greater than 200 mg. dry weight on low-temperature tar fraction CTP. *C. lipolytica* 409B and *C. tropicalis* 410 both produced more than 200 mg. of dry cells on low-temperature tar fraction CTPO. *C. lipolytica* 409B also yielded more than 200 mg. dry weight on Fischer-Tropsch fraction FTD. All cultures gave negligible or no growth on low-temperature tar fraction HSD; however, upon removal of the phenolic constituents from this fraction, *C. lipolytica* 409B and *C. tropicalis* 410 produced more than 100 mg. of dry cell material.

In terms of relative growth, *C. lipolytica* 409 was outstanding on Fischer-Tropsch fraction FTW and on low-temperature tar fraction CTP, yielding 100 and 84%, respectively, of the growth obtained on PET. *C. lipolytica* 409A gave a relative growth yield of 71% on fraction CTP. The versatility of *C. lipolytica* 409B is again illustrated by relative yields ranging from 61% (fraction CTPO) to 85% (fraction FTW) on all substrates except fractions HSD and HSDφ. *C. tropicalis* 410 was outstanding in its relative ability to grow on low-temperature tar fractions CTP (95%) and CTPO (84%), although absolute yields were less than those obtained with *C. lipolytica* 409B on the same substrate. Also interesting is the apparent correlation between the abilities of *C. lipolytica* 409B and *C. tropicalis* 410 to use a terminal olefin (Table V) and their ability to grow on low-temperature tar fraction CTPO, containing 56% of olefinic compounds (Table III). The *C. lipolytica* 409 and 409A cultures gave poorer yields on 1-octadecene relative to *n*-hexadecane (Table V) and this was reflected in their poorer absolute and relative yields on CTPO compared with CTP (Table VI).

Since the Bureau of Mines Fischer-Tropsch fractions (FTD, FTW) had been stored for a long time prior to testing, confirmation of our results was sought with fresh material. The new results (Table VII) demonstrated clearly the equivalence of fresh Fischer-Tropsch fraction SASOL and petroleum-derived fraction PET in terms of absolute and relative growth yields with the three *C. lipolytica* strains.

Pooled growth yields of five replicate cultures of *C. lipolytica* 409B grown on Fischer-Tropsch fraction SASOL (average yield, 451 mg. of dry cell material per gram of SASOL added) were analyzed for crude protein content (Kjeldahl N $\times$ 6.25) and gave 41.1% crude protein. This value compares favorably with values reported for microorganisms grown on petroleum hydrocarbons (*3, 6, 9, 13, 15*).

Table VI. Growth Yields of Yeasts on Low-Temperature Tar, Fischer-Tropsch, and Petroleum Fractions

Substrate	C. lipolytica			C. tropicalis
	409	*409A*	*409B*	*410*
Low-temperature tar		Growth Yield*a*		
HSD*b*	14(0.05)	6(0.02)	0(0)	0(0)
HSDϕ*c*	73(0.24)	72(0.22)	106(0.28)	102(0.42)
CTPO	113(0.37)	124(0.39)	233(0.61)	205(0.84)
CTP	259(0.84)	235(0.71)	287(0.75)	232(0.95)
Fischer-Tropsch				
FTD	114(0.37)	150(0.45)	243(0.63)	0(0)
FTW	306(1.00)	167(0.50)	329(0.85)	161(0.66)
Petroleum				
PET	307(1.00)	333(1.00)	385(1.00)	244(1.00)

a Average of triplicate cultures. Data in milligrams of dry weight of yield per gram of substrate added, corrected for growth in controls. Values in parentheses are growth yields relative to those on PET.
b Phenols not removed.
c Phenols removed by three passages through alumina column.

Growth Yields of Bacteria on Coal Acids and Polynuclear Aromatic Hydrocarbons. In all tests, bacteria growth yields on the coal acids and on the synthetic mixture of polynuclear aromatic hydrocarbons were below 100 mg. of dry cell material (Table VIII). Interestingly, most cultures produced higher cell yields in media without yeast extract (medium N).

Discussion

The over-all results of our experiments are summarized in Table IX, which gives the range of growth yields obtained on the various substrates (carbon sources) with yeasts and bacteria. The highest range of yields was

Table VII.   Growth Yields of Yeasts on Fischer-Tropsch (SASOL) and Petroleum-Derived (PET) Fractions

Organism	Substrate	Experiment 1		Experiment 2	
		Mg./G.	Relative yield	Mg./G.	Relative yield
C. lipolytica 409	PET	342	1.00	280	1.00
	SASOL	322	0.94	326	1.16
C. lipolytica 409A	PET	338	1.00	306	1.00
	SASOL	347	1.03	341	1.12
C. lipolytica 409B	PET	430	1.00	374	1.00
	SASOL	437	1.02	348	0.93
C. tropicalis 410	PET	287	1.00	290	1.00
	SASOL	224	0.78	261	0.90

Table VIII.   Growth Yields of Bacteria on Coal Acids and Polynuclear Aromatic Hydrocarbons

Substrate	Microorganism	Mg. Dry Wt./G. Substrate Added	
		Medium N	Medium NX
Coal acids			
DOW	D-10	10	28
DOW	D-21	68	18
DOW	D-27	14	9
HOW	H-22	51	48
Polynuclear aromatics			
CTA	CTA-23	1	68
CTA	CTA-26	32	3

obtained with n-hexadecane as substrate; yields on 1-octadecene decreased by approximately one half.   Normal paraffin fraction PET from petroleum supported growth ranging from 244 to 430 mg. dry weight.   Fischer-Tropsch fractions FTD, FTW, and SASOL, as well as low-temperature tar fraction CTP, supported growth falling within the range obtained with PET. Growth yields on low-temperature tar fraction CTPO approached the lower limit of the yields on fraction PET.   The coal acids (ANTH, DOW HOW) and the mixture of polynuclear aromatic hydrocarbons (CTA) proved inferior substrates for bacteria and were incapable of supporting the growth of yeasts.

The data in Table IX suggest that, in general, higher growth yields are favored by substrates which are higher boiling, and hence, of higher molecular weight (compare yields on FTL, FTD, and FTW); contain a high ratio of normal paraffins to olefins (compare yields on n-hexadecane with 1-octadecene; PET, CTP, and SASOL with CTPO); and are low in phenols (compare yields on HSD with HSDφ).

The range of growth yields obtained with any given substrate is related in part to the inherent variability among different species or different strains of the same species and illustrates the importance of choosing the proper strain for obtaining high yields.

Table IX. Growth Yields on Pure Hydrocarbons and Fractions Derived from Coal or Petroleum

Microbe	*Substrate*	*Growth Yield,[a] Mg./G. Substrate*
Yeasts	Low-temperature Tar	
	HSF	0
	HSFφ	0
	HSD	0–14
	HSDφ[b]	0–83
	HSDφ[c]	72–106
	CTPO	113–233
	CTP	208–294
	Fischer-Tropsch	
	FTL	0
	FTD	0–280
	FTW	127–34 l
	SASOL	224–451
	Petroleum	
	PET	244–430
	Pure Hydrocarbons	
	1-Octadecene	244–357
	n-Hexadecane	433–719
Bacteria	Coal Acids	
	ANTH	0
	DOW	9–68
	HOW	48–51
	Polynuclear Aromatics	
	CTA	1–68

[a] Mg. of dry cell material synthesized per gram of substrate added. Low and high growth yields for each range are average yields of triplicate cultures of lowest and highest yielding cultures among cultures tested.

[b] Phenols and other material removed by two passages of HSD through alumina.

[c] Phenols and other material removed by three passages of HSD through alumina. Effluents *b* and *c* showed absence of hydroxyl group by infrared spectroscopy.

In practice, over 80% conversion of hydrocarbon substrates to cell material has been obtained (1, 3, 6, 9, 13, 17). Although our absolute growth yields on pure hydrocarbons, petroleum, Fischer-Tropsch, and low-temperature tar fractions were somewhat lower, our experiments were designed solely to test the comparative feasibility of using these substrates for microbial production of food. Improvements in the nutritional quality of the growth medium, closer control of pH, more efficient aeration, and other modern fermentation practices undoubtedly will result in higher cell yields.

Conclusion

Paraffin-rich, higher molecular weight fractions derived from low-temperature coal tar and Fischer-Tropsch synthetic liquid fuel compare favorably with a petroleum-derived fraction as substrates (carbon sources) for microbial production of food. Coal, with its enormous reserves, therefore can take its place alongside petroleum as a potential source of high-protein food.

Literature Cited

(1) Azouley, E., Couchoud-Beaumont, P., Senez, J. C., Ann. Inst. Pasteur 107, 520 (1964).
(2) Champagnat, A., Filosa, J. (to Société des Pétroles), French Patent 1,297,619 (May 21, 1962).
(3) Champagnat, A., Vernet, C., Lainé, B., Filosa, J., Nature 197, 13 (1963).
(4) Chem. Eng. News 41, 49 (Feb. 2, 1963).
(5) Ibid., 42, 41 (Jan. 20, 1964).
(6) Gatellier, C., Hydrocarbon Process. Petrol. Refiner 43, 143 (1964).
(7) Hammer, M. A., Brady, G. A., Eckerd, J. W., Bur. Mines Rept. Invest. 5782 (1961).
(8) Hoerburger, W., Forschungsber. Wirtsch. Verkehrsministeriums Nordrhein-Westfalen, No. 131 (1955).
(9) Johnson, M. J., Chem. Ind. (London) 1964, 1532.
(10) Just, F., Schnabel, W., Branntweinwirt 2, 113 (1948).
(11) Just, F., Schnabel, W., Ullmann S., Brauerei 4 (8), 57, 71 (1951).
(12) Komagata, K., Nakase, T., Katsuya, N., J. Gen. Appl. Microbiol. 10, 313 (1964).
(13) Miller, T. L., Lie, L., Johnson, M. J., Biotechnol. Bioeng. 6, 299 (1964).
(14) "Recent Progress in Microbiology, VIII International Congress for Microbiology, Montreal, 1962," N. E. Gibbons, ed., p. 719, University of Toronto Press, Toronto, Canada.
(15) Takahashi, J., Kawabata, Y., Yamada, K., Agr. Biol. Chem. 29, 292 (1965).
(16) Takahashi, J., Kobayashi, K., Imada, Y., Yamada, K., Appl. Microbiol. 13, 1 (1965).
(17) Takahashi, J., Kobayashi, K., Kawabata, Y., and Yamada, K., Agr. Biol. Chem. 27, 836 (1963).
(18) Thaysen, A. C., "Yeasts," W. Roman, ed., p. 155, W. Junk, Hague, 1957.

(19) Yamada, K., Takahashi, J., Kobayashi, K., Imada, Y., *Agr. Biol. Chem.* **27,** 390 (1963).

ADDENDUM: A reviewer has pointed out that some early papers appeared on the use of kogasin, a synthetic fuel derived from coal, for microbial substrates (*8, 10, 11*).

RECEIVED March 14, 1966. Presented to the Division of Fuel Chemistry, 150th Meeting ACS, Atlantic City, New Jersey, September 1965. *Specific brand names of products are mentioned only to identify the materials used; no endorsement by the Bureau of Mines is implied.*

Index